RET

MW01097611

**The Materials
Information Society**

ASM International® is a Society whose
mission is to gather, process and
disseminate technical information.
ASM fosters the understanding and
application of engineered materials and
their research, design, reliable manufacture, use and economic and social
benefits. This is accomplished via a
unique global information-sharing
network of interaction among members
in forums and meetings, education
programs, and through publications
and electronic media.

EXTRUSION

Processes, Machinery, Tooling

EXTRUSION

Processes, Machinery, Tooling

Dr.-Ing. KURT LAUE
(Deceased) Formerly Director
Vereinigte Deutsche Metallwerke
Frankfurt/Main, West Germany

Dr.-Ing. HELMUT STENGER
Technical Director
Glyco do Brasil
Industria Metallurgica, Ltda.
Cataguases, Brazil

Translators from the German version:

A. F. Castle, B.Sc. (Eng.), Ph.D., D.I.C.
Senior Process Engineer
Fielding & Platt Limited
Gloucester GL1 5RF, England

Dipl.-Ing. Dr. mont. Gernot Lang
Head of the Extrusion Research Dept.
Vereinigte Metallwerke Ranshofen-Berndorf AG
A-5282 Ranshofen, Austria

AMERICAN SOCIETY FOR METALS
Metals Park, Ohio 44073

Originally published in 1976 as
Strangpressen
Copyright © 1976 by
Aluminium-Verlag GmbH, Düsseldorf

English translation of revised text
copyright © 1981
by the
AMERICAN SOCIETY FOR METALS
All rights reserved

Fifth printing

Library of Congress Cataloging in Publication Data
Laue, Kurt.
   Extrusion: processes, machinery, tooling.

   Translation of Strangpressen.
   Includes bibliographical references and index.
   1. Metals — Extrusion.   I. Stenger, Helmut, joint
author.   II. Title.
TS255.L3813   671.3′4   80-23076
ISBN 0-87170-094-8

PRINTED IN THE UNITED STATES OF AMERICA

Translators' Foreword

Although the original German text has been carefully followed and in some areas revised, mistakes are bound to have been made and we should be grateful if readers inform us of any they find. Additional comments and criticisms will also be useful for a revised edition of this book.

All units have been converted to SI units using the approximation that $1 \text{ kp/mm}^2 = 10 \text{ N/mm}^2$. Most of the tables have been revised, and new work has been included where appropriate.

References have been numbered in the text to assist the reader, and some additional references have been added.

A. F. CASTLE
GERNOT LANG

Preface

Extrusion has an industrial history stretching back more than 160 years. In the past 20 years its economic importance has increased, primarily as a result of spectacular technological advances that have drawn on extensive practical experience and on numerous fundamental investigations into the extrusion process, tooling, and metal flow.

The vast number of publications in international technical journals makes it difficult for students and industrial extrusion plant operators to locate the information they need. The authors of this book have therefore tried to provide a comprehensive and detailed survey of extrusion data, including the latest technology. The book is based as far as possible on their own practical experience, and on the most important and most recent technical publications.

This book is intended to provide a comprehensive introduction to this complex area of metalworking for those in industry—both the engineer and the technical sales manager—with particular reference to the problems of optimum tool design, closely linked with the economics of the extrusion process. Students, too, will be able to find detailed information to supplement their lectures, and researchers will find information of use to them in data analysis.

The aims of this book could be realized only with the collaboration of many acknowledged experts. Particular thanks are due to Dr. G. Sauer, chairman of the Extrusion Working Party of the Deutsche Gesellschaft für Metallkunde (German Metallurgical Society), for reviving the idea of publishing a comprehensive survey on extrusion. He also wrote the section on container design, completely rewrote the section on stresses in extrusion tooling, and critically read other parts of the text. Dr. R. Akeret (Neuhausen, Switzerland), Dr. A. Boden (Frankfurt/Main), R. M. L. Elkan (Bournemouth, England), R. Keller (Alsdorf/Aachen), Prof. C. Petersen (Frankfurt/Main), K. Schindler (Remscheid), W. Schulte (Schwerte), Dr. E. Tuschy (Osnabrück), W. Wilcken (Osnabrück) and F. Wyss (Chippis, Switzerland) made valuable contributions to the sections on extrusion processes, technology and installations. Dr. M. Bauser (Ulm), Dr. J. Nitsche (Düsseldorf) and D. Rohrbacher (Wutöschingen) made constructive suggestions for additions and corrections in the material used in the book.

The following companies provided photographs and technical information: Aluminium-Werke (Wutöschingen), ASEA (Västeras, Sweden), Cameron Iron Works (Houston, Texas), Collin (Aichach/Ecknach), Demag-Hydraulik (Duisberg), Fielding Plant Design, Ltd. (Bournemouth, England), Glyco-Metall-Werke, Daelen & Loos (Wiesbaden), Hoesch Profilwerk (Schwerte), Otto Junker (Lammersdorf), Kuhlmann (Bad Lauterberg), Lindemann (Düsseldorf), Metallgesellschaft (Frankfurt/Main), Schloemann-Siemag (Düsseldorf), Sutton Engineering Co. (Pittsburgh, Pennsylvania), Technica-Guss (Würzburg), Vereinigte Deutsche Metallwerke (Frankfurt/Main) and Wieland-Werke (Ulm).

The authors would like to thank all their colleagues and the firms mentioned above for their cooperation and support.

Dr.-Ing. Kurt Laue
Dr.-Ing. Helmut Stenger

Frankfurt/Main
June 1976

Contents

1. General Principles

1.1. Basic Processes

1.1.1. Method of Operation and Historical Development

Extrusion is a deformation process used to produce long, straight, semi-finished metal products such as bars, solid and hollow sections, tubes, wires and strips. The principle is very simple: under a high load, a billet is squeezed from a closed container through a die to give a reduction in size. Cross sections of varying complexity can be extruded, depending on the material and the dies used. Extrusion can be carried out at room temperature or at high temperatures, depending on the alloy and the method. Figure 1.1 shows how the extrusion load is transmitted via a hydraulically or mechanically driven ram through an intermediate dummy block to the billet. The container is constructed of several thick-wall cylinders, usually shrunk together to withstand the high radial stresses, and fitted with a wear-resistant liner. The axial load is applied to the die stack in the press platen (end housing).

The hydraulic extrusion press was invented in 1810 by the Englishman S. Bramah. His press was designed for extrusion of lead. The basic principle is

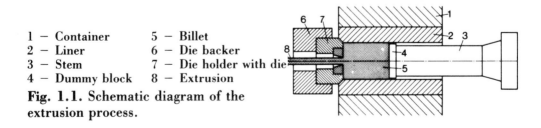

1 — Container   5 — Billet
2 — Liner   6 — Die backer
3 — Stem   7 — Die holder with die
4 — Dummy block   8 — Extrusion

Fig. 1.1. Schematic diagram of the extrusion process.

still used today in the manufacture of lead tubes. The process was first successfully applied to higher melting point alloys by the German A. Dick, in the 1890's. He located a separate dummy block in front of the extrusion stem, allowing the discard and the dummy block to be ejected together. This was the first decisive invention that led to the extrusion of metals other than lead. Further development of the process to the present state of extrusion practice has been closely connected with advances in the mechanical construction of press installations, improvements in tooling and the development of hot working steels.

There are four characteristic differences among the various methods of extrusion and the presses used:

    (*a*) The movement of the extrusion relative to the stem — direct and indirect processes.
    (*b*) The position of the press axis—horizontal or vertical presses.
    (*c*) Type of drive—hydraulic (water or oil) or mechanical presses.
    (*d*) Method of load application—conventional or hydrostatic extrusion.

1.1.2. Mechanical State of Stress and Workability in Extrusion

Extrusion is listed under the heading "compressive deformation" in the classification of deformation processes given in DIN 8582 and 8583. Deformation can be defined exactly by referring the operating mechanical stresses in the deformation zone to the axis of a three-dimensional coordinate system. Stress components in each of the three directions occur in the planes normal to each other — a normal stress σ and two shear stresses τ perpendicular to each other (Fig. 1.2). If, as is usual, the coordinates are taken to be parallel to the directions of the maximum normal stresses, the stress system can be represented simply by the three normal stresses σ_1, σ_2 and σ_3 (Fig. 1.3)—known as principal stresses because the shear stresses are zero. In this system tensile stresses are positive and compressive stresses negative. According to Tresca's yield criterion (Ref 1), plastic flow—the start

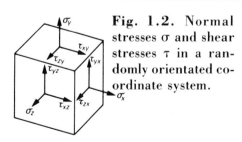

Fig. 1.2. Normal stresses σ and shear stresses τ in a randomly oriented coordinate system.

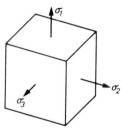

Fig. 1.3. Principal stresses in a coordinate system, the axes of which are parallel to the principal axis.

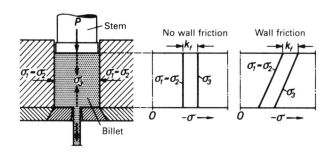

Fig. 1.4. Schematic variation of axial pressure σ_3 and radial pressure $\sigma_1 = \sigma_2$ over the length of the container for lubricated and unlubricated extrusion. *(From Ref 2)*

of deformation — occurs when the difference between the maximum and minimum principal stresses ($\sigma_1 > \sigma_2 > \sigma_3$) reaches a certain value (stress gradient):

$$\sigma_1 - \sigma_3 = k_f \tag{Eq 1}$$

k_f is the flow stress, a very important material property in deformation technology (see section 1.4.2.2).

The Tresca yield criterion states that plastic flow can be initiated by either compressive or tensile stresses, provided the stress gradient is maintained at the value k_f. However, an important feature of extrusion is that all three principal stresses are compressive, in contrast to most other deformation processes (Fig. 1.4). The axial stress σ_3 has the greatest magnitude. The radial and tangential stresses σ_1 and σ_2 have approximately the same magnitude in a cylindrical billet, but are less than σ_3. Inasmuch as all three principal stresses are negative (compressive), then:

$$\sigma_1 = \sigma_2 > \sigma_3 \text{ and } \sigma_1 - \sigma_3 = k_f$$

ignoring any friction between the billet and the container. Therefore, the axial stress is given by:

$$- \sigma_3 = k_f - \sigma_1$$

If, for example, the flow stress of the material being extruded is 100 N/mm², and σ_1 is assumed to be 50% of σ_3, then the axial load on the stem (neglecting friction) is given by:

$$- \sigma_3 = k_f - 0.5 \, \sigma_3 \; ; \; - \sigma_3 = k_f / 0.5 = 2 \, k_f = 200 \text{ N/mm}^2$$

This example shows that the load on the stem is always significantly higher than the yield stress, even without taking friction into account. The advantage of plastic deformation under a state of multiaxial compression in extrusion is the very high strain that can be attained. Although the yield stress according

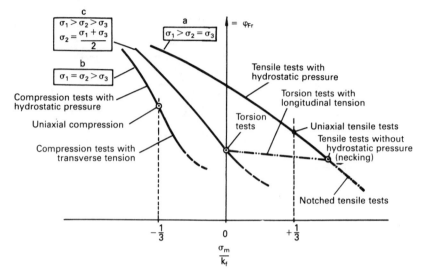

Fig. 1.5a. The effect of the type of stressing on deformability φ_{Fr} as a function of the relative mean stress σ_m/k_f (schematic). *(From Ref 18)*

to Tresca is independent of the state of stress, the workability (deformation to the point of fracture) increases with increasing mean pressure (hydrostatic pressure = pressure applied from all sides):

$$\sigma_m = \tfrac{1}{3}(\sigma_1 + \sigma_2 + \sigma_3) \tag{Eq 2}$$

or decreasing relative mean value σ_m/k_f (Fig. 1.5a).

1.1.3. Comparison With Other Deformation Processes

The favorable compressive state of stress indicates a high capacity for deformation, and therefore it is possible to extrude metals that can only be slightly deformed by using other methods. This is shown schematically in Fig. 1.5b and is well substantiated in practice. Alloys such as CuSn8 (tin bronze) or the free-cutting aluminum alloy AlCuMgPb are almost impossible to hot roll without cracking, but can be extruded with a perfect finish. Ideally, the axial stress at the die exit is zero. The effect of friction, however, can lead to the development of a tensile stress exceeding the tensile strength at the surface of heterogeneous alloys. Thus, the extrudability of many metals is limited.

1.2. Material Flow in Extrusion

Extrusion is usually carried out as a discontinuous process—that is, the second billet is not loaded until the first has been extruded. A nonsteady state of flow is caused by temperature variations in the billet and the limited billet length, as well as by friction between the container and the billet, and between the dummy block and billet. This leads to nonuniform flow from the

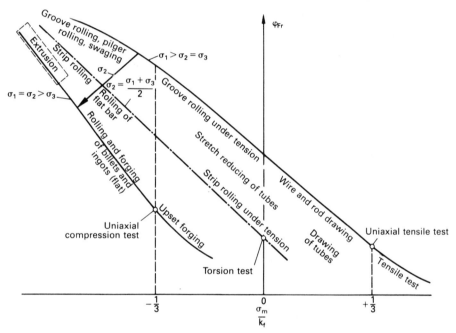

Fig. 1.5b. Deformability φ_{Fr} in various deformation processes in comparison with deformation to the point of fracture in tension, compression and torsion testing (schematic). *(From Ref 18)*

front of the billet to the end and results in a change in the extrusion load throughout the cycle, temperature differences that lead to variations in material properties over the cross section and along the extrusion, and the possibility of defects. Many investigations into material flow in the container have been carried out to study and overcome these usually undesirable effects. Many papers have been published in this field, and Dürrschnabel (Ref 4) has given a detailed description of material flow in nonferrous metal extrusion (see also Ref 1, 3 and 6).

1.2.1. Methods of Investigation

The so-called opto-plastic methods of study used can be classified by the experimental material selected:

Model materials, including wax, Plasticine (Ref 5, 7).
Metals that can easily be deformed at or just above room temperature, such as lead, tin, bismuth.
Metals similar to those in commercial use.

They can also be classified by the method used for reference-marking inside the experimental billet:

Disc method: discs similar to each other but identifiable optically or metallographically are arranged in layers to form a billet (Ref 1, 3, 8, 9). Variations of this method use billets constructed of materials of different types or colors to form the surface and the interior, or layered together longitudinally (Ref 9).
Indicator method: conclusions on material flow can be drawn from the movement of plugs inserted in the billet surface (Ref 10). This method cannot provide any information on the flow taking place in the billet center.
Longitudinal grid method (coordinate method): the billet is sectioned longitudinally along its axis, and the mating surfaces are marked with a grid. The two halves are then reassembled, using a parting compound (Fig. 1.6), and partially extruded (Ref 11, 12).

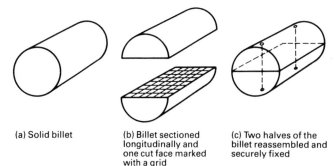

(a) Solid billet

(b) Billet sectioned longitudinally and one cut face marked with a grid

(c) Two halves of the billet reassembled and securely fixed

Fig. 1.6. Billet preparation for material flow studies using the longitudinal grid (coordinate) method.

1.2.2. Typical Flow Patterns in Extrusion

Numerous flow patterns in extrusion have been detected by many investigators using the experimental methods described above, especially the grid method (Ref 4, 6, 84). The results have shown that the flow of the billet in the container varies in a characteristic way according to the material being extruded and the process used.

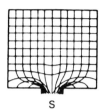 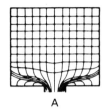 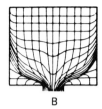 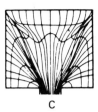

S   A   B   C

Fig. 1.7. Schematic diagram of the four different types of flow in extrusion.

The main cause of these differences is the magnitude of the resistance due to friction at the liner wall of the container. In certain cases in hot extrusion, heat losses in the container cause the billet surface to be colder than the center, and the corresponding increase in the flow stress can have a significant effect. The different types of flow patterns observed have been classified into four types: S, A, B and C, according to the increasing order of nonuniformity of flow (Fig. 1.7).

Flow Pattern S

This pattern is characterized by the maximum possible uniformity of flow in the container. Plastic flow takes place mainly in a deformation zone directly in front of the die. The major part of the nonextruded billet, pushed as a rigid body through the die, remains undeformed, as is shown in Fig. 1.7 by the undistorted grid. Hence the front of the billet moves evenly into the deformation zone. This very uniform flow can take place only when there is no friction at the liner wall or at the surface of the die and the die holder. In practice, frictionless extrusion is impossible, but flow patterns of this type are closely approximated when very effective lubrication is used — for example, in hydrostatic extrusion or steel extrusion with glass lubricant, as well as indirect extrusion with a die lubricant. Even in the absence of friction, the strain rate and strain potential vary throughout the deformation zone because of the change in direction of the material as it flows towards the die orifice. The metal cannot flow around the sharp corner between the container and the die because of material constraints, and consequently it seeks the shortest path. Thus, it flows along a funnel-shaped shear zone that develops in front of a "dead metal zone." This is very small in type S flow.

Flow Pattern A

Flow type A (Fig. 1.7) occurs when there is virtually no friction between the container and the billet but significant friction at the surface of the die and its holder. This retards the radial flow of the peripheral zones and increases the amount of shearing in this region. The result is a slightly larger dead metal zone than that in flow type S, with a correspondingly wider deformation zone. However, deformation in the center is still relatively uniform. Flow patterns of this type occur during the lubricated extrusion of soft alloys such as lead, tin, α-brasses and tin bronzes, and in the extrusion of copper billets covered with oxide, which acts as a lubricant.

Flow Pattern B

This pattern occurs if there is friction at both the container wall and at the surfaces of the die and die holder (Fig. 1.7). The peripheral zones are retarded at the billet/container interface, whereas the lower resistance causes the material in the center to be accelerated towards the die. The shear zone between the retarded regions at the surface and the accelerated material in the center extends back into the billet to an extent that depends on the extrusion parameters and the alloy. The dead metal zone is, therefore, large. At the start of extrusion the shear deformation is concentrated in the peripheral regions, but as deformation continues, it extends towards the center. This increases the danger of material flowing from the billet surface—with impurities or lubricant—along the shear zone and finishing up under the surface of the extrusion (blistering and scale formation; see section 1.2.3.3). Also, the dead metal zone is not completely rigid and can influence, even if to a limited degree, the flow of the metal (compare Fig. 1.13 and 1.17). Flow type B is seen in single phase (homogeneous) copper alloys that do not form a lubricating oxide skin and in most aluminum alloys.

Flow Pattern C

Type C flow (Fig. 1.7) occurs in hot extrusion when the friction is high, as in type B, and the flow stress k_f of the material in the cooler peripheral regions of the billet is considerably higher than that in the center; the billet surface forms a relatively stiff shell (Ref 5, 12). The conical dead metal zone is, therefore, much larger and extends from the front of the billet to the back. At the start of extrusion, only the material inside the funnel is plastic and it is severely deformed — especially in the shear zone — as it flows towards the die. The stiff shell and the dead metal zone are in axial compression as the billet length decreases and, consequently, the displaced material of the outer regions follows the path of least resistance to the back of the billet, where it turns towards the center and flows into the funnel.

This type of flow is found in the (α + β)-brasses, where the cooling of the peripheral regions of the billet leads to an increase in the flow stress (Fig. 1.8), because the flow stress of the α phase is much higher than that of the β phase during hot working (compare the curves for CuZn39Pb3 and CuZn37 in Fig.

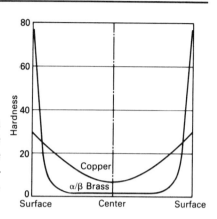

Fig. 1.8. Hardness distribution in an extrusion billet after cooling in the container (10 sec). The hardness distribution was determined from the calculated temperature distribution and the measured hardness temperature curve (temperature of the container, 200 °C). *(From Ref 5)*

1.41). As in the (α + β)-brasses, flow type C will occur when there is a hard billet shell and, at the same time, the friction at the container wall is high. It can also occur without any phase change that leads to a higher flow stress if there is a large temperature difference between the billet and the container. This can take place in the extrusion of tin as well as of aluminum and its alloys (Ref 15, 84).

The extrusion defect known as pipe is caused by type C flow. It is an annular separation in the cross section at the rear of the extrusion (see section 1.2.3.2). The nonuniform material flow in the container, together with the production and dissipation of heat (Fig. 1.3), results in an uneven distribution of the strain rate, temperature and, therefore, the flow stress (Ref 14). Figure 1.9 shows a typical example.

1.2.3. Extrusion Defects Produced by Undesirable Metal Flow, and Methods of Prevention

Extrusion defects described in this section are the result of nonuniform flow in the container. Susceptibility to defects increases with the heterogeneous nature of the flow pattern—that is, in the order S, A, B, C. Apart from the formation of a funnel in the discard, almost no defects are found with flow type S, whereas A and B can lead to the formation of a skin, and type C to pipe. If a lubricant is used, blistering can occur with these three flow types.

1.2.3.1. Funnel Formation

Movement of the peripheral zones of the billet close to the die and die holder surfaces—independent of the nonuniform flow in the container

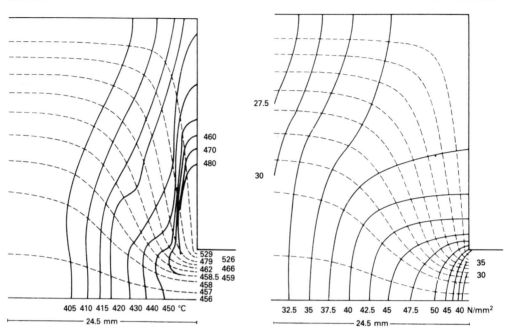

Fig. 1.9. Distribution of the temperature (a) and the calculated flow stress (b) in the adiabatic extrusion of Al99.5. *(From Ref 14)*

caused by friction — results in shearing, as discussed in 1.2.2. The material in the axis flows more rapidly towards the die orifice than that at the edge. Therefore, as the end of the billet approaches the die, a funnel-shaped hollow forms in the discard (Fig. 1.10). This funnel can extend into the rear of the extrusion; hence, the billet should not be extruded completely. The optimum length of the discard must be determined experimentally and must be greater for lower extrusion ratios — as in the production of thick rods — than for higher ratios, because the defect develops at an earlier stage. A funnel also occurs in indirect extrusion, because shearing at the die is not prevented (Fig. 1.11).

1.2.3.2. Pipe

Pipe is an internal separation of material, dividing — partially or totally — the cross section of the extrusion into an inner core and an outer zone (Fig. 1.12). This defect is found in the rear third of the extrusion and should not be confused with the funnel formation described in 1.2.3.1, which is the result of a completely different process. Pipe is of particular importance in the extrusion of $(\alpha + \beta)$-brasses; in fact, production problems with these alloys during World War I provided the impetus that led to the classification of flow patterns

Fig. 1.10. Funnel formation in the discard of a solid billet after extruding a rod. *(From Ref 84)*

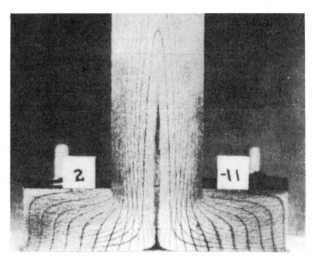

Fig. 1.11. Funnel formation in the indirect extrusion of lead. *(From Ref 85)*

Fig. 1.12. Pipe in a brass rod. The defect was revealed by cutting and then breaking the rod. *(From Ref 86)*

into types A, B, C and S. The defect occurs at the periphery of the dummy block when the oxide-clad surface of the billet turns into the more rapidly flowing material in the center. The metal layers flowing unevenly together cannot weld together because of the oxide layer. The difference in speed between the billet center and the surface layers is highest for flow type C; consequently, the extrusion defect is found only in alloys with this flow type — examples are $(\alpha + \beta)$-brasses and some aluminum alloys. Figure 1.13, taken from an $(\alpha + \beta)$-brass billet fitted with marker pins, clearly shows that the flow of metal from the rear of the billet towards the center is diagonal (Ref 10).

The following methods can be used to reduce or, ideally, eliminate the extrusion defect:

(a) *Reduction of the defect:* extrusion with a shell; machining the cast

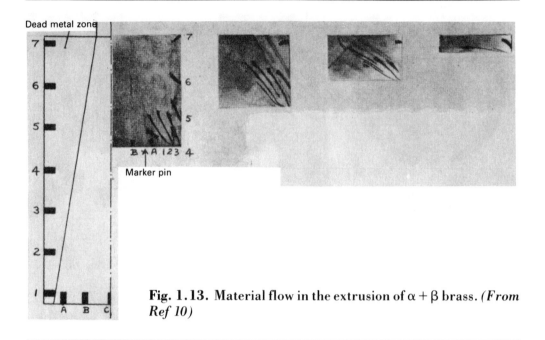

Fig. 1.13. Material flow in the extrusion of $\alpha + \beta$ brass. *(From Ref 10)*

billet; extrusion with a long discard; equalizing the billet and container temperatures.

(*b*) *Elimination of the defect:* all methods that replace the uneven type C flow with the more homogeneous type A or B can be used, including indirect extrusion and reduction of surface friction.

These methods are discussed briefly below.

Extrusion With a Shell

In this method (see also Chap. 2), which is often used in extrusion of brass, the diameter of the dummy block is 3 to 5 mm less than that of the container. The shell sheared off by the dummy block during extrusion remains, together with all the impurities, as a cylinder and is pushed out after each extrusion (Fig. 1.14). It is important to have the dummy block in the center of the container, in order to leave a shell with a constant wall thickness. However, it should not be more than 3 mm thick, because of the danger of back extrusion. The shell must be completely removed after each extrusion if pipe is to be avoided. If it remains in the container or is only partly removed, the as-cast surface of the next billet will end up in the center of the extrusion (Ref 84, 86). Good-quality dummy blocks and a clean, undamaged liner are also very important (Ref 86).

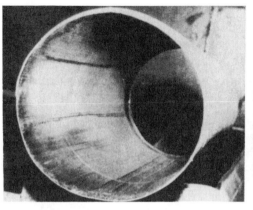 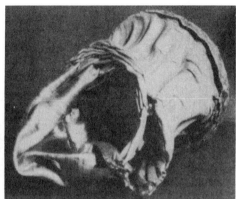

a) Perfect   b) Defective

Fig. 1.14. Brass extrusion shell. *(From Ref 86)*

Machined Billets

To a certain extent, surface impurities and oxide skins can be removed by machining off the dirty, uneven, as-cast surface of the billet. The success of this method is limited only by the oxidation of the machined surface during billet heating. This can be influenced by the furnace atmosphere and the duration of heating.

Extrusion With a Long Discard

In this method, extrusion is interrupted before the defect appears, leaving a correspondingly large discard of up to 30% of the billet length. This method is generally successful but expensive. Extrusion with smaller discards and the use of fracture tests to determine the starting point of the defect are, therefore, preferable. These tests are carried out in special machines and involve bending the end of the extrusion backward and forward until it breaks. The two separate layers of the defect can then be clearly seen.

Similar Billet and Container Temperatures

When type C flow is caused by a temperature gradient resulting in heterogeneous plastic deformation, altering the container temperature to that of the billet can reduce or prevent the danger of pipe formation. However, this method is applicable only with temperatures up to a maximum of 450 °C; for example, for aluminum alloys. It is not possible to match perfectly the temperatures in the case of metals that have to be extruded at high tempera-

(a) Container temperature 100 °C; flow type C

Fig. 1.15. Extrusion of CuZn31Si with a flat die, shell thickness ≈ 0.5 mm,

tures, such as copper alloys, because the container material cannot withstand such temperatures over a long period of time. Nevertheless, even if the temperatures cannot be equalized, it has been found that the ratio of the billet temperature to that of the container has a significant effect on the flow behavior of brass (Fig. 1.15). Results have demonstrated that an increase in the container temperature reduces the severity of type C flow. Although raising the container temperature has a favorable effect on the flow characteristics of copper, brass and other heavy metals, it increases the tendency of aluminum alloys to stick to the container wall.

Reduction of Surface Friction

Type C flow can be avoided and replaced by type B or even A if a lubricated container and a conical die are used. An example is shown in Fig. 1.16 for CuZn41. This method could be used to prevent pipe formation at the end of extrusion. Lubrication in normal hot extrusion is, however, often impractical, because other defects, including scale or blister formation, develop from the trapped lubricant, particularly on the surface of the product.

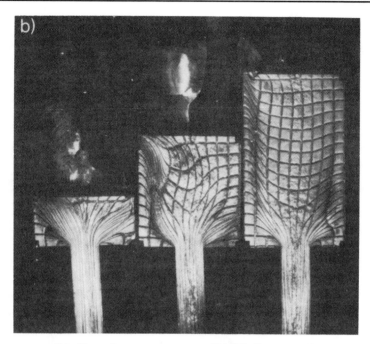

(b) Container temperature 350 °C; flow type B
5 MN press, container diameter 90 mm, billet temperature 725 °C. *(From Ref 15)*

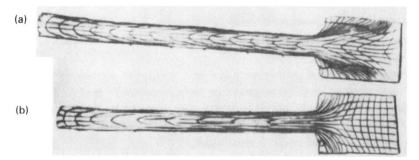

Fig. 1.16. Deformed grid network of CuZn41 after extrusion: **(a)** without container lubrication; **(b)** with container lubrication. *(From Ref 87)*

Theoretically, lubricated cold extrusion with a conical die, as in hydrostatic extrusion, would be another way to avoid friction and, therefore, pipe formation, but the high stresses in the tooling and the reduced output prevent the use of these processes for mass-produced alloys such as brass.

Indirect Extrusion

This method is very effective for changing the flow pattern in the container (see Chap. 2). There is no relative motion between the billet surface and the container, and type A or S flow patterns occur (see section 1.2.2). Consequently, the conditions leading to the formation of pipe are absent. Indirect extrusion has not been used for brass rod production in Germany, even though indirect extrusion presses are used for this material in other countries — for example, France (Ref 86).

1.2.3.3. Scale and Blister Formation

Defects close to the extrusion surface resulting from the formation of scales or blisters can develop if flow patterns of type A or B occur during deformation. This type of defect is caused when the billet surface flows towards the center—following the dead metal zone—as it enters the deformation zone (Fig. 1.7 and 1.17). If there are any impurities, oxide or lubricant on the surface, small particles or even complete layers are dragged along the shear zone and — worst of all — can be trapped under the surface of the extrusion. The likelihood of this occurrence increases proportionately with larger dead metal zones and toward the end of extrusion. Scaling is characterized by thin, and therefore often invisible, scales or folds, depending on the number and types of trapped material; by scales that have been torn open or flakes on the surface of the extrusion; or by lines or blisters if the trapped impurities — for example, a lubricant — form a gas at the deformation temperature. Sometimes the blisters do not appear immediately after extrusion but during a subsequent heat treatment. Extruded copper-chromium alloys, which have to be solution treated at 950 to 1000 °C in order to develop the necessary age-hardening effect, are a typical example, with blisters frequently appearing if impurities are present near the surface.

Because scaling usually appears in the extrusion of metals of flow types A and B, this defect also occurs in indirect extrusion (Fig. 1.18). Three methods that tend to hinder the flow of the billet surface towards the center of the billet can be used to prevent scale formation:

(a) Extrusion without a lubricant and with flat dies.
(b) Extrusion with a shell.
(c) Lubricated extrusion and conical dies.

Extrusion Without a Lubricant and With Flat Dies

Extruding without a lubricant not only removes the possibility of lubricant inclusions but also increases the friction between the billet and the container. This restricts the movement of the billet surface along the container wall to such an extent that it cannot flow into the extrusion. The material,

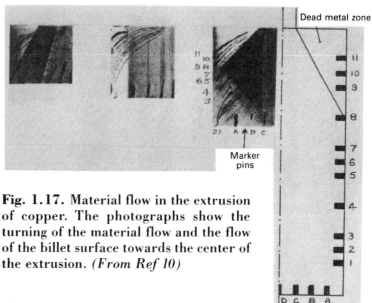

Fig. 1.17. Material flow in the extrusion of copper. The photographs show the turning of the material flow and the flow of the billet surface towards the center of the extrusion. *(From Ref 10)*

Fig. 1.18. Shell formation in indirect extrusion. *(From Ref 84)*

therefore, flows beneath the surface of the billet by shearing and the residual surface layer containing the impurities collects in front of the dummy block. This method, similar to extrusion with a shell, is used in extrusion of aluminum. Metals with oxide skins that act as a lubricant and are, consequently, susceptible to scaling and blistering—for example, copper, copper-chromium and copper-tin alloys — can also be extruded by this method without any defects, provided the billet surface is clean and virtually oxide-free. Low

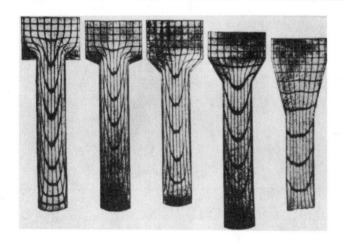

Fig. 1.19. Metal flow in the extrusion of tin billets 22 mm in diameter and 30 mm long through different conical dies with an exit diameter of 11 mm. *(From Ref 12)*

container temperatures and a low billet length-to-diameter ratio are also helpful.

Extrusion With a Shell

If scales and blisters still appear even when no lubricant is used, extrusion with a shell (the same method used to combat pipe formation; see section 1.2.3.2) can be used.

Extrusion With a Lubricant and a Conical Die

An alternative approach to the methods mentioned above is to reduce the dead metal zone to such an extent that there is virtually no possibility that the billet surface will flow into the extrusion. This can be done by using a good lubricant in the container and on the die (Fig. 1.7, flow type S or A). The billet surface will then form the surface of the product; thus, it is essential that billets with clean, smooth (usually, machined) surfaces be used. Conical dies are also employed when extruding with a lubricant, because they increase the desired homogeneity of flow (Fig. 1.19). Nevertheless, blistering cannot be completely eliminated even with lubricated extrusion and conical dies. This sometimes necessitates experimentation to determine the optimum die angle for any given alloy and its extrusion parameters.

1.2.3.4. Internal Defects in Tube Extrusion

Longitudinal strain in piercing a solid billet is relatively small, and therefore friction between the billet and the container does not lead to any problems. On the other hand, friction between the mandrel and the internal billet surface, depending on the alloy and the lubricant, can give rise to a significant distortion of the material flow at the internal surface (Ref 11). Alloys that tend to weld to steel during hot working—including pure aluminum, some aluminum alloys, and various bronzes — deform in a manner similar to type C flow during piercing, and shear zones occur below the internal surface of the billet. In extreme cases material separation can occur. The result is a blotchy, torn internal surface, and material that has welded to the mandrel and is difficult to remove. The flow in extrusion and piercing can be improved by using a lubricant, which helps to obtain a better inner surface. In many cases, however, a lubricant is dangerous, because it can easily be trapped under the tube surface during extrusion, resulting in blistering at higher temperatures (Ref 9).

1.2.3.5. Variations in Structure Along the Length and Cross Section of the Extrusion

Ideally, the extruded product has the same structure throughout its length and cross section, with uniform properties. However, the inhomogeneous nature of the flow in the container results—to varying degrees, according to the flow pattern — in the following:

(a) The peripheral zone of the extrusion undergoes a much more severe plastic deformation than the center because of the effect of friction and shearing (Fig. 1.20 and Ref 9).

(b) The deformation caused by friction and shearing in the peripheral zone increases toward the end of the extrusion and, therefore, covers a larger fraction of the cross section (Fig. 1.15).

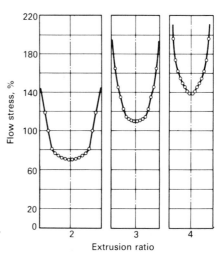

Fig. 1.20. Variations in deformation in extrusion. *(From Ref 11)*

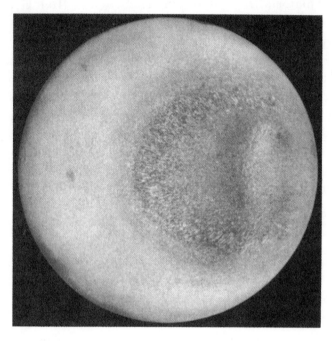

Fig. 1.21. Peripheral (crescent-shaped) and core zones of a transverse section taken from an AlMgSi1 extruded rod (not solution heat treated); both zones are un-recrystallized. *(From VDM Frankfurt)*

(c) The shear deformation in the peripheral zone and at the end of extrusion results in higher temperatures than those in other parts of the deformed billet.

In most cases, cast structure in hot extrusion is removed by recrystallization. Only in the extrusion of heat treatable aluminum alloys is recrystallization during deformation suppressed, because it gives better mechanical properties in the extrusion direction after heat treatment (press effect). The recrystallization that takes place during deformation (dynamic recrystallization) and the resulting distribution in grain size depend on the strain, strain rate and temperature profiles in the deformation zone and the emerging extrusion. Therefore, not only can structural differences and defects be explained by a knowledge of these relationships, but they can also be influenced to some degree. Different alloys, however, exhibit different phenomena, according to the recrystallization temperature.

Low Melting Point Metals Such as Lead and Tin

These metals recrystallize during cold extrusion. The recrystallized grain size in large diameter bars is much finer on the outside than in the center. If critical cold working (5 to 12%) occurs, secondary grain growth and coarse grain recrystallization take place at room temperature.

Aluminum Alloys

Pure aluminum and alloys with a low recrystallization temperature are completely recrystallized under normal hot extrusion conditions. On the other hand, the recrystallization temperature is raised to such an extent in alloys containing recrystallization-retarding elements (e.g., AlMgSi or AlCuMg with Mn, Cr or Zr) that no spontaneous recrystallization takes place during deformation. The rate of recrystallization is lower than the rate of deformation (see Chap. 3 for exceptions). The usual structural changes first occur during the subsequent solution treatment. The unrecrystallized extruded structure of an AlMgSi1 rod is shown in Fig. 1.21. It was extruded through a multihole die, and therefore the heavily deformed peripheral region is distinguished from the less severely deformed central zone by its asymmetrical crescent shape. The recrystallization behavior of the regions originating in

Fig. 1.22. Crescent-shaped coarse-grain recrystallization in an AlMgSi1 rod after solution heat treatment at 530 °C. *(From VDM Frankfurt)*

the shear zones is different from that of the core during solution treatment (≈530 °C). The outer regions can develop a very coarse-grained structure because the unfavorable extrusion conditions and the presence of the recrystallization-inhibiting elements combine to just exceed the critical strain, whereas the central zone does not recrystallize. Figure 1.22 shows a typical example of crescent-shaped coarse-grain recrystallization (multihole extrusion). The increasing tendency to recrystallize toward the end of the extrusion after solution heat treatment can be seen in Fig. 1.23, which

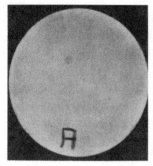 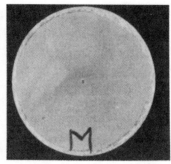 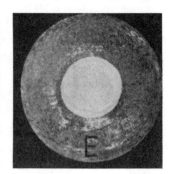

A = Front of rod, unrecrystallized
M = Middle of rod, peripheral zone recrystallized
E = End of rod, larger recrystallized peripheral zone

Fig. 1.23. Macrosections from the front, middle and back of an extruded AlMgSil rod, solution heat treated at 530 °C. *(From VDM Frankfurt)*

shows a rod of AlMgSil extruded through a single-hole die. Attempts have been made to prevent the very undesirable asymmetrical structure that develops during multihole extrusion by selecting the most favorable pitch circle diameter for the die apertures in relation to the container diameter. However, it is almost impossible to prevent this crescent formation in multihole extrusion with only one circle of die orifices. If several concentric pitch circles are used, the shear zone is seen only in the extrusions nearest the edge of the die. The others are screened by the outside ones (Ref 16).

Coarse-grain formation in aluminum alloys can be avoided in several ways. The first is by raising the recrystallization temperature to such a value that both core and peripheral-zone recrystallization is reduced as much as possible or even prevented. This is used especially in the extrusion of high-strength heat treatable alloys, because higher strengths can be attained in the extrusion direction with an unrecrystallized structure than with a recrystallized one (press effect).

At first, the increase in the recrystallization temperature by additions of manganese, chromium and zirconium was attributed only to their influence when in solution (Ref 19). However, Gruhl and Scharf (Ref 20-22) have shown that the retarding effect is due more to the finely dispersed precipitates than to the fraction in solid solution, and that their effect is determined only by their size and distribution — the chemical composition and time of formation being of secondary importance. The important precipitates in the alloys are Al_6Mn, $AlMnFeSi$, Al_3Zr and Mg_2Si. Consequently, methods that provide an optimum distribution of the recrystallization-retarding precipitates can be used to produce extrusions with an unrecrystallized structure. These include moderate homogenization temperatures, short homogenization times or no homogenization at all, and high extrusion temperatures, as well as the lowest possible extrusion ratio. If subsequent heat treatment (solution heat treatment) or hot working is required after extrusion, the methods described above must be used to prevent the critical strain condition from developing, because it leads to coarse-grain formation.

The second method of preventing coarse-grain formation in aluminum alloys is to reduce the recrystallization temperature so that the whole cross section recrystallizes with a fine-grain structure. In this case, the addition of recrystallization-inhibiting elements has to be avoided as far as possible, or else a suitable heat treatment (high homogenizing temperature and a long homogenization time) must be used in order to precipitate certain phases (e.g., phases containing Mn or Mg_2Si) from the supersaturated solid solution. The presence of coarse precipitates lowers the recrystallization temperature, and — in comparison with a structure containing finely dispersed precipitates — the rate of nucleation is increased. Also, the maximum possible extrusion ratio should be used in order to exceed the critical strain by as much as possible and thus obtain a fine-grain recrystallized structure.

Heavy Metals and Steels

Spontaneous recrystallization almost always takes place during the hot extrusion of heavy metal alloys and steels. The large temperature gradient between the billet and the tooling results in a rapid fall in the billet temperature. Hence, from the point of view of the danger of coarse-grain formation, these alloys differ greatly from aluminum alloys. The high extrusion temperature at the start of the process can lead to coarse-grain formation by secondary grain growth if the initial, unsteady deformation is severe enough. A finer-grain structure — with its associated better mechanical properties — develops towards the end of extrusion, as the temperature decreases. If it is impossible to prevent coarse-grain zones and a nonuniform structure by any other means, one almost certain method for the subsequent removal of these defects in rods and tubes is cold drawing with a reduction in area of at least 15%, followed by a recrystallization anneal.

This approach is especially suitable for alloys that must subsequently be solution heat treated or forged after heating at a hot working temperature above the recrystallization temperature. As well as metallurgical methods of preventing coarse-grained structures, practical steps that influence the heterogeneous nature of the internal shearing flow can be used, including that of changing type C or B flow to A or S, indirect extrusion (Fig. 1.24) and lubricated extrusion. A more detailed discussion is given in Chap. 2 and 3.

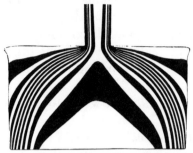 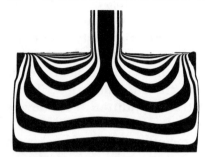

Fig. 1.24. Material flow in extruding two billets of the same material by the indirect (right) and the direct (left) processes; container diameter 130 mm; billet length 500 mm; billet temperature 480 °C; disc method: white, AlMgSi0.5; black, AlSi5 — both anodized 20 μm. *(From Lang, unpublished)*

1.3. Heat Balance and Temperature Changes in Extrusion

Temperature is one of the most important parameters in extrusion. The flow stress is reduced if the temperature is increased and deformation is, therefore, easier but, at the same time, the maximum extrusion speed is reduced, because localized temperature peaks can lead to the melting of eutectics and heterogeneities with low melting points, and a torn surface. The temperature changes during extrusion depend on the billet temperature, the heat transfer from billet to container, and the heat developed by deformation and friction.

1.3.1. Temperature Profile in Hot Billets

During induction heating, heat is developed in the surface of the billet; the depth of penetration depends on the frequency used, and also the permeability and electrical conductivity of the alloy. At a frequency of 50 Hz, the penetration depth for copper is about 15 mm, for brass about 22 mm, and for aluminum about 18 mm. Induction heating gives a very uniform temperature distribution around the billet circumference and, under normal operating conditions with successive billets, a temperature difference of 3 to 4% of the surface temperature between the center and the edge on leaving the furnace. The difference can hardly be measured by the time the billet has reached the press. The temperature variation along the billet length is usually less than 3%

of the surface temperature (Ref 23). Uniformity of heating in gas furnaces depends on the type of furnace and heat transfer. The heat is not developed internally but is transferred to the billet surface by radiation and convection. This can cause large temperature variations if the billet location and method of heat transfer are not carefully controlled. However, in modern gas furnaces the billet is heated, in effect, from all sides and a temperature profile as uniform as that obtained with an induction furnace is developed within a heating cycle of 15 to 20 minutes.

1.3.2. Heat Balance in Extrusion

Very complex thermal changes commence as soon as the hot billet is loaded into the usually preheated container and extrusion started. They consist of the following individual processes:

(a) Production of heat by deformation carried out in the zone in front of the die.
(b) Production of heat by friction between the billet and the container and by shearing at the dead metal zone.
(c) Transfer of heat as the billet moves towards the die.
(d) Conduction of heat to the tooling (container, ram, die).
(e) Conduction of heat to the billet.
(f) Conduction of heat to the extrusion.
(g) Production of heat by friction through the die.

The decisive temperature in extrusion is the exit temperature of the extruded product, which depends on all the above factors. It increases if the heat produced by deformation and friction exceeds the heat losses, and decreases if the reverse is true. Heat conduction requires a definite time and, therefore, depending on the alloy and the extrusion conditions, heat production predominates above a certain ram speed. This explains the dependence of the temperature profile along the length of the extrusion on the ram speed. In borderline cases, adiabatic extrusion occurs: no heat is lost to the surroundings and all the heat developed is retained in the deformed material. The temperature increases by a corresponding amount. The natural laws governing heat balance must be known if the extrusion process is to be under optimal control (a constant exit temperature maintained). Several methods of calculating the quantities of heat evolved and the thermal balances mentioned above have been developed.

1.3.2.1. Akeret's Numerical Method

In this method (Ref 24, 25) the temperatures are calculated point by point or cell by cell. The billet is assumed to be divided into a number of uniform cells (Fig. 1.25), and the heat developed and transferred by the movement of the billet is individually calculated for each element, together with the heat losses to the tooling. The partial numerical solutions for the heat produced and the heat lost can be combined linearly and the temperature profile along the billet in the container and the extrusion obtained. Figure 1.26 gives an example of this type of calculation, using broad steps for four different ratios of billet-to-container temperature in aluminum extrusion.

If the container is at a higher temperature than the billet, the exit temperature increases during extrusion (Fig. 1.27); if it is lower, it increases only at the start of deformation until a constant state is reached (the heat of deformation predominates) and decreases towards the end of extrusion (heat

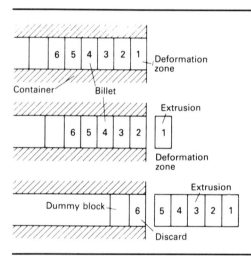

Fig. 1.25. Cell model for calculating the axial temperature profile. **(a)** Billet in container before extrusion: **(b)** front of billet extruded; **(c)** billet extruded as far as the discard (6). *(From Ref 24)*

losses predominate; see Fig. 1.27b). Calculated temperature profiles are compared with experimental results in Fig. 1.27 and 1.28. The combined effect of the individual thermal processes and their effect on the exit temperature are shown schematically in Fig. 1.29 for aluminum (increasing exit temperature) and a heavy metal (decreasing exit temperature, for the most part).

1.3.2.2. Lange's Analytical Method

Lange (Ref 26) developed an analytical solution for the temperature distribution in the deformation zone and the exit temperature of the extrusion. It has the advantage that each calculated quantity is expressed as a direct function of the extrusion and alloy parameters. Relatively complicated mathematical expressions for the radial and axial temperature profiles in the billet and container are obtained from the heat balance by using linear equations for the heat developed and the heat lost.

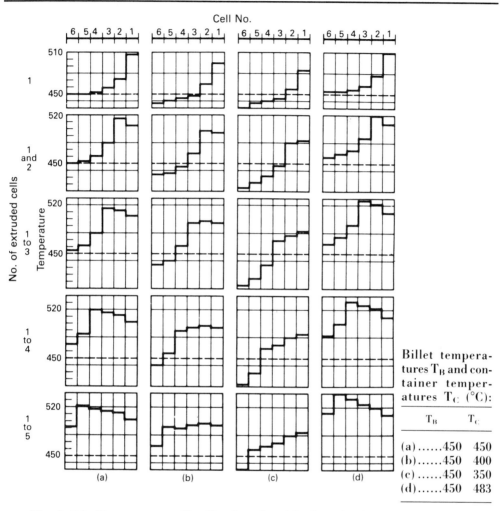

Cell No.

Fig. 1.26. Temperature distribution along the length of the unextruded billet and exit temperature of the extrusion. Extrusion data assumed: billet diameter 200 mm; billet length 600 mm; extrusion pressure 300 N/mm²; temperature increase under adiabatic extrusion 95 °C; ram speed 1 mm/sec; die temperature, constant. *(From Ref 24)*

Billet temperatures T_B and container temperatures T_C (°C):

	T_B	T_C
(a)	450	450
(b)	450	400
(c)	450	350
(d)	450	483

1.3.2.3. Calculation of the Exit Temperature From the Work of Deformation

In comparison with the theoretical method described above, a very simple estimation of the temperature changes during extrusion can be made using the approximate equations of Stüwe (Ref 27). He assumes that

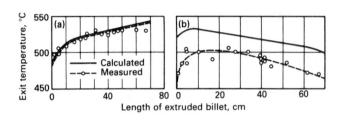

Fig. 1.27. Calculated and measured exit temperature profiles: (a) container hotter than billet; (b) container colder than billet. *(From Ref 24)*

the increase in temperature of the emerging extrusion consists of three components:

(*a*) A temperature increase caused by the work of deformation that is almost entirely converted into heat (adiabatic):

$$\Delta_1 T \approx \frac{k_f \cdot \varphi}{\rho \cdot c_p} \qquad \text{(Eq 3)}$$

where φ is the natural logarithm of the extrusion ratio ($= \ln A_0/A_1$).

(*b*) A temperature increase at the billet surface caused by friction at the container wall, taking the temperature balance within a given surface layer of the billet into account but assuming adiabatic deformation:

$$\Delta_2 T \approx \frac{k_f}{4\rho \cdot c_p} \sqrt{\frac{v_a \cdot L_0}{a \cdot R}} \qquad \text{(Eq 4)}$$

[Typical values of $1/(\rho \cdot c_p)$ in (mm$^2 \cdot$ K)/N are given in the first table under item *c*, below.]

This equation assumes that the heat developed by friction is divided equally and uniformly between the billet and the container to a depth of:

$$y \approx \sqrt{\frac{a \cdot L_0 \cdot R}{v_a}} \qquad \text{(Eq 5)}$$

(*c*) A temperature increase at the extrusion surface caused by friction at the die lands:

$$\Delta_3 T \approx \frac{k_f}{4\rho \cdot c_p} \sqrt{\frac{s \cdot v_a}{a}} \qquad \text{(Eq 6)}$$

The depth of heating caused by this temperature difference is:

$$y_s \approx \sqrt{\frac{a \cdot s}{v_a}}$$

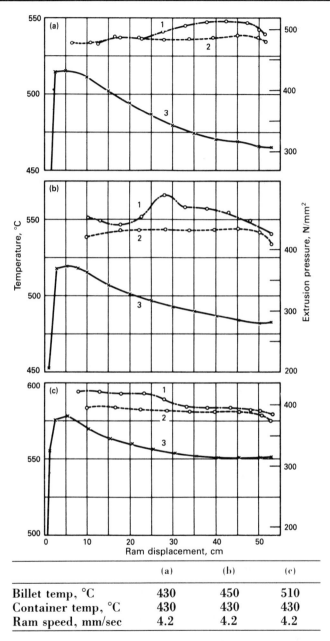

	(a)	(b)	(c)
Billet temp, °C	430	450	510
Container temp, °C	430	430	430
Ram speed, mm/sec	4.2	4.2	4.2

Fig. 1.28. Measured and calculated profile of the extrusion exit temperature in the extrusion of AlMgSi0.5. **Curve 1:** measured temperature; **Curve 2:** calculated temperature for a container temperature of 480 °C; **Curve 3:** extrusion pressure. *(From Ref 80)*

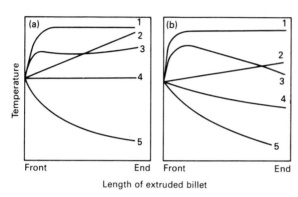

1 — Heat produced by deformation
2 — Heat produced by shearing
3 — Exit temperature of the product
4 — Initial temperature of the billet
5 — Cooling due to heat losses to the tooling

Fig. 1.29. Combined effect of heat production and heat conduction: (a) for aluminum at low to average extrusion temperatures *(from Ref 25)*; (b) for heavy metals or high extrusion temperatures, respectively.

The following data are used to calculate the values of ΔT:

Material	$\dfrac{1}{\rho \cdot c_p} \left(\dfrac{mm^2 \cdot K}{N} \right)$
Al	0.409
Cu	0.291
Pb	0.686
Fe	0.283
Mg	0.560
Zn	0.360

The values in the following table were obtained for the extrusion of aluminum and copper, with an extrusion ratio of 30, corresponding to $\varphi = \ln 30 = 3.4$; a billet length of 800 mm; a k_f (N/mm^2) of 39.2:

Material	Temp, °C	v_a(a) (m/min)	$\Delta_1 T$ (°C)	$\Delta_2 T$ (°C)	$\Delta_3 T$(b) (°C)
Al	450	60	54	71	27
Cu	800	150	39	81	31

(a) Assumed values. (b) Assuming that s = 4 mm.

1.3.2.4. Temperature Increase at the Extrusion Surface Caused by Friction at the Die Lands

The temperature rise caused by friction between the metal and the die lands calculated in section 1.3.2.3 using Stüwe's method (Ref 27) shows that this heat source cannot be neglected. On the contrary, it has a decisive

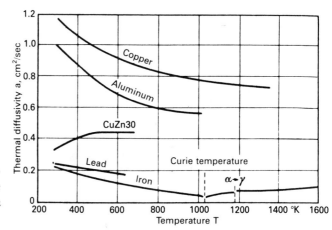

Fig. 1.30. Thermal diffusivity as a function of the absolute temperature. *(From Ref 27)*

influence on the maximum admissible billet temperature and extrusion speed for the following reasons:

(a) The usually relatively high exit speed and the related brief contact time (< 0.005 sec) mean that the temperature increaee is concentrated in a thin surface layer, which endangers the total surface.

(b) The heating of the outside regions leads to a concentration of heat, especially at sharp edges on the extrusion, which increases the danger of hot shortness.

(c) The temperature of the surface regions is already higher than that on the inside, because of the shearing and friction in the container (Ref 14).

In practice, if the exit temperature or speed is too high, tearing initially starts at the edges of the extrusion and then develops over the remainder of the surface (Fig. 1.31). The press operator uses these observations to regulate the press speed. Lange (Ref 26) has also attempted to calculate the temperature increase at the surface, especially at the edges. Sections that are not too small are extruded at relatively high speeds, and therefore the temperature at the center remains almost constant. Based on experience, Lange assumes the temperature rise at the edges to be twice that at the midpoint of the sides, and he arrives at:

$$T = \frac{2.26 \cdot b_e \cdot \tau}{(b_d + b_e) \cdot \lambda} \sqrt{a \cdot s \cdot v_a} \qquad \text{(Eq 7)}$$

The index e refers to the extrusion; the index d to the die.

The temperature increase at the edges of a square section was calculated using Eq 7, and the results are shown in Fig. 1.32. The importance of the length of the die land on the temperature rise is illustrated in Fig. 1.33. This effect

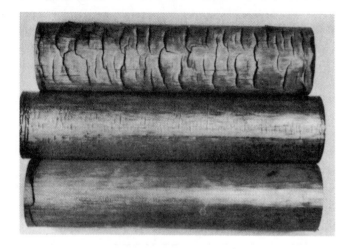

Fig. 1.31. Surface cracks (hot shortness) of differing degrees of severity on an extruded CuSn8 tube. *(From Ref 91)*

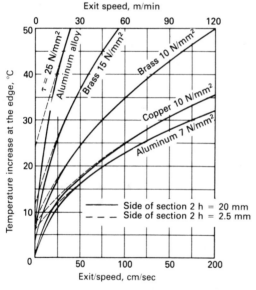

Fig. 1.32. Temperature increase at the edge of an extruded square bar. *(From Ref 26)*

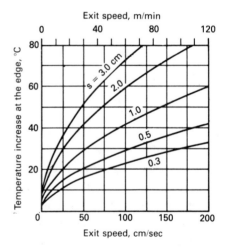

Fig. 1.33. Effect of the ram speed and die land length on the temperature rise at the edge of an extruded square aluminum bar (side of section 2 h = 20 mm). *(From Ref 26)*

should be of special consideration in die design. For example, Fig. 1.33 and Eq 7 show that it is possible to extrude with double the exit speed and the same temperature increase only if the length of the die lands is reduced by half. The exit temperature profile in complicated sections apparently has not yet been studied.

1.3.3. "Isothermal" Extrusion

As discussed in previous sections, the exit temperature can increase or decrease during extrusion with a constant ram speed, depending on whether the predominating factor is the development of heat by friction and deformation in the container or heat losses to the tooling, especially the container. A temperature increase towards the end of extrusion is observed—in agreement with the theoretical calculation — if either the exit speed is high or the container temperature is only slightly below or equal to that of the billet (Ref 28-30). Extrusion with a constant exit temperature is of practical interest for achieving a uniform product quality or for making the most efficient use of the maximum speed that the alloy can withstand without hot shortness developing. The basic idea of so-called isothermal extrusion developed from a knowledge of the relationship between the exit temperature and the ram speed. The exit speed is varied via the press control system to give a constant exit temperature.

The practical—that is, economic—value of so-called isothermal extrusion is that, except at the very beginning, it allows the use of the optimum extrusion speed over the complete extrusion cycle. On the other hand, if the exit temperature varies during extrusion by an unknown amount, the press speed is usually adjusted in accordance with the maximum prevailing temperature. This sets the speed for the whole cycle and there is a wasted surplus speed capacity in the region of low exit temperature. This is shown schematically in Fig. 1.34. The temperature profile at a constant speed must first be determined by measurement in each case in order to decide whether isothermal extrusion is feasible and how the press control system should be modified. In the first example in Fig. 1.34, with a continually increasing exit temperature typical of aluminum alloy extrusion, isothermal extrusion can be carried out in the following ways:

(a) Reducing the extrusion speed during the extrusion according to the measured exit temperature. This requires continuous temperature measurement. The method is illustrated in Fig. 1.35 and isothermal extrusion is obtained in the fifth extrusion.

(b) Reducing the extrusion speed according to a preselected speed program. On a modern press the ram displacement can be divided into steps of varying lengths, each with its own programed speed.

(c) Nonuniform heating of the billet to give a lower temperature at the back of the billet. This is known as "taper heating" and can be achieved by induction heating with suitable coil connections or by using additional burners, which transfer more heat to the front of the billet than to the rear, in gas furnaces. Another method is to heat the billet uniformly and then quench the back end with a water spray as the billet is transferred from the furnace to the container. Lange has calculated the necessary profile in the billet (Ref 26).

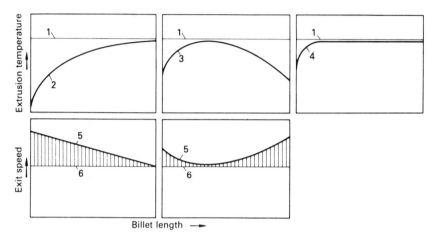

1 — Maximum permitted extrusion temperature (start of cracking)
2 — Exit temperature increases
3 — Exit temperature reaches a maximum, then decreases
4 — Exit temperature profile for "isothermal" extrusion
5 — Possible extrusion speed in "isothermal" extrusion
6 — Actual extrusion speed
Shaded area: unused speed reserve

Fig. 1.34. Relationship between temperature profile and usable extrusion speed in "isothermal" extrusion (schematic). *(From Ref 30)*

Only the first two methods can be used in the second example in Fig. 1.34, which is characterized by a maximum exit temperature followed by a decrease. A profile of this type can occur in aluminum extrusion if the container is relatively cold, but it is more typical of heavy metals — that is, at higher extrusion temperatures (>500 °C). It is possible to compensate for the heat losses only towards the end of extrusion of high speed alloys by raising the ram speed with a hydraulic accumulator system or a mechanical crank drive, provided the press has the power given by $P = F \cdot v$.

1.3.4. Maximum Extrusion Speed

The extrusion load is a function of the flow stress of the alloy being extruded. The essence of hot working is that the deformation is carried out at a high temperature in order to reduce the yield stress to a value that enables high strains to be attained economically. Alloys with high flow stresses have to be heated to very high deformation temperatures. However, if the exit temperature resulting from the initial billet temperature and the extrusion speed is

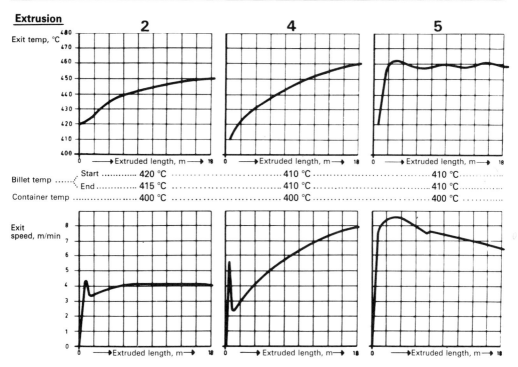

Fig. 1.35. Increase in the extrusion exit temperature at a constant extrusion speed (left), an increasing extrusion speed (center) and "isothermal" extrusion with a decreasing speed (right); the difference in speed between the 5th and the 2nd extrusion illustrates the increase in output. *(From Ref 30)*

too close to the solidus temperature, the surface tears and roughens and is unacceptable. A plot of the maximum speed against the extrusion temperature gives two limiting curves, Fig. 1.36. One represents the extrusion load limiting line, above which deformation is impossible, and the other the metallurgical limit, where the alloy starts to tear (Fig. 1.31 and Ref 81). The area between the two curves gives all possible working parameters for the extrusion of the alloy and, in particular, provides information about the theoretical maximum possible speed and the corresponding optimum exit temperature. It must be stressed that this optimum refers only to the extrusion speed and not to the physico-metallurgical properties of the product.

There are two basic types of work diagrams. The first has a wide operating range, similar to that shown schematically in Fig. 1.37a, which is typical for alloys that are easy to extrude, including Al99.5, AlMgSi0.5, E-Cu and the β-brasses. The second is found with the more difficult alloys and has a

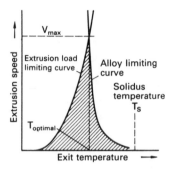

Fig. 1.36. Limit diagram for extrusion speed. *(From Ref 81)*

narrow working range below the maximum speed of the press (Fig. 1.37b). In both cases the extrusion load limiting curve is favorably displaced to the left as the press capacity increases or the deformation efficiency is improved. On the other hand, the working range decreases if the extrusion ratio, billet diameter, billet length, or the flow stress increases or if the section requires a higher load (Ref 69). These parameters have to be varied to increase the exit speed. Metallurgical methods can also be used, including heat treating the alloy to decrease the yield stress (Ref 68, 82, 83).

Systematic optimization of the extrusion parameters is simplified if the location and magnitude of the working range — the shape of the limiting curves — are described mathematically and a solution obtained for the point of intersection. This solution can be used to study the influences of the different press parameters on the maximum speed. Limit diagrams for hot shortness have been determined using experimental results obtained with aluminum alloys, and it has been shown that they can be described adequately by an exponential function:

$$v_{RA} = a^* \cdot e^{-b^* T^2} \tag{Eq 8}$$

where a^* and b^* are constants, and T is the exit temperature referred to a reference temperature (index A = alloy).

The extrusion load curve is obtained from elementary theory (see section 1.4) and the maximum possible ram speed for a given press capacity is given as a function of the material and the extrusion parameters by:

$$v_{KP} = \left[\frac{F_{max}}{k_{f0} \left(\dfrac{6\varphi}{D_0} \right)^{m^*} e^{-d^* T^2} \left(A_0 \cdot \varphi \dfrac{1}{\eta_F} + \pi D_0 \cdot L_0 \mu_F \right)} \right]^{\frac{1}{m^*}} \tag{Eq 9}$$

This equation describes the dependence of the attainable extrusion speed on all the factors that influence the load.

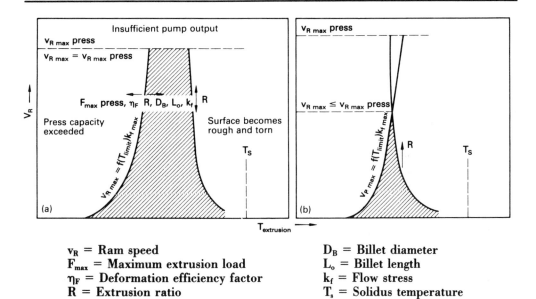

v_R = Ram speed
F_{max} = Maximum extrusion load
η_F = Deformation efficiency factor
R = Extrusion ratio

D_B = Billet diameter
L_o = Billet length
k_f = Flow stress
T_s = Solidus temperature

Fig. 1.37. Working range of an extrusion press in a v-T diagram for: **(a)** an easily extruded alloy; **(b)** a difficult alloy. *(From Ref 81)*

The point of intersection of the load limiting curve and the limiting curve for the onset of hot shortness gives the maximum extrusion speed. Equating v_{RA} and v_{RP}:

$$v_{R\ max} = \left[\frac{F_{max} \cdot a^{*f^*}}{k_{f0} \left(\dfrac{6\varphi}{D_0} \right)^{m^*} \left(A_0 \varphi \dfrac{1}{\eta_F} + \pi D_0 L_0 \mu_F \right)} \right]^{\frac{1}{m^* + f^*}} \qquad (Eq\,10)$$

The maximum extrusion speed is fully defined only when the extrusion parameters are specified and the constants known. After the constants have been obtained experimentally from production data (Ref 81), the influence of the extrusion parameters on the maximum speed can be studied. Figure 1.38 shows, for example, the calculated dependence of the maximum extrusion speed on the press capacity (F_{max}) and the container diameter for the alloy AlMgSi0.5. Even a relatively small increase in the press capacity yields a significant increase in the maximum speed. The diagram also gives the container sizes with which the maximum exit speed is too low to be economically viable. This kind of optimization is of particular importance for alloys that are difficult to extrude. The working range of these alloys is very limited because the load limit curve (sticking billet) and the hot shortness curve are very close together (Fig. 1.37b).

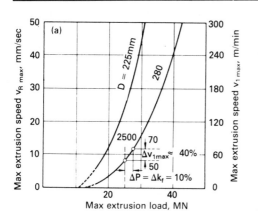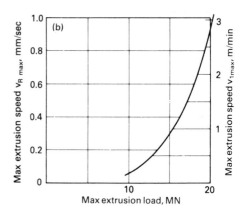

Fig. 1.38. Dependence of the maximum exit speed on the press capacity calculated for the alloys: **(a)** AlMgSi0.5; **(b)** AlCuMg1 ($v_{1\ max} = R\cdot v_{R\ max} =$ max exit speed).

1.4. Load and Energy Requirements in Extrusion

1.4.1. Survey of Methods of Calculation

Methods of calculating the loads and stresses that occur during extrusion are an important aid for the production engineer in determining the ease with which a certain product can be extruded, and, for the toolmaker, press manufacturer and plant designer, in the design and layout of new plants.

Several methods for calculating the deformation load have been developed since the start of systematic extrusion research. They differ from each other in the assumptions made, the method and complexity of analysis, the theoretical basis and the degree of approximation of the solution. The solution obtained by elementary analysis has proved to be the most useful in practice, because of its simplicity. Therefore, this method is given priority but the basic principles of the most important other methods are also compared.

1.4.1.1. Elementary Analysis

The starting point of this approach is the influence of the material, extrusion ratio, temperature and friction between the billet and the container on the magnitude of the work of deformation (Ref 12, 31, 34).

A considerable amount of calculation would be required to obtain the total work of deformation from the nonuniform distribution of strain and deformation energy in the deformation zone. Therefore, the billet is assumed to deform homogeneously with plane sections remaining plane. Tresca's yield criterion (Ref 1) is used for the three-dimensional state of stress — with principal stresses of $\sigma_1 > \sigma_2 > \sigma_3$ — that develops in each element of volume under the applied ram load (section 1.1.2, Eq 1). Frictionless deformation of an element of volume by a change in length of dL requires the ideal deformation load F_{id}. The ideal work of deformation is:

$$dW_{id} = FdL \qquad \text{(Eq 11)}$$

For uniaxial loading:

$$F = A \cdot k_f \qquad \text{(Eq 12)}$$

which can be extended to:

$$F = \frac{V}{L} \cdot k_f \qquad \text{(Eq 12a)}$$

giving:

$$dW_{id} = V \cdot k_f \cdot \frac{dL}{L} \qquad \text{(Eq 13)}$$

Therefore:

$$W_{id} = V \cdot k_f \int_{L_1}^{L_0} dL/L \qquad \text{(Eq 14)}$$

$$\int_{L_1}^{L_0} \frac{dL}{L} = \ln L \int_{L_1}^{L_0} = \ln \frac{L_1}{L_0} = \varphi \qquad \text{(Eq 15)}$$

The volume remains constant. Therefore:

$$A_B \cdot L_0 = A_1 \cdot L_1 \qquad \text{(Eq 16)}$$

$$\ln L_1/L_0 = \varphi = \ln \frac{A_B}{A_1} \qquad \text{(Eq 17)}$$

Hence:

$$W_{id} = V \cdot k_f \cdot \varphi \qquad \text{(Eq 18)}$$

$$F_{id} = \frac{W_{id}}{L} = A_B \cdot k_f \cdot \varphi \qquad \text{(Eq 19)}$$

1.4.1.2. Plasticity Analysis Using Slip-Line Field Theory

This method, based on plasticity theory, can be applied to plane strain (two-dimensional) deformation, where one of the three principal stresses is

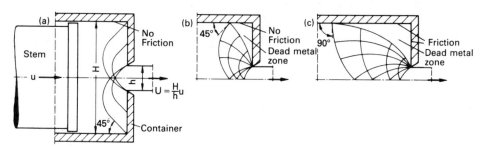

Fig. 1.39. Typical slip-line field solutions for extrusion: **(a)** lubricated extrusion without a dead metal zone; **(b)** lubricated extrusion with a dead metal zone; **(c)** unlubricated extrusion with a larger dead metal zone. *(From Ref 33)*

zero or, in exceptional cases, to three-dimensional axially symmetrical deformation. The basic principle is that a network of slip-lines is constructed in the deformation plane and the stress condition deduced from it (Ref 32). Slip-lines indicate the direction of the principal shear stress at every point. Two effective principal shear stresses operate perpendicular to each other at every point in the surface. The construction, therefore, gives two slip-lines intersecting at 90°. The net result is an orthogonal field of slip-lines in the plane of deformation. The first solution for extrusion was given by Hill (Ref 33) and further ones for specific cases have since been obtained from his model, similar to those in Fig. 1.39 (Ref 35-38).

The mean extrusion pressure is obtained from the slip-line field by mathematical analysis and by solving the differential equations for the slip-lines using the Hencky integrals, and can be expressed approximately in the form:

$$\frac{F}{k_f} = A^* + B^* \cdot \ln \frac{A_B}{A_l} + C^* \cdot L = A^* + B^* \cdot \varphi + C^* \cdot L \qquad \text{(Eq 20)}$$

where L is the actual billet length in the container. The term A^* represents the losses due to shearing (redundant work), $B^* \cdot \varphi$ the work of deformation, and $C^* \cdot L$ the friction in the container. Values for A^*, B^* and C^* have been determined by Hirst and Ursell (Ref 40) and discussed in detail by Alexander (Ref 41).

1.4.1.3. Estimating an Upper and Lower Bound for the Extrusion Load

This method is based on the basic plasticity equations and — in contrast to an exact solution — gives an upper and a lower bound for the deformation load without involved mathematics. The true value of the deformation load is situated between the two limits, and the closer these are the more accurate is the solution. The calculation, however, is then more complex. Lippmann (Ref 43) applied this method to plane strain extrusion (Fig. 1.40; the strain perpendicular to the plane of the diagram is zero) and also to axisymmetric extrusion, where Y is the radius r, H is the container diameter D_0, and h is the extrusion diameter d. Equations for the upper and lower bounds of the mean ram pressure $\bar{p}$, referred to the flow stress k_f, are obtained from the assumed stress and velocity conditions, which are assumed to be constant in fields I to IV (Fig. 1.40). There is a considerable discrepancy in the values obtained for $\bar{p}/k_f$ for steady state extrusion, but the upper bound solution is supposed to give better agreement with experimentally measured ram pressures than does the lower bound (Ref 43). The upper bound solution for the steady state is:

$$\frac{\bar{p}}{k_f} \leq C^* + \left(1 - \left[\frac{d}{D_0}\right]^2\right) + \frac{2}{\sqrt{3}} \cdot \frac{D_0}{d} \cdot \frac{a_l}{D_0}$$

$$+ \frac{1}{6\sqrt{3}}\left(1 - \frac{d}{D_0}\right)\left(\left[\frac{d}{D_0}\right]^2 + \frac{d}{D_0} + 2\right)\frac{D_0}{a_l} \qquad \text{(Eq 21)}$$

where C^* is an integration constant:

$$C^* = \frac{1}{\sqrt{3}}\left\{2 - \sqrt{1 + \left[\frac{d}{D_0}\right]^4} - \frac{1}{2}\ln\left(3\frac{\sqrt{1 + 3\left[\frac{d}{D_0}\right]^4} - 1}{\sqrt{1 + 3\left[\frac{d}{D_0}\right]^4} + 1}\right)\right\} \qquad \text{(Eq 22)}$$

For the symbols used, see Fig. 1.40.

---

d = Exit diameter (h)

v_R = Ram speed (u)

D_0 = Container diameter (dummy block diameter) (H)

$D_0/d \cdot v_R$ = Exit speed for plane deformation ($\frac{H}{h} \cdot$ u)

a_l = Length of deformation zone (a)

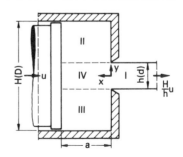

Fig. 1.40. Stress and velocity condition constant in each field, I to IV. *(From Ref 43)*

1.4.2. Methods Used in Practice Based on Elementary Analysis

1.4.2.1. Calculation of the Work of Deformation and the Extrusion Load

In practice, problems are usually solved by elementary analysis because it is easy to understand and simple to use. For frictionless extrusion the ideal extrusion load F_{id} is obtained from the ideal work of deformation (section 1.4.1.1). However, additional work W_S is required, over and above the homogeneous work of deformation, to overcome the shearing deformation — redundant work — in the deformation zone (and friction at the die), as well as the work W_F needed to overcome the friction between the billet and the container, or to shear the material close to the billet surface if sticking friction occurs:

$$W_T = W_{id} + W_S + W_F \qquad \text{(Eq 23)}$$

W_S is difficult to determine theoretically, and so it is combined with W_{id}, and the efficiency of the deformation is defined as:

$$\eta_f = \frac{W_{id}}{W_{id} + W_S} \qquad \text{(Eq 24)}$$

which can be measured and which enables the redundant work to be allowed for empirically.

The following expression is then obtained:

$$W_{id} + W_S = \frac{W_{id}}{\eta_F} = V \cdot \varphi \cdot \frac{k_f}{\eta_F} \qquad \text{(Eq 25)}$$

The term k_f / η_F is known as the deformation resistance k_w. It differs from the flow stress k_f, which is a material constant, inasmuch as it includes the internal shearing losses that depend on the geometry of deformation and the die friction. The additional work that has to be expended to overcome the friction between the billet surface and the container is:

$$W_F = F_F \cdot L = U \cdot L^2 \cdot \mu_F \cdot k_f = \pi \cdot D_0 \cdot L^2 \cdot \mu_F \cdot k_f \qquad \text{(Eq 26)}$$

The expression for the total work then becomes:

$$W_T = V \cdot \varphi \cdot k_w + \pi \cdot D_0 \cdot L^2 \cdot \mu_F \cdot k_f \qquad \text{(Eq 27)}$$

and the total load is given by:

$$F_T = A_0 \cdot \varphi \cdot k_w + \pi \cdot D_0 \cdot L \cdot \mu_F \cdot k_f \qquad \text{(Eq 28)}$$

This is identical to the equation given by Siebel and Fangmeier (Ref 31). Other workers have used a different approach, especially for the friction at the container wall — for example, using an exponential function (Ref 12, 34 and others) or, when sticking friction occurs, replacing $\mu_F \cdot k_f$ by τ (Ref 27, 44). They have also made allowances for the dead metal zone. These minor differences will not be discussed in detail.

1.4.2.2. Flow Stress

The flow stress k_f is a material constant for homogeneous deformation. It varies with temperature, strain (in cold working) and strain rate (especially in hot working), and is measured experimentally as a function of these factors. The method used is usually selected to give uniaxial stressing, because this simplifies the analysis.

In uniaxial tension (i.e., up to the onset of necking in a normal tensile test):

$$\sigma_2 = \sigma_3 = 0$$

$$k_f = \sigma_1 = \frac{F}{A} \tag{Eq 29}$$

where F is the tensile load, and A the corresponding cross-sectional area. In compression tests (where uniaxial pressure is obtained if friction at the ends of the specimen is eliminated):

$$\sigma_1 = \sigma_2 = 0$$
$$k_f = -\sigma_3 = \frac{F}{A} \tag{Eq 30}$$

where F is the compressive load.

In torsion tests (pure shearing):

$$k_f = 2\tau_F \tag{Eq 31}$$

where τ_F is the measured shear stress.

Diagrams of the variation in flow stress with strain $\varphi = \ln A_0/A_1$ are known as stress-strain curves. The flow stress increases with increasing strain in cold working by an amount depending on the alloy (work hardening), whereas in hot working the stress is almost independent of the strain because no work hardening takes place. Only a low uniform strain can be attained in tensile tests, and so the flow stress is measured by a compression or a torsion test. The latter gives constant stress conditions up to failure and, consequently, k_f can be measured up to high strains together with the strain to fracture, which can be used as a measure of the workability (see Chap.

3). However, because the high temperature flow stress depends on the strain rate, it is important to keep the strain rate constant during the test. The constant speed of rotation used in torsion tests fulfills this need. In compression tests the rate of compression has to be varied as a function of the height of the specimen.

1.4.2.3. The Effect of Temperature and Strain Rate on the Flow Stress

The decrease in flow stress with increasing temperature and the increase at higher strain rates have been measured in several studies. The effect of temperature measured in these experiments can be directly applied to extrusion. On the other hand, a relationship between the experimental strain rate (tensile, compression or torsion tests) and that in extrusion has to be found. The strain rate is defined as the strain per unit time (usually seconds):

$$\dot{\varphi} = \frac{d\varphi}{dt} \qquad\qquad (Eq\ 32)$$

for a constant strain:

$$\dot{\varphi} = \frac{\varphi}{t} \qquad\qquad (Eq\ 33)$$

The complex flow pattern in the deformation zone creates problems in determining the strain rate. The material undergoes a rapid acceleration as it passes through the deformation zone and, therefore, a mean strain rate has to be estimated for determining the extrusion load (Ref 27, 45). The deformation zone is assumed to be conical for simplicity. The mean strain rate is given by (Ref 27):

$$\dot{\varphi}_{mean} \approx 6v_R \cdot \frac{\varphi}{D_0} \qquad\qquad (Eq\ 34)$$

The maximum strain rate at the entry to the die is given approximately by:

$$\dot{\varphi}_{max} \approx \frac{2v_a}{d} \qquad\qquad (Eq\ 35)$$

where d is the diameter or the equivalent diameter calculated from the cross sectional area of the extrusion.

Experimental values of flow stress have been published by many authors (Ref 46-64). Figure 1.41 gives a summary of the dependence of the flow stress on the temperature for several alloys. The effect of the strain rate is shown in Fig. 1.42. A straight-line relationship is obtained by plotting the results on a double logarithmic scale and can be expressed by the exponential equation:

$$k_f = K^* \cdot \dot{\varphi}^{m^*} \qquad\qquad (Eq\ 36)$$

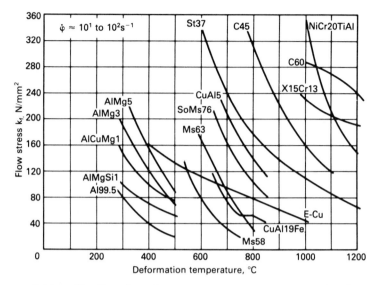

St37 = Unalloyed steel 37 (tensile strength ≈ 370 N/mm^2)
SoMs76 = CuZn20Al
Ms58 = CuZn39Pb3
Ms63 = CuZn37
E-Cu = Copper, conductor grade
X15Cr13 = Chromium steel (0.15% C, 13% Cr)
C45 = Carbon steel, 0.45% C
C60 = Carbon steel, 0.60% C

Fig. 1.41. Dependence of the flow stress on the deformation temperature.

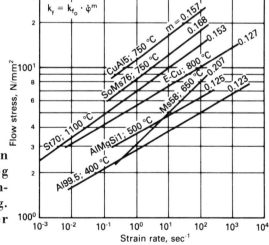

Fig. 1.42. Influence of the strain rate on the flow stress (log-log plot). St 70 = Unalloyed steel (tensile strength ≈ 700 N/mm^2); see Fig. 1.41 for identification of other designations.

Inasmuch as the starting point of any calculation is always a known value k_{f0} at a known strain rate $\dot{\varphi}_0$, Eq 36 is better expressed as:

$$k_f = k_{f0} \left(\frac{\dot{\varphi}}{\dot{\varphi}_0} \right)^{m^*} \qquad \text{(Eq 37)}$$

The gradients of the straight lines shown in Fig. 1.42 are very similar in spite of the very different alloys. The exponent m^* is obtained by:

$$m^* = \frac{\log \dfrac{k_f}{k_{f0}}}{\log \dfrac{\dot{\varphi}}{\dot{\varphi}_0}} \qquad \text{(Eq 38)}$$

The values for m^* are included in Fig. 1.42.

Example: the flow stress k_{f0} of an alloy is 69 N/mm^2 at a strain rate $\dot{\varphi}_0$ of 1 sec^{-1}. If m^* is 0.14, the flow stress at the strain rate of $\dot{\varphi} = 100$ sec^{-1} is given by:

$$k_f = k_{f0} \left(\frac{\dot{\varphi}}{\dot{\varphi}_0} \right)^{m^*} = 69 \cdot 100^{0.14} = 131 \text{ N/mm}^2$$

Approximate values for the flow stresses of different alloys are given in Table 1.1.

Table 1.1. Approximate Values of the Flow Stress k_f for the Most Common Working Temperatures(a)
$\varphi = 2.5 \, [= \ln (A_0/A_1)]$

Material	Temp, °C	Strain rate, $\dot{\varphi}$ (s^{-1})	k_f (N/mm^2)	Material	Temp, °C	Strain rate, $\dot{\varphi}$ (s^{-1})	k_f (N/mm^2)
Al99.5	400	1	32	AlCuPbBi	400	1	53
	500	1	18		500	1	42
AlMn	400	1	43	AlCuMg1(b) . . .	400	0.2	80
	500	1	23		500	0.2	18
AlMg1	400	1	67	AlCuMg2	350	1	88
	500	1	42		450	1	63
AlMg3	400	1	83	AlZnMgCu1.5	350	1	88
	500	1	53		400	1	74
AlMg5	400	1	95	E-Cu(99.98) . . .	690	0.0006	85
	500	1	56	SE-Cu	850	3.3	56
AlMgMn(b)	360	0.25	98		950	3.8	37
	480	0.25	55	SF-Cu	500	1.23	148
AlMg4.5Mn(b)	360	0.25	115		700	1.23	78
	480	0.25	55		900	1.23	42
AlMgSi0.5	400	1	38	CuZn1.5	600	2.5	142
	500	1	24		800	2.5	67
AlMgSi1	400	1	39	CuZn10	600	2.5	186
	500	1	30		800	2.5	88
AlZnMg1	400	1	66	CuZn20	600	2.5	197
	500	1	42		800	2.5	83

Table 1.1 (continued). Approximate Values of the Flow Stress k_f for the Most Common Working Temperatures(a)

$\varphi = 2.5 \, [= \ln \, (A_0/A_1)]$

Material	Temp, °C	Strain rate, $\dot{\varphi}$ (s^{-1})	k_f (N/mm^2)	Material	Temp, °C	Strain rate, $\dot{\varphi}$ (s^{-1})	k_f (N/mm^2)
CuZn28	600	3	195	CuNi30Fe	1000	2.8	120
	800	3	65		1100	3.1	97
CuZn30	600	2.5	183	CuNi30Cr3 ...	1000	0.9	113
	800	2.5	65	CuAl5........	700	3	190
CuZn35	600	2.5	155		800	3	130
	800	2.5	40	CuAl8Fe......	900	3	75
CuZn37	600	3	145	CuAl10Fe.....	650	3	100
	800	3	35		750	3	45
CuZn40	600	2.5	62	CuBe2	700	10	215
	800	2.5	12		800	10	150
CuZn20Al	700	3	150	CuAg	950	3.3	48
	800	3	90	CuSi3Mn	700	2.9	128
CuZn28Sn	700	3	140		900	3.4	55
	800	3	85	LC-Ni........	1000	1.9	128
CuZn35Ni	700	3	63	NiCr20Ti.....	1000	2.5	275
	800	3	14		1200	2.5	147
CuZn38Pb1 ...	500	0.1	86	NiCr20TiAl ...	1000	2.5	314
	600	0.1	50		1200	2.5	147
CuZn39Pb3 ...	600	3	70	NiCr20Co18Ti	1000	2.5	324
	700	3	30		1200	2.5	157
CuSn2	600	2.5	260	Sn...........	RT	0.01	34
	800	2.5	140	Pb...........	RT	0.01	20
CuSn5	600	2.5	270	Mg	350	0.01	29
	800	2.5	145	In	RT	0.01	2
CuSn6	600	2.5	310	St37	1000	75	177
	800	2.5	120		1200	75	118
CuSn8	800	2.9	125	C15..........	1000	360	226
CuSn10	600	2.5	275		1200	360	167
	700	2.5	190	C45..........	1000	79	196
CuNi3Si......	800	3	230		1200	79	118
	900	3	145	C60..........	1000	400	226
CuNi5Fe	890	1.2	80		1200	400	172
CuNi10Fe.....	800	3	125	C100W2......	1000	400	226
	1000	3	67		1200	400	167
CuNi17Zn20 ..	800	3	153	X15Cr3	1000	400	221
	1000	3	68		1200	400	186
CuNi20.......	920	1.9	103	X15Cr13	1000	400	231
CuNi30.......	1000	2	142		1200	400	191

(a) From *Atlas of Hot Working Properties of Nonferrous Metals*, Ref 89. (b) $\varphi = 0.5$.

1.4.2.4. Deformation Resistance and the Efficiency Factor

The deformation resistance k_w includes the flow stress k_f, the internal shearing losses that arise during deformation, and the losses due to friction of the die. It does not take into account friction between the container and the billet. From Eq 28:

$$F_T = A_0 \cdot k_w \cdot \varphi + F_F \qquad \qquad \text{(Eq 39)}$$

The deformation resistance is measured by extruding most of the billet and, because the billet length is then small, the component caused by friction on the container is virtually eliminated and $F_F \approx 0$. Therefore:

$$k_w \approx \frac{F_T}{A_0 \cdot \varphi} \qquad \qquad \text{(Eq 40)}$$

With this assumption, k_w and the efficiency factor η_F obtained from k_w and k_f by:

$$\eta_F = \frac{k_f}{k_w} \qquad \qquad \text{(Eq 41)}$$

have been measured, using a small research press. The values are given in Table 1.2. These results also demonstrate that the efficiency factor increases

Table 1.2. Deformation Resistance k_w and Deformation Efficiency Factor η_F in Extrusion With and Without a Lubricant (From Ref 2)

Material	Temp, °C	Billet lubricant	k_w (N/mm²)	η_F
Al99.5	350	Oil/graphite	152 to 168	0.33 to 0.30
	400	Oil/graphite	147 to 178	0.26 to 0.21
	450	Oil/graphite	83 to 125	0.34 to 0.22
	500	Oil/graphite	74 to 94	0.34 to 0.21
CuZn39Pb2	650	Oil/graphite	102 to 166	0.44 to 0.27
	700	Oil/graphite	79 to 98	0.32 to 0.26
	750	Oil/graphite	79 to 98	0.23 to 0.21
	800	Oil/graphite	46 to 79	0.33 to 0.19
	800	None	39 to 48	0.39 to 0.31
CuZn40	800	None	35 to 46	0.51 to 0.39
	800	Rough surface	29 to 34	0.69 to 0.59
CuZn37	750	Oil/graphite	180 to 186	0.28 to 0.27
	800	Oil/graphite	104 to 110	0.34 to 0.32
	850	Oil/graphite	72 to 79	0.35 to 0.32
E-Cu	800	Oil/graphite	159 to 166	0.37 to 0.35
	900	Oil/graphite	106 to 109	0.41 to 0.39
	900	Rough surface	106 to 148	0.41 to 0.29
	1000	Oil/graphite	93 to 94	0.32
Steel Cq45	1150	Glass	198 to 208	0.45 to 0.43

with increasing extrusion speed. This might be attributable to the speed-dependent formation of a lubricating film at the die. The billet lubrication used in these experiments had practically no effect on k_w and η_F, because the friction between the billet and the container was virtually eliminated by measuring the minimum load at short billet lengths. The efficiency factor η_F, according to Table 1.2, is usually less than 0.5 and generally between 0.3 and 0.4. No systematic measurements of k_w and η_F on larger presses are available in the literature.

Since relatively few reliable measurements exist of k_w and η_F for the wide range of alloys extruded, the calculation of extrusion loads is very difficult. Geleji (Ref 44) tried to overcome this difficulty by assuming a conical dead metal zone with an included angle of 45° and a coefficient of internal friction $\mu_i = 0.58$ (shearing). He calculated the maximum extrusion load to be

$$F_{max} = p\,(A_0 + \psi \cdot V) \qquad (Eq\ 42)$$

where ψ is a speed-dependent function of the internal friction:

$$p = 2\,k_m - k_f$$

where k_m is the mean deformation resistance given by:

$$k_m = \frac{k_f}{1 - 0.93 \cdot \Delta A / A_0} \qquad (Eq\ 43)$$

This cannot be directly compared with the deformation resistance defined above because the form of the equation for F, the deformation, is already included in the term for the deformation resistance. This is not the case in Siebel's equation.

1.4.2.5. The Influence of Friction at the Container Wall and of the Billet Length on the Extrusion Load

Friction is allowed for in Siebel and Fangmeier's (Ref 31) equation by the term:

$$F_F = \pi \cdot D_0 \cdot L \cdot \mu_F \cdot k_f \qquad (Eq\ 44)$$

According to this, the load arising from friction decreases linearly with decreasing billet length and, therefore, explains the typical shape of the extrusion load ram displacement diagram for direct extrusion (Fig. 1.43, a and b). It is characterized by a maximum at the start of extrusion followed by a gradual decrease in the load to a minimum and then a steep increase at the end of extrusion. The latter occurs when the billet has been extruded to a very small discard and there is a very high resistance to radial flow towards the center. The coefficient of friction at the container wall can vary considerably,

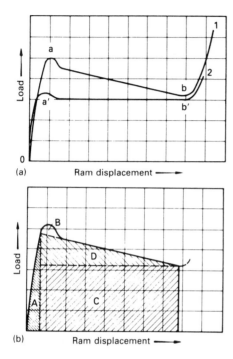

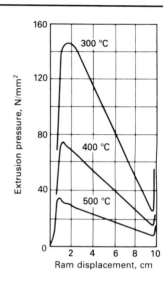

Fig. 1.44. Influence of the temperature on the variation in extrusion pressure with ram displacement in the extrusion of Al99.99. *(From Ref 65)*

(a) Dependence of the extrusion load on the ram displacement:
   a—b = Direct extrusion
   a′—b′ = Indirect extrusion
(b) Division of the work of deformation *(from Ref 88)*:
   A = Work of upsetting
   B = Work needed to initiate deformation
   C = Work of deformation
   D = Work to overcome friction and shearing in direct extrusion

Fig. 1.43. Load required during extrusion.

depending on the alloy and the lubricant. At temperatures close to room temperature and with good lubrication, μ_F can vary from 0.05 to 0.15. In nonlubricated extrusion without a shell, it varies from 0.35 to 0.45, whereas, under conditions of sticking friction — extrusion with a shell being sheared off — it has a theoretical value of:

$$\mu_{max} = \frac{1}{\sqrt{3}} = 0.577 \tag{Eq 45}$$

In this case, shearing work equivalent to the term $\mu \cdot k_f$ has to be carried out; thus, the friction component of the extrusion load is very temperature dependent. This is clearly shown in the load ram displacement diagrams published by Krysko and Lui (Ref 65) for Al99.99 (Fig. 1.44). The maximum load increases with decreasing temperature in the same ratio as the flow stress increases (compare with Fig. 1.41). According to elementary analysis, the relationship between the billet length and the extrusion load is linear. However, the experimental results illustrated in Fig. 1.45 demonstrate that there is a positive or negative deviation from linearity, depending on the alloy. The largest positive deviations occur with the heavy metals, which are extruded rather slowly. The extrusion takes so long that the temperature decreases significantly, with a corresponding rise in the flow stress. The component of the total extrusion load caused by friction can vary from 30 to 80% in direct extrusion. It is negligible in lubricated extrusion and completely eliminated in indirect extrusion (Fig. 1.43, load profile a' − b').

1.4.2.6. The Influence of the Extrusion Ratio on the Extrusion Load

From Siebel and Fangmeier's equation (Ref 31), the load should be a linear function of the logarithm of the extrusion ratio. This has been confirmed by measurements made on several alloys (Fig. 1.46). Nevertheless, if A_1 is very small, a pressure increase can occur, because the shearing and die friction components of the load are then the dominating factors.

1.4.2.7. The Effect of the Section Shape on the Extrusion Load

A section with a complicated profile will require a higher deformation load than a round bar of the same cross sectional area, because additional

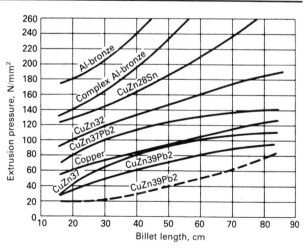

Fig. 1.45. Influence of the billet length on the extrusion pressure of different heavy metal alloys; the deviations from linearity are the result of temperature changes during extrusion.

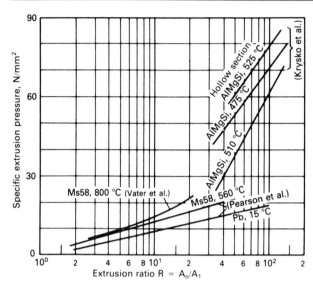

Fig. 1.46. Dependence of the specific extrusion pressure on the extrusion ratio. Ms58 is CuZn39Pb3. *(From Ref 2, 65, 69, 84 and others)*

shearing has to take place in the deformation zone. The larger die land area will lead to an increase in friction and, therefore, can also contribute to an increase in the extrusion load. Hornauer (Ref 66) suggested that these two influences could be allowed for by applying two correction factors to the deformation resistance k_w: a shape factor f_S and a die friction factor f_F:

$$k_w = k_{w0} \cdot f_S \cdot f_F \qquad \qquad \text{(Eq 46)}$$

where k_{w0} is the measured deformation resistance of a standard cross section, for example, a round bar. In this case, $f_S = 1$ and it is assumed that $f_F = 1$ for the standard die (90° angle, sharp edges, constant die land of 6 mm). Hornauer gave $f_S = 1.5$ for the open section with walls of different thicknesses, shown in Fig. 1.47, and, because the die lands must have different lengths to control the flow, $f_F = 1.4$.

The total correction factor for this example that must be applied to k_w — that is, the deformation contribution to the extrusion load — is given by: $f_S \cdot f_F = 1.5 \cdot 1.4 = 2.1$.

Another approach is to combine the two factors and write:

$$F = F_T \cdot f_E = \text{total load (round bar)} \cdot \text{section factor}$$

The increase in load in this case is not only included in the deformation term of Siebel and Fangmeier's equation (section 1.4.2.1), as has often been recommended (Ref 59, 67, 68), but also in the term for friction between the billet and the container. The additional increase in the friction at the container wall is

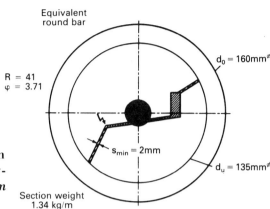

Equivalent
round bar

R = 41
φ = 3.71

d_0 = 160mm⌀

s_{min} = 2mm

d_u = 135mm⌀

Section weight
1.34 kg/m

D_0 = Container diameter
D_c = Circumscribing circle diameter
s_{min} = Minimum wall thickness

Fig. 1.47. Comparison of an open section (wt 1.34 kg/m) with an equivalent round bar (25 mm diam). *(From Ref 66)*

based on the fact that an increase in the total load also increases the normal stress between the billet surface and the container (Ref 69). The effect of the section shape on the extrusion load (Ref 70-73), which has been confirmed in many studies, was studied systematically by Vater and Heil (Ref 69). They related the extrusion loads measured during the lubricated extrusion of aluminum sections on a 1.25 MN press to the circumferential ratio:

$$\frac{U_E}{U_0} = \frac{\text{circumference of the section}}{\text{circumference of a round bar of the same cross sectional area}}$$

Lubrication was used to prevent the friction component in the model from becoming too high. The results suggested that the section factor f_E is a function of the circumferential ratio:

$$f_E = \frac{F_E}{F_0} = f\left(\frac{U_E}{U_0}\right) \qquad \text{(Eq 47)}$$

This is illustrated in Fig. 1.48, which also contains values measured in other works as well as those of Vater and Heil. The results of Ogashi and Yamashita (Ref 74) should be emphasized, because they were made on a production press and show good agreement with the laboratory results. Whether the influence of the section shape is described with sufficient accuracy by the function $f_E = f$ (U_E/U_0) or whether better agreement could be obtained with another function cannot, at the moment, be decided. It must also be remembered that the shape factors used in practice, which are often defined in completely different ways, are not designed to determine the influence of the shape on the load but to give a reasonable estimate of the degree of difficulty of

	Material	Symbol	Load	Lubricant	φ
Ref 69	Lead	—·—·—	$F_{max.}$	None	2.15
		———	$F_{min.}$		
	Al99.5	———	F_A	Oil-graphite	
	AlMgSi1	– – – –			
Ref 74	Al alloy	△	$F_{min.}$		4.3
Ref 75	Al99.5	◊	$F_{max.}$ $F_{min.}$	None	3.7
Ref 76	Pure lead	□	$F_{min.}$	Not stated	
Ref 12	Tin	○	$F_{max.}$ $F_{min.}$	None	1.4

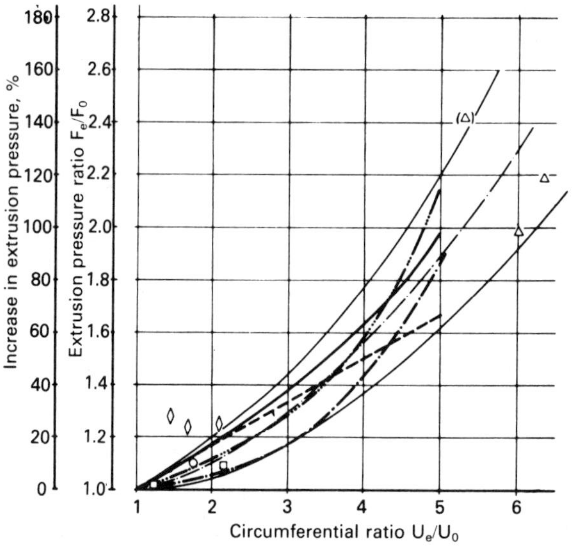

Fig. 1.48. Increase in extrusion load as a function of the circumferential ratio U_e/U_0 in the direct extrusion of sections. *(From Ref 69)*

the section. Used in this way, the shape factor can be a useful aid in assessing the extrudability of sections and production costs (Chap. 3, aluminum sections).

When hollow sections and tubes are extruded with bridge or porthole dies, the billet has to divide into several strands, which necessitates higher shearing and friction loads to overcome the increase in die friction in the long internal channels. The extrusion load can be 2 to 2.6 times that for a normal section (factor = 1) in the single-hole extrusion of difficult aluminum hollow sections through modern bridge and porthole dies (Ref 66). The factor can increase to 2.5 to 3.2 times for multihole dies. A factor of 1.3 is typical for AlMgSi hollow sections of moderate complexity (see also Ref 65).

1.4.2.8. The Extrusion Load in Multihole Extrusion

Bars and simple shapes are extruded through multihole dies to increase productivity. The number of die apertures that can be used increases with smaller and simpler sections but rarely exceeds 12 for aluminum alloys; 2 to 6 is the usual range. In special cases, up to 100 round sections are extruded. For a constant billet diameter, the extrusion ratio reduces as the number of strands n is increased; consequently, the extrusion load decreases linearly with the natural logarithm of the extrusion ratio, according to the relationship:

$$F_{id} = A_0 \cdot k_w \cdot \ln \frac{A_0}{n \cdot A_1}$$

The cross sectional area of the extrusion — that is, the number of strands — must, therefore, be increased by 7 to reduce the deformation load by 50%. However, friction in the container remains unchanged and, therefore, the maximum extrusion load is only reduced by a relatively small amount. The effect of increasing the number of die apertures on the extrusion load from 1 to 2 or 3 should not be overestimated. If the number of strands is increased and the extrusion ratio remains constant, the change in the flow pattern and the increase in friction result in a slightly higher deformation resistance (Ref 76). Sometimes this effect can be so large that an increase in the number of die apertures leads to an increase rather than a decrease in the extrusion load.

1.4.2.9. The Influence of the Die Shape on the Extrusion Load

Apart from the shape of the section and the number of apertures, the die can influence the load in several ways:

(*a*) The angle of the die surface.
(*b*) The die entry radius on flat dies.
(*c*) The length of the die land.
(*d*) The type of construction used.

Die Angle

Eisbein (Ref 12) studied the extrusion of tin through flat and conical dies at room temperature (Fig. 1.19) and found that the minimum extrusion load was obtained with a die angle 2α of 80 to 120° (Fig. 1.49) — approximately 30% less than the load for a flat, sharp-cornered die ($2\alpha = 180°$). This was

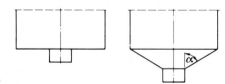

Fig. 1.49. Flat and conical die entry.

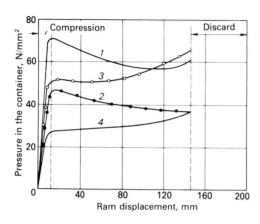

1 — Flat die, container temp 100 °C, extruded with a shell
2 — Flat die, container temp 350 °C, extruded with a shell
3 — Die with an entry angle of $2\alpha = 150°$, container temp 100 °C, extruded without a shell (lubricated)
4 — Die with an entry angle of $2\alpha = 120°$, container temp 350 °C, extruded without a shell (lubricated)

Fig. 1.50. Variation in pressure in extruding CuZn31Si at different container temperatures. *(From Ref 15)*

later confirmed by further experiments and production experience where die angles of 80 to 110° gave the lowest loads for lubricated extrusion. However, the billet surface is also extruded and, if it is of poor quality, defects occur in the surface of the product. To reduce this effect, dies with slightly higher angles, between 120 and 130°, are used. A dead metal zone then develops in the container and this restrains surface impurities (Ref 77 and Chap. 3, CuSn8).

Boes and Pouw (Ref 78) give an extrusion load factor for aluminum alloys of 1.2 for a flat die and 1 for a die with an included angle 2α of 120°. The variation in extrusion pressure with ram displacement has been measured for CuZn31Si using both flat dies ($2\alpha = 180°$) and conical dies ($2\alpha = 120$ and 150°); the experimental results are given in Fig. 1.50. Only a rough comparison between the two types of die can be made, because — following standard industrial practice — unlubricated extrusion with a shell was used with the flat die and lubricated extrusion without a shell with the conical die. This explains the different profiles of the load displacement curves. The load needed to overcome friction between the billet and the container is practically eliminated in lubricated extrusion with a conical die. The maximum pressure for T = 350 °C at the start of extrusion is, in Fig. 1.50, about 450 N/mm² for a flat die with a shell, reduced by 40% to 270 N/mm² with a die angle of 120° and no shell. The flow pattern is also more uniform.

Die Entry Radius

Flat dies have sharp, 90° corners on the entry side after manufacture (usually spark erosion). They are rounded off with large or small radii for several reasons, including: to influence the material flow, guarantee a good surface finish, and prevent cracks. Only a few systematic investigations have been made into the effect of the radius on the extrusion load, and most of them were on experimental presses.

There are two basic types of die entry:

(a) conical, used in lubricated extrusion (see previous section).
(b) flat dies with sharp corners, used for unlubricated extrusion (e.g., aluminum).

Experience has shown that sharp-edged dies give the lowest loads in unlubricated extrusion because the longer entry with conical dies increases the friction. Extrusion experiments with high-purity aluminum have verified these results. The material flow is retarded by filing the edges at an angle — one method of die correction.

Die Land Length

In comparison with dies with sharp corners and constant die land lengths, dies with very different land lengths (see Chap. 5) can cause significant increases in the extrusion load. This applies to irregular sections with large variations in wall thicknesses. These shapes can be extruded successfully — without any distortion, waves or twisting — only if the dies are manufactured with long lands, which can then be shortened by different amounts during testing and die correction until a uniform flow is obtained.

No exact and systematic studies of the effect of the die land length are available. However, friction at the die is only a small fraction of the total load; according to Stüwe (Ref 27), it is approximately:

$$F_{FD} = U_E \cdot s \cdot \tau \cdot R \qquad \text{(Eq 48)}$$

and, therefore, its effect on the load cannot be significant.

1.4.2.10. Extrusion Load and Mandrel Load in Tube Extrusion

The following loads occur during tube extrusion from solid billets (see Chap. 2): (a) Piercing load (compressive load on the mandrel) to pierce the solid billet; (b) Extrusion load, and (c) Tensile load on the mandrel during extrusion. There is no piercing load when hollow billets are used.

Piercing Load

According to Siebel (Ref 79), piercing requires a load given by:

$$F_P = A_0 \cdot \varphi_P \cdot k_f + F_{PS} \qquad \text{(Eq 49)}$$

where F_{PS} is the load for additional shearing, and φ_P is the strain in piercing. If the shearing component is replaced by $A_M \cdot \tau$, then:

$$F_P \, A_0 \cdot \varphi_P \cdot k_f + A_M \cdot 0.577 \, k_f \qquad \text{(Eq 50)}$$

A simpler equation, also from Siebel, gives a good approximation:

$$F_P \approx 3\, A_M \cdot k_f \qquad\qquad\qquad\qquad\qquad\text{(Eq 51)}$$

Extrusion Load

The load required in tube extrusion with a mandrel is increased by an amount representing the friction between the billet and the mandrel:

$$F_{FM} = \pi D_M \cdot L_M \cdot \mu_M \cdot k_f \qquad\qquad\qquad\qquad\text{(Eq 52)}$$

Therefore:

$$F_T = A_0 \cdot \varphi \cdot k_w + \pi D_0 \cdot L \cdot \mu_F \cdot k_f + \pi \cdot D_M \cdot L_M \cdot \mu_M \cdot k_f \qquad\text{(Eq 53)}$$

The coefficient of friction μ_M at the mandrel is not necessarily the same as that for friction at the container μ_F — for example, if the mandrel is lubricated.

Tensile Load on the Mandrel

The component of the total extrusion load due to friction on the mandrel in Eq 53 applies a tensile load on cylindrical or slightly tapered mandrels. For a fixed mandrel the tensile stress is:

$$\sigma_M = \frac{F_{FM}}{A_M} = \frac{\pi \cdot D_M \cdot L_M \cdot \mu_M \cdot k_f}{A_M} = \frac{4\, L_M \cdot \mu_M \cdot k_f}{A_M} \qquad\text{(Eq 54)}$$

This tensile load can be high enough to cause fracture. The effect of friction is partly offset by tapering the mandrel; the stresses on the mandrel are thus reduced. Tensile loads can also be reduced by extruding with a stepped mandrel — extrusion over the tip — because the tip is very short and an axial load acting backwards is developed at the heel of the mandrel. The mandrel load can also be reduced by extruding with a moving mandrel (see Chap. 2).

Bibliographic References

1. Tresca, H.: On the Flow of Solid Bodies Under High Pressure. Comptes Rendus Acad. Sci. Paris 2 (1864) 59, p. 754/758; 1 (1867) 64, p. 809/812; Sav. Ac. Sci. 18 (1868) p. 733/799; 20 (1872) p. 75/135.
2. Vater, M., and Rathjen, C.: Untersuchungen über die Größe der Stempelkraft und des Innendruckes im Aufnehmer beim Strangpressen von Metallen. Fortschrittsberichte VDI, Reihe 2 (1969) p. 9.
3. v. Obermeyer, A.: Versuche über den Ausfluß plastischen Tones. Sitzungsbericht der Kaiserl. Akad. d. Wissenschaft, Vienna, Bd. 58 II (1868) p. 737/755; Bd. 75 I (1877) p. 665/678; Bd. 113 (1904) p. 511/566.
4. Dürrschnabel, W.: Der Materialfluß beim Strangpressen von NE-Metallen (literature survey) I: Metall 22 (1968) p. 426/437; II: p. 995/998; III: p. 1215/1219.
5. Sandin, A.: Zusammenhang zwischen Preßfehlern und Fließvorgang beim Pressen von Kupfer und Messing. Z. f. Metallkunde 55 (1964) p. 49/52.

6. Tuschy, E.: Unterschiede im Fließverhalten beim Strangpressen verschiedener Werkstoffe. Z. f. Metallkunde 62 (1971) p. 513/516.

7. Hertel, H.; Modelltechnische Untersuchung der Fließvorgänge beim Strang- und Gesenkpressen. Automobil Industrie 11 (1966) No. 3

8. Doernickels, F., and Trockels, J.: Fließvorgänge im Messingblock beim Strangpressen. Z. f. Metallkunde 13 (1921) p. 466/472.

9. Unckel, H.: Einiges über die Fließbewegung beim Pressen von Stangen und Rohren sowie beim Ziehen. Z. f. Metallkunde 20 (1928) p. 323/330.

10. Weber, R. D.: The Effect of Metal Flow on Extrusion Force During Hot Extrusion. The Wire Industry, Febr. (1966) p. 165/167.

11. Siebel, E., and Hühne, H.: Untersuchungen über den Formänderungsverlauf bei technischen Formgebungsverfahren. Mitt.-Kais.-Wilh.-Inst.-Eisenforschg. 13 (1931) p. 43/62.

12. Eisbein, W.: Kraftbedarf und Fließvorgänge beim Strangpressen. Z. f. Metallkunde 24 (1932) p. 79/84.

13. Eisbein, W.: Spanlose Formgebung der Metalle (1931), Verlag Springer, Berlin, p. 67/98.

14. Fister, W.: Fließverhalten und Kraftbedarf bei verschiedenen Strangpreßverfahren. Techn. Mitt. 54 (1961) p. 77/78 (also thesis 1963, TH Aachen).

15. Laue, K.: Praktische Erkenntnisse zu den Umformungsvorgängen beim Strangpressen. Z. f. Metallkunde 55 (1964) p. 559/567.

16. **Berger, W. G.: Maßnahmen zur Verbesserung des Gefüges und der mechanischen Eigenschaften in ein- oder mehrstranggepreßten Stangen und Profilen. Thesis, TH Hannover (1943).**

17. Siebel, E.: Kräfte und Materialfluß bei der bildsamen Formgebung. Stahl und Eisen 45 (1925) p. 1563/1566.

18. Stenger, H.: Bedeutung des Formänderungsvermögens für die Umformung. Bänder-Bleche-Rohre 8 (1967) p. 599/606.

19. Rosenkranz, W.: Untersuchungen über die Grobkornbildung bei Strangpreßprofilen und Preßteilen aus der Legierung AlCuMgSi. Aluminium 41 (1965) p. 555/567.

20. Scharf, G., and Gruhl, W.: Der Einfluß von Ausscheidungen auf das Rekristallisationsverhalten von AlMgSi-Legierungen. Z. f. Metallkunde 60 (1969) p. 413/421.

21. Scharf, G., Achenbach, D., and Gruhl, W.: Beeinflussung der Grobkornbildung bei Preßprofilen aus Aluminiumlegierungen. Z. f. Metallkunde 60 (1969) p. 515/520.

22. Scharf, G., and Gruhl, W.: Der Einfluß von Ausscheidungen auf Warmverformung und Rekristallisationsverhalten von Aluminiumlegierungen. Dokumentation 5. Internationale Leichtmetall-Tagung, Leoben (1968) p. 173/178.

23. Putz, J.: Gegenüberstellung von gas- bzw. widerstandsbeheizten Öfen zum Erwärmen von Blöcken aus NE- und E-Metallen für hydraulische Strangpressen. Metall 2 (1958) p. 113/122.

24. Akeret, R.: A Numerical Analysis of Temperature Distribution in Extrusion. J. Inst. Met. 95 (1967) p. 204/211.

25. Akeret, R.: Untersuchungen über das Strangpressen unter besonderer Berücksichtigung der thermischen Vorgänge. Aluminium 44 (1968) p. 412/415.

26. Lange, G.: Der Wärmehaushalt beim Strangpressen. Z. f. Metallkunde 62 (1971) p. 571/584.

27. Stüwe, H.P.: Einige Abschätzungen zum Strangpressen. Metall 22 (1968) p. 1197/1200.

28. **Singer, A. R. E., and Coakham, J. W.: Temperature Changes Occurring During the Extrusion of Aluminium, Tin and Lead. J. Inst. Metals 89 (1960) p. 177/182.**

29. Singer, A. R. E., and Sammarrai, S. K. H.: Temperature Changes Associated with Speed Variation During Extrusion. J. Inst. Metals 89 (1960) p. 225/231.

30. Laue, K.: Isothermes Strangpressen. Z. f. Metallkunde 51 (1960) p. 491/495.

31. Siebel, E., and Fangmeier, E.: Untersuchungen über den Kraftbedarf beim Pressen und Lochen. Mitt.-Kais.-Wilh.-Inst.-Eisenforschg. 13 (1931) p. 29/43.

32. Storoschew, M. W., and Popow, E. A.: Grundlagen der Umformtechnik (1968), VEB-Verlag Technik, Berlin.

33. Hill, R.: A Theoretical Analysis of Stress and Strains in Extrusion and Piercing. J. Iron & Steel Inst. 159 (1948) p. 177/185.

34. Sachs, G.: Spanlose Formung der Metalle. Handbuch der Metallphysik .Bd. 3, Lieferung 1.

35. Johnson, W., and Kudo, H.: The Mechanics of Metal Extrusion. Manchester University Press, Manchester (1962).

36. Johnson, W.: Extrusion Through Wedgeshaped Dies. J. Mech. Phys. Solids 3 (1955) p. 218/230.

37. Johnson, W.: Extrusion Through Square Dies of Large Reduction. J. Mech. Phys. Solids 4 (1956) p. 191/198.

38. Green, A. P.: On Unsymmetrical Extrusion in Plane Strain. J. Mech. Phys. Solids 3 (1955) p. 189/196.

39. Bishop, J. F. W.: The Theory of Extrusion. Metallurgical Reviews Vol. 2, p. 361/390.

40. Hirst, S., and Ursell, D. H.: Proc. Conf. on the Technology of Engineering Manufacture (1958) Paper 32, also Metal Treatment 25 (1958) p. 409.

41. Alexander, J. M.: The Application of Experimental and Theoretical Results to the Practice of Hot Extrusion. J. Inst. Metals (1961) p. 193/215.

42. Pawelski, O.: Grundbegriffe und Grundgleichungen der bildsamen Formgebung. Verlag Stahleisen, Düsseldorf (1966).

43. Lippmann, H.: Abschätzen oberer und unterer Schranken für Umformungsleistungen und -kräfte, besonders bei Strangpressen. Grundlagen der bildsamen Formgebung, Verlag Stahleisen, Düsseldorf (1966).

44. Geleji, A.: Bildsame Formgebung der Metalle in Rechnung und Versuch. Neue Hütte 8 (1963) p. 475/479.

45. Feltham, P.: Extrusion of Metals. Metal Treatment and Drop Forging 23 (1956) p. 440.

46. Nadai, A., and Manjoine, M.: High Speed Tension Test at Elevated Temperatures. Part I: Proc. Am. Soc. Test. Mat. 40 (1940) p. 822. Part II and III: J. Appl. Mech. (1941) p. 77/91.

47. Schulte, O.: Einfluß kleiner Formänderungsgeschwindigkeiten auf die Formänderungsfestigkeit verschieden legierter Stähle und NE-Metalle bei Warm-Formgebungstemperaturen. Forschungsbericht No. 1190 des Landes Nordrhein-Westfalen, Westdeutscher Verlag (1966).

48. Lueg, W., and Müller, H. G.: Formänderungsverhalten von Stahl C45 beim Stauchen und Scheren in Abhängigkeit von Temperatur und Formänderungsgeschwindigkeit. Arch. Eisenhüttenw. 28 (1957) p. 505/516.

49. Fink, K., Lueg, W., and Bürger, G.: Formänderungsfestigkeit von unlegierten und niedrig legierten Stählen beim Warmstauchen unter einem Fallhammer. Arch. Eisenhüttenw. 26 (1955) p. 655/668.

50. Cook, P. M.: True Stress-Strain Curves for Steel in Compression at High Temperatures and Strainrates for Application to the Calculation of Load and Torque in Hot Rolling. Inst. Mech. Eng., Westminster (1957).

51. Meyer, H.: Zahlenwerte über die Umformfestigkeit von unlegierten und legierten Stählen nach neueren Schrifttumsangaben. Werkstatttechnik und Maschinenbau 48 (1958) p. 673/676.

52. Weber, K. H.: Berechnungsunterlagen zur Ermittlung von Walzkraft und Drehmoment beim Warmwalzen. Freiberger Forschungshefte B 46 (1956).

53. Gärtner, G.: Versuche zur Übertragung des Kegelstauchverfahrens auf das Warmstauchen von Metallen. Freiberger Forschungshefte B 27 (1958) p. 28/51.

54. Heinemann, H. H.: Formänderungsfestigkeit verschiedener Aluminium- und Kupferlegierungen bei hohen Formänderungsgeschwindigkeiten und Umformtemperaturen. Thesis TH Aachen (1961).

55. Kühne, H.: Ermittlung der Formänderungsfestigkeit k_f von C-Stahl bei Warmformgebung. Fertigungstechn. u. Betrieb Part 1: 2, p. 105/106. Part 2: 4, p. 262/266, 12 (1962).

56. Walter, M., and Winter, G.: Ermittlung der Formänderungsfestigkeit und der bezogenen Formänderungsarbeit gebräuchlicher Schmiedewerkstoffe bei der Warmformgebung. Part 3: Fertigungstechn. u. Betrieb 12 (1962), 7, p. 469/475.

57. Höpfner, G.: Die Staucheigenschaften von Aluminium and Aluminiumlegierungen und ihr Werkstoffzustand nach dem Umformen. Thesie TH Hannover (1968).

58. Bühler, H., Höpfner, G. and Löwen, J.: Die Formänderungsfestigkeit von Aluminium und einigen Aluminiumlegierungen. Bänder-Bleche-Rohre 11 (1970) p. 645/649.

59. Akeret, R., and Künzli, A.: Ermittlung der Formänderungsfestigkeit k_f von Aluminiumlegierungen mit Hilfe von Torsionsversuchen und Vergleich der Ergebnisse mit denjenigen von Strangpreßversuchen. Z. f. Metallkunde 57 (1966) p. 789/792.

60. Akeret, R.: Ermittlung der Formänderungsfestigkeit k_f etc. Aluminium 44 (1968) p. 412.

61. Schmidt, W.: Untersuchung des Formänderungsverhaltens hochwarmfester Werkstoffe mit Warmtorsionsversuchen. Bänder-Bleche-Rohre 11 (1970) p. 528/536.

62. Suzuki, A., et al.: Studies on the Flow Stress of Metals and Alloys. Rep. Inst. Ind. Sci. Univ. Tokyo 18 (1968) No. 3.

63. Vater, M., and Lienhart, A.: Überblick über die allgemeinen Grundlagen der bildsamen Formgebung. Bänder-Bleche-Rohre 12 (1971) p. 252/260.

64. Borchers, H. M., and Ehrhardt, H.: Verformungsvermögen von Aluminium und Aluminium-Magnesium-Legierungen bei verschiedenen Probenzuständen und Versuchstemperaturen. Aluminium 44 (1968) p. 546/550.

65. Krysko W.W., and Lui, M. W.: Untersuchungen über das Strangpressen kubisch flächenzentrierter Metalle. Z. f. Werkstofftechnik/J. Mat. Technol. 1 (1970) Part 1: p. 83/89, Part 2: p. 127/137.

66. Hornauer, H.: Vorausbestimmung der Umformungskräfte beim Strangpressen von Leichtmetallprofilen. Aluminium 32 (1956) p. 350/356.

67. Fister, W.: Fließverhalten und Kraftbedarf bei verschiedenen Strangpreßverfahren. Techn. Mitt. 54 (1961) p. 77/78.

68. Zoller, H., and Ried, A.: Metallkundliche Grundlagen der leichtpreßbaren AlMgSi-Legierungen. Aluminium 41 (1965) p. 625/629.

69. Vater, M., and Heil, H. P.: Der Einfluß der Profilform auf den Kraftbedarf beim Strangpressen. Aluminium 45 (1969) p. 141/149.

70. Siebel, E.: Die Formgebung im bildsamen Zustande. Verlag Stahleisen, Düsseldorf (1932).

71. Laue, K., and Hornauer, H.: Grenzen der Umformung beim Strangpressen. Z. f. Metallkunde 47 (1956) p. 117/121.

72. Laue, K.: Möglichkeiten werkstoffgerechter Gestaltung von Leichtmetallprofilen. Z. f. Metallkunde 54 (1963) p. 667/671.

73. Zolobow, W. W., and Zwerew, G. I.: Pressowanie Metallow, Vol. 1, Moscow (1959); German Translation: Das Strangpressen der Metalle, DGM, Cologne (1967).

74. Ogashi, H., and Yamashita H.: A Study on the Extrusion Force of Aluminium Alloys. Sumitomo Light Metal Techn. Reports 3 (1962) p. 87/93.

75. Grüning, K.: Umformtechnik. Verlag Vieweg & Sohn, Braunschweig (1966).

76. Johnson, W.: Experiments in the Cold Extrusion of Rods of Non-Circular Section. J. Mech. Phys. Solids 1 (1958) p. 37/44.

77. Landichow, A. D.: Herstellung von Rohren, Stangen und Profilen aus NE-Metallen.

Fachbuchverlag, Leipzig (1955).

78. Boes, P. J. M., and Pouw, H. P.: A Practical Calculation Method for Extrusion Pressures. Sheet Metal Industry (1966) p. 377/390.

79. Siebel, E.: Mechanik der bildsamen Formgebung. Eisenhütte, 5. ed., Verlag Ernst & Sohn (1961), p. 191.

80. Kemppinen, A. I.: Computer Simulation of Temperature Rise During Extrusion. International Extrusion Technology Seminar, New Orleans, 1969, Paper No. 15, Aluminum Association, New York.

81. Stenger, H.: Die maximale Preßgeschwindigkeit beim Strangpressen. Drahtwelt 59 (1973) p. 235/240 and 371/376.

82. Akeret, R.: Die Produktivität beim Strangpressen von Aluminium-Werkstoffen. Einfluß von Werkstoffen und Verfahren. Dokumentation des DGM Symposiums "Strangpressen" (1970), Dr. Riederer-Verlag, p. 63/68.

83. Stenger, H.: Besonderheiten bei der Herstellung von Strangpreßprofilen aus Aluminium-Eloxal- und Glänzwerkstoffen. Bänder-Bleche-Rohre 13 (1972) p. 454/461.

84. Pearson, E. C., and Parkins, R. N.: The Extrusion of Metals. 2nd ed., London 1961.

85. Thomsen, E. G., Young, C. T., and Bierbower, J. B.: University of California, Publ. in Engineering, Vol. 5 (1954), No. 4, p. 89/144.

86. Lotz, W., Steiner, U., Stiehler, H., and E. Schelzke, E.: Preßfehler beim Strangpressen von Kupfer-Zink-Legierungen. Symposium "Strangpressen" der DGM (1970), Dr. Riederer-Verlag, p. 30/35.

87. Camutal, N. M.: Sm. Report Lpj. (1937) USSR (also Zolobow/Zwerew: Pressowanie Metallow).

88. Suchoversky, I.: Erkenntnisse über das Strangpressen von Aluminium. Aluminium 36 (1962) p. 295/299.

89. Atlas of Hot Working Properties of Nonferrous Metals: Volume 1: Aluminium and Aluminium Alloys. Volume 2: Copper and Copper Alloys. Deutsche Gesellschaft für Metallkunde (1978), Oberursel.

90. Laue, K.: Die thermische und mechanische Beanspruchung der Strangpreßwerkzeuge. Z. f. Metallkunde 46 (1955) p. 1/6.

91. Wieland Werke, Ulm (Germany): Catalogue of Extrusion Defects, No. Ma 10842, 21.01.

2. Extrusion Processes

The different flow characteristics of the various alloys extruded and the complex relationship between the extrusion parameters and the flow pattern in the container mean that it is impossible to use the same method for all materials. Special methods are generally used, according to the typical flow behavior of the alloy under consideration, to obtain the optimum in quality and productivity. Also, the wide range of products obviously requires special production methods. The two basic methods are shown in Fig. 2.1:

(a) Direct or forward extrusion.
(b) Indirect or backward extrusion (using a hollow stem).

2.1. Conventional Direct Extrusion

The most important method used in extrusion is the direct process (Fig. 2.2), which follows the five-step sequence given below:

(a) Loading the billet and dummy block into the press.
(b) Extrusion of the billet.

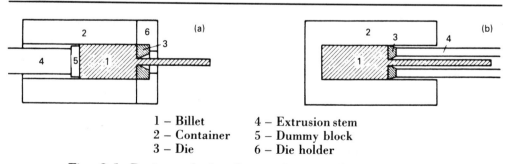

1 – Billet	4 – Extrusion stem
2 – Container	5 – Dummy block
3 – Die	6 – Die holder

Fig. 2.1. Basic methods of extrusion: **(a)** direct extrusion; **(b)** indirect extrusion.

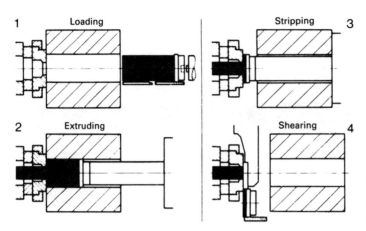

Fig. 2.2. Sequence of operations in direct extrusion (schematic).

(c) Decompression of the press and opening the container to expose the discard and the dummy block (stripping).

(d) Shearing the discard.

(e) Returning the shear, container and ram to the loading position.

The surface of the billet slides along the container wall, and the ease with which this is carried out depends on the alloy and whether a lubricating film is present. In every case, part of the extrusion load—depending on the length of the billet—is expended in overcoming the friction between the billet and the container, or in shearing the inner material from the slower-moving peripheral layer adjacent to the container wall.

As Fig. 1.43 in Chap. 1 shows, the load in direct extrusion initially increases very rapidly as the billet upsets to fill the container. There is then a further increase in pressure (Fig. 1.43a) and extrusion commences. A somewhat cone-shaped deformation zone then develops in front of the die aperture. The maximum strain rate is developed in this zone. After the maximum load, the extrusion pressure falls as the billet length decreases until a minimum is reached (Fig. 1.43b) and then rapidly increases again. This pressure increase occurs because only a disc of the billet remains and the metal has to flow radially towards the die aperture. The deformation resistance increases considerably with decreasing thickness. The load profile for indirect extrusion is also shown in Fig. 1.43; this is considered in more detail in section 2.2.

2.1.1. Direct Extrusion With and Without Lubrication or a Shell

Direct extrusion can be carried out with or without a lubricant and, in the latter case, with or without a shell. If the material has a strong tendency to stick to the container wall, nonuniform flow occurs; the central region of the billet first flows towards the die and the peripheral region is extruded only towards the end of the process. The separation of the pure material, forming the inside of the billet, from the outside layer, which usually has a rough cast surface and is coated with oxide and impurities, can be improved still further by leaving this layer in the container. This is known as extrusion with a shell and is used mainly with heavy metal alloys to suppress the formation of pipe in the rear of the extrusion (Fig. 2.3a). The process is also known as Dick's method of extrusion, after Alexander Dick. The diameter of the dummy block is about 1.5 to 2 mm less than that of the container and this "cuts" the clean core material from the impure outside region. The shell is pushed out (Fig. 2.4) at the end of extrusion with a dummy block of a larger diameter (cleaning pad).

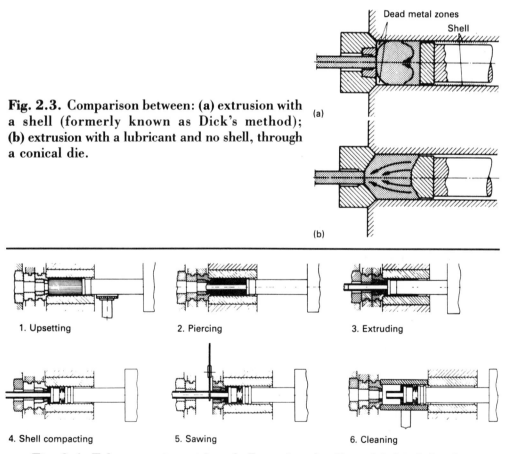

Fig. 2.3. Comparison between: **(a)** extrusion with a shell (formerly known as Dick's method); **(b)** extrusion with a lubricant and no shell, through a conical die.

1. Upsetting   2. Piercing   3. Extruding

4. Shell compacting   5. Sawing   6. Cleaning

Fig. 2.4. Tube extrusion with a shell, sawing the discard behind the die.

Aluminum alloys are preferably extruded using a dummy block with a very close fit in the container. Consequently, hardly any shell is sheared off. The surface is not drawn into the billet because, in contrast to heavy metals, aluminum sticks to the container wall and impurities on the surface are held back. Also, there is only a small temperature difference between the billet and the container, and the difference in velocity between the center of the billet and the periphery is much less than in the case of heavy metals. As the dummy block advances, impurities on the billet surface and the peripheral segregation are sheared off and collect in the discard, which must be large enough to meet the quality desired.

In comparison with the production methods using no lubricant and possibly a shell, the presence of a good lubricant between the billet and the container results in a relatively uniform strain rate over most of the cross section of the billet. The large reduction in friction reduces any flow from the center of the billet; as in drawing, the whole billet is more uniformly deformed. Therefore, the billet surface also forms the surface of the extruded product. Uniform flow is prevented if a dead metal zone is allowed to form, and so conical dies are used with included angles similar to those of the dead metal zones (Fig. 2.3).

Use of the lubricated process in the extrusion of heavy metals and steels naturally results in a lower extrusion load and makes the extrusion of some very difficult alloys possible. Also, higher speeds can be attained. Impurities on the surface are not drawn into the billet and, therefore, a very small discard suffices—with the advantage of reduced scrap losses. The lubricant used and the extrusion temperature vary from alloy to alloy. The self-lubricating oxide layer is sufficient for copper, whereas the container, die and mandrel have to be well lubricated for extrusion of steel and brass.

The use of special lubricants, including graphite, salts and even glass, led to the large-scale extrusion of steel tubes. In spite of the potential advantages, little use can be made of lubricated extrusion for aluminum. If too much or too little lubricant is used, several types of surface defects occur that are not encountered in the usual method of unlubricated extrusion. In the latter case, the surface of the extruded product is formed from the interior of the billet by shearing.

2.1.1.1. Extrusion of Rods and Solid Shapes

The direct extrusion of rods and solid shapes is the simplest production method in use. Nevertheless, in order to achieve an acceptable quality, many factors have to be considered, depending on the material and the section shape. The metallurgical aspects of rod and section extrusion are discussed in Chap. 1; Chap. 3 describes the methods used for various alloys. Particular emphasis is given to the defects associated with a coarse-grain structure.

With the exception of billet-to-billet extrusion, rods and sections are extruded with a separate dummy block and a discard, the length of which depends on the flow pattern (material, funnel formation, extrusion defect; see Chap. 1). Billet-to-billet extrusion is very suitable for continuous lengths of coiled products (section 2.1.2). The design of the tooling is a decisive factor in rod extrusion—even more so for sections — especially the correct layout of the die apertures. At the same time, the shrinkage of the extrusion upon cooling has to be considered, together with the influence on the material flow through the die land. This flow is of particular importance when extruding complicated sections to close tolerances, and is considered in more detail in Chap. 5.

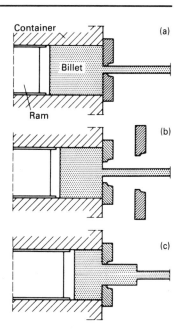

Fig. 2.5. Extrusion of stepped products. (a) Extrusion of the small cross section; (b) exchanging the die for the small section with that for the larger; (c) extrusion continued with the large cross section. *(From Kaiser Aluminum, Oakland)*

Sections with gradual variations in cross section along the length of the extrusion can be manufactured by interrupting the extrusion stroke after a certain ram displacement and changing the die. Extrusion begins with the smallest cross section; the die, which is made up of two or more sections, is then replaced by a larger one and the ram stroke is continued. A schematic illustration is given in Fig. 2.5. This process is used in the United States for aircraft sections and saves on machining. Stepped posts for street lamps, and the like, are produced in the same way. Dies have also been developed to give a continuous increase in the size of the aperture and allow conical sections to be extruded.

2.1.1.2. Extrusion of Tubes and Hollow Sections

In order to extrude tubes, the billet has to be pressed through a die that determines the outside diameter, and over a centrally located mandrel that determines the inside diameter. The metal must, therefore, flow through an annular gap. The various methods of producing tubes are characterized by the following points:

    (*a*) Type of mandrel location:
        On the extrusion stem.
        On the die (welding chamber die).
    (*b*) Method of axial movement of the mandrel (for those fitted to the stem):
        Fixed mandrel screwed to the stem.
        Moving mandrel controlled independently of the ram displacement.
        Stationary mandrel controlled independently of the ram displacement.
    (*c*) Method of billet piercing:
        Solid billet pierced in the press.
        Hollow billets.
        Billets with a pilot hole.

2.1.1.2.1. Extrusion With the Mandrel on the Stem

The mandrel has two main functions: the first production step is to pierce the solid billet in the container by pushing the piercing mandrel axially through the billet with the required piercing load; the whole billet is plastically deformed. The volume of metal displaced by the mandrel moves axially, and there is a corresponding increase in the billet length. At the end of the piercing process, the mandrel is centrally located in the die. The pierced billet is then extruded to a tube. Predrilled billets can also be used; this is described below.

The axial position of the mandrel relative to the die and its variation during extrusion, and hence during the deformation of the pierced or bored billet, are important for a number of reasons. With the continuing development of the extrusion process, control of the mandrel location and its movement has kept pace with the requirements of modern tube production. Because some older presses are still in use today, a description of the simpler methods of tube extrusion is given below.

Tube Extrusion With a Moving Mandrel (Screwed to the Stem)

The mandrel is securely screwed into an axial hole in the front of the stem (Fig. 2.6). Therefore, after piercing, the mandrel speed during extrusion is the same as the ram speed. Because the mandrel moves with the ram, it has to be cylindrical if a constant wall thickness along the length of the tube is required. In practice, slightly tapered mandrels are used to reduce friction. The rigid attachment of the mandrel to the ram means that the loading daylight (stroke of the main cylinder) must be very large or, if a press of normal construction

1 – Mantle. 2 – Intermediate sleeve. 3 – Liner. 4 – Extrusion die. 5 – Die backer. 6 – Die holder. 7 – Bolster. 8 – Die slide. 9 – Mandrel. 10 – Extrusion stem. 11 – Dummy block.

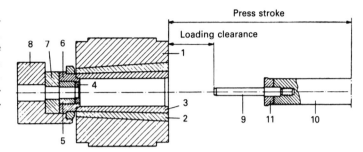

Fig. 2.6. Extrusion with a moving mandrel.

> Note on Fig. 2.6. to 2.11: The container format illustrated, with conical intermediate sleeves, does not reflect the contemporary state of container construction. The diagrams serve merely to illustrate the extrusion process.

is used, only billets with half the normal length can be extruded. The process is therefore uneconomical; it is used only if tubes occasionally have to be extruded in a simple press and a welding chamber die cannot be used.

Tube Extrusion With a Floating Mandrel

The method is an improvement of that described above. The mandrel is not attached to the stem but is inserted with the dummy block, after the press has been loaded with a hollow billet. The mandrel is secured in the dummy block during extrusion either by a cylindrical hole of suitable length (Fig. 2.7) or by a taper fit (Fig. 2.8). Solid billets cannot be pierced with a floating mandrel, but normal length billets can be extruded.

Tube Extrusion With a Limited-Movement Mandrel

In this method (Fig. 2.9) the extrusion stem is drilled along its axis and the mandrel is fitted into the bore in such a way that it can move freely over a certain distance. The mandrel retracts into the stem by this amount during loading, which increases the loading clearance, and then moves forward as the tube is extruded until it reaches its limit of travel. The advantage over the floating mandrel is that solid billets can be pierced.

Extrusion With Independent Mandrel Movement

The methods described above can be used with normal extrusion presses but have numerous disadvantages from the point of view of output and quality. Therefore, special presses for tube extrusion have been developed, in which the mandrel location and movement can be controlled independently from the ram movement (Fig. 2.10). The construction of these presses

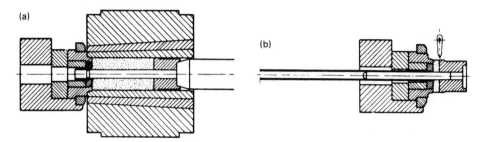

Fig. 2.7. Extrusion with a floating mandrel: **(a)** at the start of extrusion; **(b)** final position before shearing the discard. (See note below Fig. 2.6.)

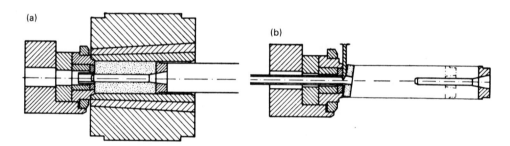

Fig. 2.8. Floating mandrel with conical end: **(a)** at the start of extrusion; **(b)** final position before shearing the discard. (See note below Fig. 2.6.)

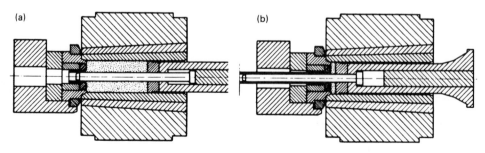

Fig. 2.9. Extrusion with a limited-movement mandrel: **(a)** at the start of extrusion; **(b)** final position. (See note below Fig. 2.6.)

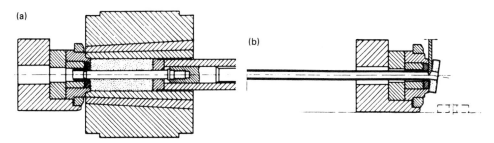

Fig. 2.10. Extrusion with independent mandrel movement: **(a)** start of extrusion; **(b)** final position before shearing the discard. (See note below Fig. 2.6.)

is described in Chap. 4. The independent mandrel movement and the ram displacement are operated hydraulically. The main advantages of this method are:

(*a*) Solid billets can be pierced.

(*b*) The piercing load is independent of the load applied by the extrusion stem. It is usually 10 to 20% of the nominal press capacity.

(*c*) Extrusion can be carried out with a moving, leading or stationary mandrel. In the last instance, the position of the mandrel is adjusted so that its tip remains stationary during extrusion — that is, as the ram advances (extrusion over a tip, Fig. 2.11).

(*d*) The use of a stationary mandrel allows both tubes and hollow sections to be produced to close tolerances. The mandrel tip conforms to the internal shape of the section, and hollow billets are used.

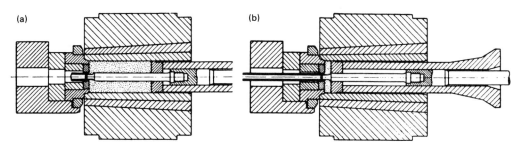

Fig. 2.11. Extrusion with stationary mandrel: **(a)** start of extrusion; **(b)** final position. (See note below Fig. 2.6.)

(e) Extrusion with a stationary mandrel over the tip has the advantage that tubes or hollow sections with small inside diameters can be produced by using mandrels of sufficient diameter and stability, with a suitable stepped tip. Fracture of the mandrel is thus prevented.

(f) Mandrels with stepped tips can be designed to have replaceable tips according to the extruded product, tolerances, wear, and the like. In the extrusion of tubes to very close tolerances, mandrel caps with a diameter larger than that of the mandrel are used. These center themselves in the die during extrusion.

(g) Because the relative motion between the ram and the mandrel is adjustable, it is also possible to extrude with a mandrel speed faster than that of the ram. The stroke at the higher speed can be adjusted to correspond with the length of the mandrel by adjusting the relative displacement. The advantage of this method is that the tensile load on the mandrel is lower than that during extrusion with a moving mandrel, resulting in an increased working life.

2.1.1.2.2. Tube and Hollow Section Extrusion Using Welding Chamber Methods

Tubes and hollow sections can also be produced by the welding chamber method. This process has found a wide range of application, especially in the manufacture of aluminum hollow sections (Fig. 2.12). However, it is suitable only for materials that can easily be deformed at normal extrusion temperatures — that is, pure aluminum, AlMn and AlMgSi alloys and, under certain conditions, AlMg alloys. Tubes are extruded by this method if long lengths are required, which — depending on the application and total length — can be extruded using billet-to-billet extrusion. The welding chamber process represents a great advance in the production of the very complicated sections used in architecture, instrument construction and vehicle manufacture.

The internal shape of the tube or hollow section is formed by a short mandrel supported on two or more arms by the die and its support tooling. The metal is divided by the arms into several strands of large cross section and, as deformation continues, these enter the inlets, flow around the arms and are rewelded in the welding chamber to form the section (high-temperature pressure welding). The metal flows out between the tip of the mandrel and the die aperture to form a tube or a hollow section according to the shape selected. This method of extrusion necessitates dies of a very high quality. Three types of dies are illustrated in Fig. 2.12, a to c. The main difference between them is the method of supporting the mandrel. The individual aspects of the design of the die are discussed in more detail in Chap. 5.

2.1.1.2.3. Tube Extrusion on Vertical Presses

There is no major difference between tube extrusion in a vertical and in a horizontal press; the various methods mentioned in section 2.1.1.2 can be used

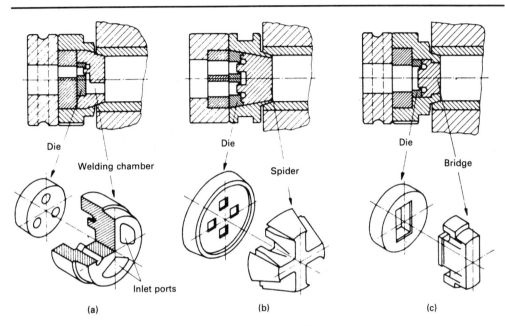

Fig. 2.12. Construction of dies for the welding chamber process used for aluminum. **(a)** Multihole porthole die; **(b)** multihole spider die; **(c)** bridge die (recessed bridge).

in both cases. Since about 1960, extrusion in vertical presses has decreased in popularity in favor of the horizontal process. The main reasons for this are:

(a) Dimensional tolerances — vertical presses were once considered more suitable for tube production because the concentricity of the tube was better than in horizontal presses. The technology of modern presses, with their accurate controls and methods of adjustment, has eliminated this advantage of vertical presses.

(b) Size of installation and efficiency — vertical presses require high buildings and have the additional disadvantage that the product has to be turned from the vertical to the horizontal position. This is difficult with long extrusions and with those of large or complicated sections. Hence, 20 MN is about the maximum size for vertical presses. These relatively small presses can accept only small billets (e.g., 150 mm diameter by 300 mm); the yield per extrusion is low. The increasing need to economize requires much larger billets (e.g., 300 mm diameter by 800 mm) — approximately ten times heavier — even for tube production, and, of course, only horizontal presses can then be used.

Nevertheless, it must be pointed out that, more recently, a special tube extrusion process for the production of large-diameter steel tubes (e.g., for pipelines) has been developed. Tubes are vertically extruded upwards on large forging presses (Fig. 4.69 and 4.70, Chap. 4).

2.1.1.2.4. Billets for Tube Extrusion

Solid or hollow billets can be used for tube extrusion, depending on the method used and the type of press. Normally, solid ones are used, for reasons of economy. After upsetting and ram retraction, the billets are pierced in the press by the mandrel — either cylindrical (up to a length-to-diameter ratio of about 7:1) or (in the case of an unfavorable length-to-diameter ratio or hollow sections) tipped (see section 2.1.1.2.1). Stepped mandrels are used for the extrusion of tubes and hollow shapes over a mandrel tip (Chap. 5). In this case, the bore of the billet is smaller than the diameter of the mandrel shaft and serves merely as a pilot hole (mandrel guide).

2.1.2. Billet-to-Billet Extrusion

Billet-to-billet extrusion is a special method for alloys that easily weld together at the extrusion temperature. Using this process, continuous lengths can be produced by discontinuous extrusion. Initially, it was of particular importance in cable sheathing with lead or aluminum, where the aim was a continuous metallic casing around the cable. Billet-to-billet extrusion is also a viable process in the production of coiled semifinished products for further processing — for example, wire and tube production (Chap. 3, aluminum). In addition to lead, the aluminum alloys that easily weld together during extrusion — Al99.5, AlMn, AlMg1, AlMgSi0.5, AlMgSil; i.e., the low-alloy types — are suitable. Perfect welding of the billet in the container with the following billet must take place as the junction passes through the deformation zone, and therefore the following requirements have to be fulfilled:

(a) Good weldability at the temperature of deformation.
(b) Accurate temperature control.
(c) Clean, but not necessarily machined, billet surfaces with no impurities, porosity or surface defects (brush cleaning immediately before billet heating).
(d) Sawn, clean billet ends free of grease.
(e) Bleeding the air from the container at the start of extrusion to avoid the problem of pockets of compressed air that later re-expand to form blisters and other defects.

A very simple and efficient method used for bleeding, especially in aluminum extrusion, is illustrated in Fig. 2.13. After the billet has reached a uniform "base" temperature, an axial temperature gradient of about 90 to 100 °C over its length is produced by rapidly heating the front of the billet (Ref 41). It is then quickly loaded into the container. As the billet upsets,

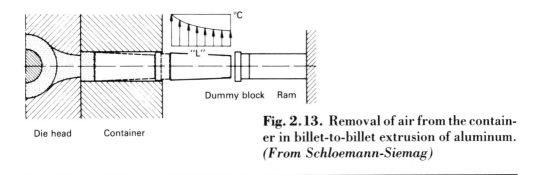

Die head   Container

Fig. 2.13. Removal of air from the container in billet-to-billet extrusion of aluminum. *(From Schloemann-Siemag)*

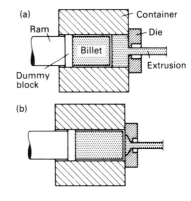

Fig. 2.14. Two methods of billet-to-billet extrusion: **(a)** normal die — discard remains in the container and the next billet is pressed onto it; **(b)** feeder plate die — discard is sheared off before a new billet is loaded.

it fills the container from the front to the back and the air is squeezed out of the container past the stem. Two methods of billet-to-billet extrusion have been developed (Fig. 2.14). In the first method (Fig. 2.14b), the discard is removed and the following billet is welded to the one remaining in the feeder plate. The second method (Fig. 2.14a) does not need a discard: the subsequent billet is pressed directly onto the billet still in the container. In this case a separate dummy block cannot be used. The dummy block shears an aluminum ring from the container during each return stroke, and this has to be removed from the ram. With aluminum the return load in this cleaning operation can be as high as 10% of the press capacity (Ref 41).

2.2. Indirect Extrusion

2.2.1. Load and Friction

In indirect extrusion (Fig. 2.1b) the die at the front end of the hollow stem moves relative to the container but there is no relative displacement between

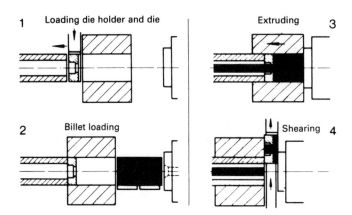

Fig. 2.15. Sequence of operations in indirect extrusion. (*From Schloemann-Siemag*)

the billet and the container. Therefore, this process is characterized by the absence of friction between the billet surface and the container (in indirect extrusion without a shell) and no displacement of the billet center relative to the peripheral regions. The load required is therefore decreased. Figure 2.15 shows the working cycle in indirect extrusion. The individual steps are:

(*a*) Loading of the die holder and die.
(*b*) Loading of the billet.
(*c*) Extrusion.
(*d*) Separation of the die holder with the die and the discard from the extrusion.

According to Fister (Ref 4) the percentage of the extrusion load needed to push the billet through the container is 22% for the extrusion of an aluminum rod (Fig. 2.16). Petsch quotes an average saving of 30% in the load requirements compared with direct extrusion (Ref 5).

2.2.2. Advantages and Disadvantages of Indirect Extrusion

The advantages of indirect extrusion are partly related to the lower load needed and partly to the more uniform flow pattern developed because of the absence of relative motion between the billet and the container — no heat is produced by friction. The main advantages are:

(*a*) A 25 to 30% reduction in load compared with direct extrusion.
(*b*) The resultant higher extrusion load available can be used either to extrude smaller cross sections or to decrease the billet temperatures, permitting the use of higher speeds.
(*c*) The extrusion pressure is not a function of the billet length, because there is no relative displacement of the billet center relative to the peripheral

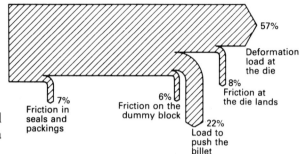

Fig. 2.16. Distribution of load requirements in extruding a round bar. *(From Ref 4)*

57%
Deformation load at the die

8%
Friction at the die lands

6%
Friction on the dummy block

7%
Friction in seals and packings

22%
Load to push the billet

region. The billet length is therefore not limited by the load required for this displacement but only by the length and stability of the hollow stem needed for a given container length.

(d) No heat is produced by friction between the billet and the container, and consequently no temperature increase occurs at the billet surface towards the end of extrusion, as is typical in the direct extrusion of aluminum alloys. Therefore, there is less tendency for the surfaces and edges to crack in the indirect process and significantly higher extrusion speeds can be used.

(e) The service life of the tooling is increased, especially that of the inner liner, because of the almost total absence of friction.

(f) There is a more uniform deformation of the complete billet cross section with no tendency to form an extrusion defect or a coarse-grained peripheral zone.

(g) Impurities on the billet surface do not finish up inside the extrusion — there is no metal turbulence in the container — but can be found on the surface of the product.

The disadvantage of indirect extrusion is that impurities or defects on the billet surface affect the surface of the extrusion and are not automatically retained as a shell or discard in the container. Therefore, machined billets have to be used in many cases. In addition, the cross sectional area of the extrusion is limited by the size of the hollow stem. The often negative attitude to indirect extrusion is partly due to the fact that the press cannot be used for all products.

2.2.3. Tool Design

Without doubt, tooling design is the major problem in indirect extrusion. The tooling on the hollow stem consists of a combination of die and die holder. The outside diameter of the tooling determines the thickness of the shell left on the container wall. The thicker the shell, the smaller the danger that impurities from the billet surface will end up on the extrusion surface. However, the container has to be cleaned more often, with a cleaning pad in an idle cycle, which increases the dead cycle time.

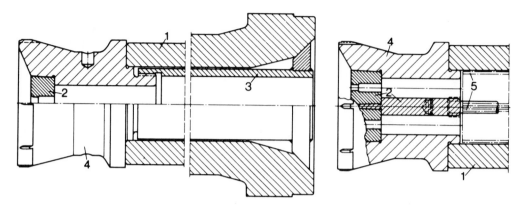

1–Hollow stem. 2–Dies. 3–Tubular clamp. 4–
Indirect special die holder. 5–Feed tubes for wire.

Fig. 2.17. Special die holder for indirect extrusion. *(From Ref 5)*

One method of eliminating the cleaning cycle is provided by the tool design shown in Fig. 2.17 for the indirect extrusion of wire. The distinguishing feature is that the thin shell is sheared off during the extrusion stroke by the leading edge of the special die holder, not as a complete shell but in the form of long strips cut by teeth on the circumference of the die holder. These strips are compressed or coiled up together at the second circumferential edge on the tooling. The discard and the shell strips can be sheared off from the die holder at the end of extrusion without the strips breaking off.

This method is very ingenious, but practice has shown that the teeth in the dummy block are very subject to wear; the shell then has to be stripped with a cleaning disc in an idle cycle.

The size of the die aperture is limited by the diameter of the bore of the hollow stem, and consequently the production of sections is limited to those of a rather small circumscribing circle diameter.

One design that provides for the use of dies for complex sections or multihole dies has been patented in France (Fig. 2.18). The die and a series of backers are arranged one behind the other in a hollow stem. The first backer has openings conforming to the shape of the section, whereas the others have normal openings. This arrangement has the following advantages:

(*a*) The die and backers can be made in the same way as the tooling for direct extrusion.

(*b*) The arrangement of the tools one behind the other simplifies their installation.

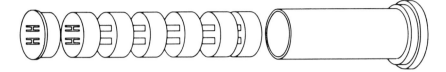

Fig. 2.18. Construction of tooling for indirect extrusion with a hollow stem and die backer arranged one behind the other. *(From Ref 11)*

(c) The stem is not subjected to bending stresses.
(d) Extrusion can be carried out with or without a shell; the tooling remains in the stem during the stroke of the container.

The absence of friction at the container wall means that the length of the billet in indirect extrusion is limited only by the length of the stem, and much longer containers can be used. Consequently, the influence of the cooling at the faces on the temperature profile in the container is appreciably lower than for direct extrusion — that is, apart from the regions at the ends of the container, the temperature variation over the container length is much less (Ref 10). The design of an extrusion stem for multihole indirect extrusion is of particular importance (Fig. 2.19). This design has overcome the main stumbling block of tooling design that prevented the general application of indirect extrusion until recently. Indirect extrusion is gaining in importance because of the influence of larger billets and constant exit temperature on productivity and quality.

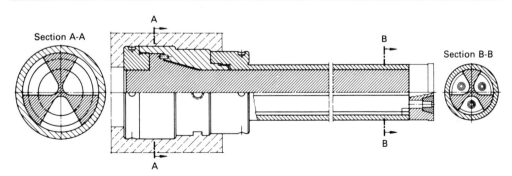

Fig. 2.19. Extrusion stem for three-hole indirect extrusion. *(From Ref 12)*

2.2.4. Temperature Control

Temperature control in indirect extrusion, especially for aluminum, has been discussed in an earlier section and the importance of isothermal extrusion (extruding with a constant exit temperature) has been stressed. In the direct process, the following methods can be used:

(a) Nonuniform heating of the extrusion billet (taper heating; see section 1.3.3).
(b) Varying the ram speed (sections 4.2.1 and 4.2.5) according to the measured exit temperature or practical experience.

Compared with direct extrusion, a constant exit temperature is much easier to achieve in the indirect extrusion of aluminum using the following methods:

(a) *A constant initial temperature over the length of the billet.* In indirect extrusion the deformation zone traverses the complete length of the container (in contrast to direct extrusion), and as a result there is no temperature drop over this length caused by conduction of the heat of deformation.
(b) *Equal billet and container temperatures.* In certain cases the initial billet temperature and the container temperature have to be adjusted so that the heating of the liner by the absorption of the heat of deformation is compensated for the cooling between extrusions. A temperature level, therefore, develops that allows the maximum and, at the same time, constant extrusion speed to be used (compare with section 1.1.3.4). At high ram speeds, heat losses from the deformation zone to the undeformed billet are negligible.

The advantages of a maximum billet length from the point of view of temperature control is mentioned in section 2.2.3. This process offers significant economic advantages for "isothermal" extrusion.

2.3. Combined Direct/Indirect Extrusion

One disadvantage of direct extrusion is that the pressure available for deformation decreases from the back end of the billet to the die because of friction at the wall of the container (Ref 17). Pressure reaches its lowest point exactly where it is most needed. Because the majority of presses use the direct process, attempts have been made to try to develop a method combining the advantages of indirect extrusion with the mechanical capabilities of direct presses. Ziehm (Ref 40) used a die with a hollow-stem extension piece (Fig. 2.20, a to c). The process begins with indirect extrusion, and therefore the initial peak load associated with the direct process is avoided. The container is free to move axially 25 to 50 mm during this initial phase (Fig. 2.20b), and any relative movement with its associated wall

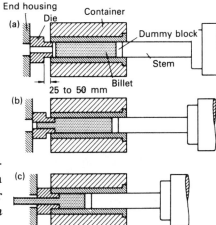

Fig. 2.20. Combined indirect/direct extrusion. (a) Tooling; (b) indirect extrusion with a floating container; (c) direct extrusion after the container has reached its stop. *(From Ref 40)*

friction is eliminated. Consequently, all the load applied by the ram is transmitted to the deformation zone in front of the die. After this initial phase, the container reaches a stop on the die holder and normal direct extrusion takes over (Fig. 2.20c). The major advantage of this combined method is that conventional presses can be used — provided the container movement is sufficient.

2.4. Cable Sheathing by Extrusion

The production of metallic cable sheaths is an important process in the cable industry. The sheath has to fulfill the following requirements:

(a) Narrow tolerances for the wall thickness — that is, the wall thickness must not fall below a specified minimum.
(b) The sheath has to be completely impervious to liquids and gases.
(c) There must be no stopmarks (bamboo rings), which can form if the press is stopped and reloaded incorrectly.
(d) The cable itself must not be thermally damaged by using too high a deformation temperature or too long a deformation time.

Numerous methods of cable sheathing have been developed to meet these requirements. The aim is to extrude the sheath continuously around the cable without interrupting the process for reloading. The basic principle of a cable press is illustrated in Fig. 2.21. The cable runs axially through a hollow point holder. The distance between the point and the die can be adjusted to form a sheath in the shape of a tube. An extensive description of the various methods

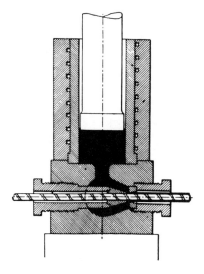

Fig. 2.21. Cross section through the container and die of a vertical cable sheathing press. *(From Ref 47)*

of extrusion has been given by Pearson and Parkins (Ref 47) and by Riemann (Ref 48).

2.4.1. Extrusion of Lead-Sheathed Cables Through Welding Chamber Dies

The charge of molten lead under a vacuum flows past the withdrawn solid ram of the vertical hydraulic press into the container (Fig. 2.22a). Then the ram is lowered to seal the container, and the lead solidifies under a low pressure applied by the ram. Lead is then pressed into the die around the cable. The upper container is connected to a hollow ram, through which the lead is pressed, and a reservoir. The reservoir is filled as the lead is forced through the hollow stem by the solid ram. When this has reached its lower limit of travel, the die is hydraulically pushed upwards, without interrupting the extrusion cycle, and hence the hollow stem is pressed into the reservoir. Solid lead then flows from the reservoir through the stem into the die. The operation is continued until the upper container has been recharged and is ready to continue the extrusion. A valve closes the entrance to the upper container.

2.4.2. Extrusion of Aluminum-Sheathed Cables Through Welding Chamber Dies

The difference between cable extrusion with lead, described above, and with aluminum is that aluminum is loaded in the form of solid preheated billets. The tooling — die, container, etc. — is also heated to ensure that the plastic deformation and the welding of the metal are not impeded by heat losses. The sheathing process usually follows the same pattern as that used for lead, including the reloading sequence (Fig. 2.22, b to d). However, complete removal of air from the container before each extrusion is important in aluminum cable sheathing. The methods used include taper heating (section 2.1.2) and the removal of air by pumping. The complicated tooling, with the thin-wall hollow stem at the front end, is of course sensitive to pressure applied from one side: it can result in unacceptable variations in wall thickness (section 3.2.1.4). Stresses in the tooling can be balanced by using the double extrusion method — that is, with two containers directly opposite each other (Fig. 2.23) and by methods giving concentric flow.

2.4.3. Lead Cable Sheathing by Concentric Metal Flow

Longitudinal welds are the characteristic feature of the cable sheathing processes described above, which are the ones most commonly used. This is true of all products extruded through welding chamber dies. Although modern extrusion technology guarantees sound and substantially homogeneous bonding of the metal strands in the welding chamber, many attempts have been made in cable sheathing to provide a continuous concentric flow of metal to the die.

2.4.3.1. The Judge Method

In the Judge method (Fig. 2.24) molten lead is fed discontinuously into the container of a press inclined at approximately 10° to the horizontal. The cable is fed concentrically to the container, and the lead flows parallel to the cable direction and solidifies only after it has passed the segmented openings of the discharge die. Therefore, no longitudinal welds are developed. Nevertheless, the work cycle is discontinuous and an oxide skin can form on the surface of the molten lead during reloading.

2.4.3.2. Sheathing With a Screw-Driven Press

The advantages of a concentric supply of metal and a completely continuous process have been realized in the principle of the screw-driven press; one designed for lead is shown in Fig. 2.25. The extrusion screw (4) rotates around a stationary inlet tube (13). The molten lead is fed internally and externally into the first compression chamber. It then flows through the ports of a spider die (12), where it is again compressed and extruded as a tube. The induction heating coils (29) and the cooling channels are used for accurate temperature control.

According to Pearson and Parkins (Ref 47), the main advantages of this continuous machine are:

(text is continued on page 88)

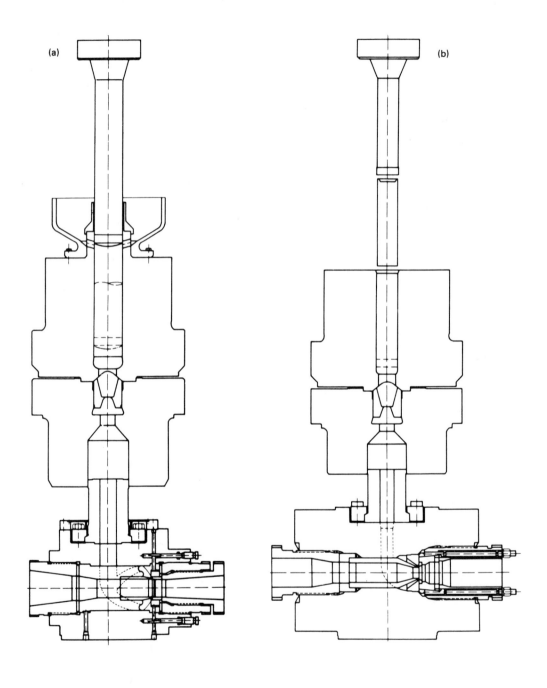

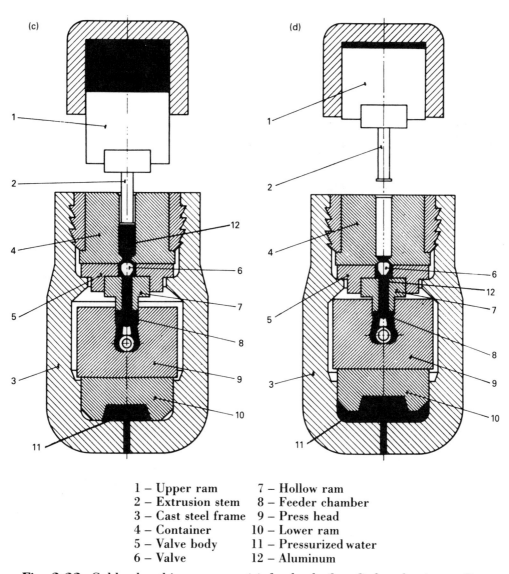

1 – Upper ram	7 – Hollow ram
2 – Extrusion stem	8 – Feeder chamber
3 – Cast steel frame	9 – Press head
4 – Container	10 – Lower ram
5 – Valve body	11 – Pressurized water
6 – Valve	12 – Aluminum

Fig. 2.22. Cable sheathing presses: **(a)** for lead; **(b,c,d)** for aluminum. Extrusion of aluminum is shown in **(c)**; extrusion and reloading, in **(d)**. *(From Demag-Hydraulik)*

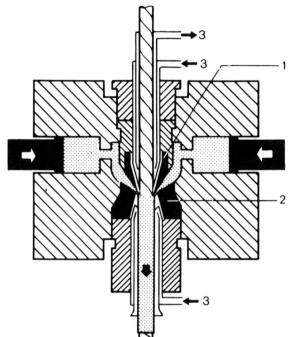

1 – Extrusion mandrel
2 – Adjustable die
3 – Cooling medium

Fig. 2.23. Section from the die head of a twin-acting cable sheathing press. *(From Schloemann-Siemag)*

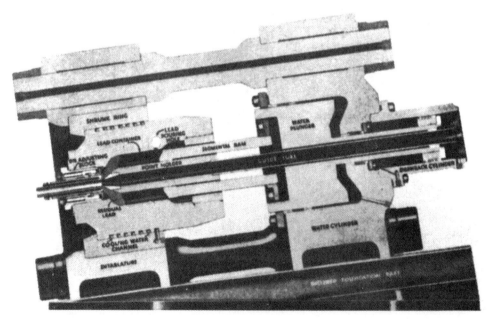

Fig. 2.24. Cross section of a Judge cable sheathing press. *(From Ref 47)*

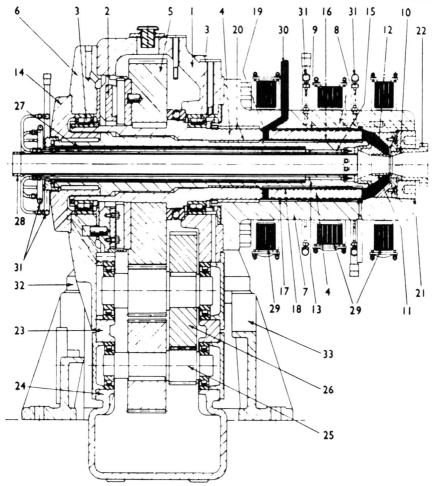

1 – Main steel casing. 2 – "Michell" thrust bearing. 3 – Double-row roller journal bearings. 4 – Extrusion screw. 5 – Final drive gear. 6 – Back flange. 7 – Extrusion barrel. 8 – Extrusion barrel cooling channels. 9 – Longitudinal slots. 10 – Ring die. 11 – Core die. 12 – Spider die (four ports, ring and core die support). 13 – Stationary inlet tube. 14 – Steel flange, locating stationary tube. 15 – Stationary tube cooling channels. 16 – Stationary tube outer longitudinal grooves. 17 – Outer extrusion passage. 18 – Inner extrusion passage. 19 – Portholes for lead access to inner extrusion. 20 – Lead retainers on stationary tube and extrusion screw. 21 – Spider front screw. 22 – Ring die adjusting screw. 23 – Two-piece subsidiary casing. 24 – Two-piece subsidiary casing. 25 – First reduction gear. 26 – Second reduction gear. 27 – Outer protecting tube — stationary tube. 28 – Inner protecting tube — stationary tube. 29 – Induction heating coils. 30 – Point of lead entry into machine. 31 – Circular pipe manifolds — cooling channels. 32 – Bottom flange. 33 – Cast iron stool.

Fig. 2.25. Sectional drawing of continuous lead extrusion machine. The lead flow from inlet pipe to the dies is shown in solid black. *(From Ref 47)*

(a) The molten lead does not oxidize, because the machine does not have to be opened for recharging.
(b) There are no longitudinal welds or stopmarks.
(c) Close dimensions and uniform properties can be achieved because of the accurate temperature control.
(d) The economic advantages of continuous production.

2.5. Hydrostatic Extrusion

2.5.1. Basic Method

In hydrostatic extrusion the billet in the container is extruded through a die by a liquid acting as a pressure medium, instead of by the direct application of the load with a ram. The principle is not new; the first patent was granted in 1894 (Ref 13) but it did not find any industrial application at that time. The idea was taken up again by Bridgman (Ref 14), whose work, together with that of Pugh (Ref 15), made a significant contribution to the technical realization of the process. Mechanical problems, especially that of sealing fluid pressures as high as 20 kbar, had to be overcome. The English firm Fielding & Platt and the Swedish firm ASEA have been particularly successful in this field. Today many hydrostatic extrusion presses up to 40 MN are in use all over the world as research and production presses.

Hydrostatic extrusion is suitable not only for working brittle metals but also for ductile metals including aluminum and copper. The process cannot be classified as either hot or cold extrusion: both cold and preheated billets are used. The basic difference between hydrostatic extrusion and the conventional methods is that, in the latter, the radial pressure on the container is 20 to 80% lower (depending on the alloy and the extrusion conditions) than the axial pressure applied by the ram. In hydrostatic extrusion the radial and axial pressures are equal. Therefore the tooling has to withstand a significantly higher pressure and more stringent requirements have to be placed on the design of the tooling and the material used (Ref 16, 17 and Chap. 4). The die extends into the container, where it is supported on all sides by the fluid pressure, and therefore it is constructed with relatively thin walls and a long conical lead-in.

2.5.2. Hydrostatic Extrusion Without Back Pressure

2.5.2.1. Method

In the simplest method of hydrostatic extrusion, the metal is extruded through the die into the atmosphere, much as in conventional extrusion

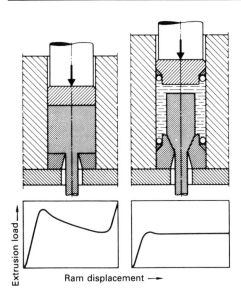

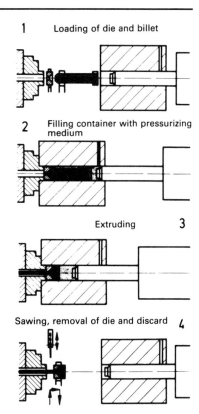

1   Loading of die and billet

2   Filling container with pressurizing medium

Extruding   3

Sawing, removal of die and discard   4

Fig. 2.26. Comparison of simple hydrostatic extrusion with conventional extrusion. **(a)** Load profile in conventional extrusion with a flat die; **(b)** load profile in hydrostatic extrusion with a conical die. *(From Fielding & Platt, Gloucester)*

Fig. 2.27. Sequence of operations in hydrostatic extrusion.

(Fig. 2.26, a and b). The container with the pressure-transmitting fluid is sealed with high-pressure seals at the ram and the die. Extrusion begins as soon as the hydrostatic pressure has reached a high enough value — depending on the flow stress of the material and the extrusion ratio. A conical die is used to allow a film of lubricant to develop. The four stages in the working cycle are shown in Fig. 2.27. The main advantages of simple hydrostatic extrusion over conventional methods are:

(a) There is no friction between the billet and the container. Therefore the load at the start of extrusion is much lower and, theoretically, billets of any length can be used (Fig. 2.28).

(b) Friction at the die is considerably reduced by the film of lubricant between the deforming metal and the die surface.

(c) The lower extrusion load and the reduced die friction allow higher extrusion ratios to be used.

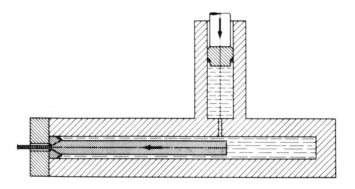

Fig. 2.28. Method for hydrostatic extrusion of very long billets. *(From Ref 18)*

(*d*) Provided the heat developed by deformation is not excessive (dependent on the properties of the material, the extrusion ratio and speed), cold worked materials can be produced by extrusion, as in normal cold extrusion (Chap. 3).

One disadvantage of the process is the laborious preparation of the billets. Every billet has to be tapered to match the die angle in order to form a seal at the start of extrusion. Also, the entire surface of the billet generally has to be machined — particularly if cast billets are being used — to remove surface defects, which would reappear in an elongated form on the extruded product, especially if low extrusion ratios are used. The same can happen with machining marks. This problem is also encountered in cold extrusion. The uniform hydrostatic pressure in the container does not cause any deformation — for example, billet buckling — and, consequently, the billets used do not have to be straight; coiled wire can also be extruded (Fig. 2.29). It is also possible to extrude tubes over a floating mandrel (Fig. 2.30).

2.5.2.2. Applications of Simple Hydrostatic Extrusion

The basic process described above is particularly suitable for extruding metals of average or good ductility at high extrusion ratios, thereby reducing some of the usual intermediate steps. An example is extrusion of copper wire (Fig. 2.31). Other commonly extruded products are aluminum wire, thin-wall copper tubes, copper sections, aluminum and special alloys, as well as steel tubes with narrow tolerances and high surface quality (Ref 23). This method has also been used successfully for the economical production of gearwheels with straight or helical teeth (Fig. 2.32); however, the extrusion ratio was low. Of particular importance is cladding or plating by extrusion, especially coating aluminum with copper for electrical conductors. Aluminum billets

Fig. 2.29. Reduction of wire by hydrostatic extrusion. 1 – High-pressure container; 2 – feed coiler; 3 – inlet for pressurizing medium; 4 – extruded wire. *(From Ref 18)*

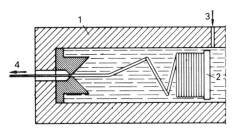

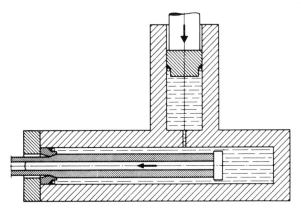

Fig. 2.30. Hydrostatic extrusion of tubes with a moving mandrel. *(From Ref 18)*

Fig. 2.31. At a pressure of 16 kbar (16 000 atm), the reduction in area of the extruded copper bar is 50:1 with a cold billet (left), and 800:1 with a billet preheated to 300 °C (right). *(From Ref 22)*

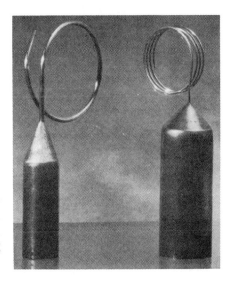

Fig. 2.32. Helical gear blanks extruded from cylindrical steel billets by hydrostatic extrusion. *(From Ref 22)*

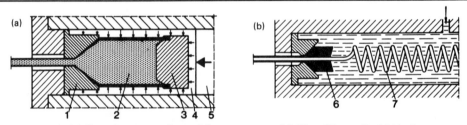

(a) Starting extrusion with a compound billet *(From Ref 22)*: 1 – die; 2 – compound billet (aluminum billet in a copper tube); 3 – steel backer; 4 – pressurizing medium; 5 – pressurizing ram.
(b) Extruding the cladding metal around wire *(From Ref 18)*: 6 – aluminum billet (hollow); 7 – copper wire.

Fig. 2.33. Cladding by hydrostatic extrusion.

packed inside copper tubing are used (Fig. 2.33a), or wire is extruded with the cladding material (Fig. 2.33b). The absence of container friction and the relatively homogeneous deformation result in a coating of constant wall thickness over the entire length of the product.

2.5.2.3 Heat Produced During Hydrostatic Extrusion

The higher extrusion ratios (and therefore, strains) used in hydrostatic extrusion result in an increase in the work of deformation, which is converted to heat. Under adiabatic conditions there is a corresponding increase in the exit temperature of the product, given by:

$$\triangle T = \frac{p}{c \cdot \rho} \qquad \text{(Eq 55)}$$

where p is the extrusion pressure (section 2.5.2.4).

The temperature increase for each 10 kbar increase in pressure is 400 °C for aluminum, 290 °C for copper, and 280 °C for steel.

Aluminum recrystallizes at pressures of less than 10 kbar and copper at about 13 kbar; therefore, cold working does not occur with these metals, even at relatively low extrusion ratios.

2.5.2.4. Extrusion Pressure

A pressure peak is also found at the start of extrusion in the hydrostatic process. It is needed to initiate the flow hindered by friction at the die until a lubricating film and steady state conditions have developed. This pressure peak is particularly high in comparison with that needed to continue extrusion if the cross-sectional area of the extrusion is low (Ref 19). The rapid decrease in pressure after the initiation of extrusion can, in some cases, lead to the development of periodic oscillations in the pressure — the slip-stick effect — which causes annular stopmarks on the product. Viscous dampers can be used to eliminate this effect (Ref 24, 25).

After the initial pressure, the steady state pressure remains constant because there is no friction at the wall of the container (Fig. 2.34). The pressure required depends on the material and is linearly related to the natural logarithm of the extrusion ratio according to the empirical equation:

$$p = a^* \cdot \ln R + b^* \qquad \text{(Eq 56)}$$

This relationship is illustrated in Fig. 2.35 for the extrusion of round billets to rod for several alloys. The gradient of the lines would be slightly steeper for more complex sections (Ref 20).

Losses in hydrostatic extrusion are mainly governed by the redundant work needed to shear the material at the die; therefore, the extrusion pressure

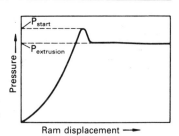

Fig. 2.34. Pressure variation as a function of ram displacement during hydrostatic extrusion. *(From Ref 20)*

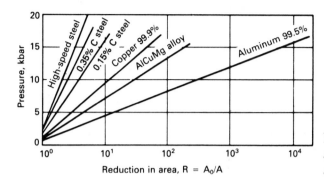

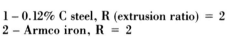

Fig. 2.35. Extrusion pressure as a function of the reduction in area. *(From Ref 20)*

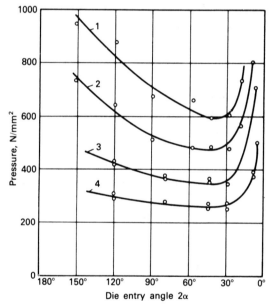

1 – 0.12% C steel, R (extrusion ratio) = 2
2 – Armco iron, R = 2
3 – Electrolytic copper E-Cu, R = 2
4 – Al99.5, R = 4

Fig. 2.36. Influence of the die angle 2α on the extrusion pressure in hydrostatic extrusion. *(From Ref 15)*

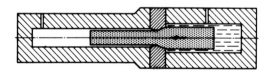

Fig. 2.37. Hydrostatic extrusion, back pressure method.

depends on the magnitude of the die angle. Experiments with aluminum have shown that the pressure decreases with decreasing die angle (Fig. 2.36 and Ref 21). Ignoring redundant deformation, the ideal extrusion pressure is given by:

$$p = k_{fm} \cdot \varphi = k_{fm} \cdot \ln \frac{A_0}{A_1} \qquad \text{(Eq 57)}$$

Comparisons between the ideal extrusion pressure and measured values have been made by Pugh and his colleagues (Ref 15, 21).

2.5.3. Hydrostatic Extrusion With Back Pressure (Fluid-to-Fluid Extrusion)

Brittle materials that cannot be extruded by the conventional process or by cold extrusion also fracture during simple hydrostatic extrusion, because of the low ductility and the fall in the hydrostatic pressure towards zero at the die exit. However, if the product is extruded into a hydraulic pressure chamber containing a sufficiently high back pressure, instead of into the atmosphere, the hydrostatic pressure at the die exit can be increased. The ductility is therefore improved, and a crack-free extrusion can be produced. This is the principle of the back pressure method shown schematically in Fig. 2.37. The back pressure increases the fluid pressure needed in the container to continue extrusion, and the pressure in the container must exceed the back pressure by an amount at least equal to the flow stress and the internal redundant work. This is a disadvantage, because the working pressure in the container can rarely exceed 20 kbar and, if this is the case, the maximum extrusion ratio is reduced.

The back pressure method is also known as the differential pressure process — from the pressure difference needed. Fielding & Platt has built experimental presses using the simple method shown in Fig. 2.37. The design and construction of the back pressure chamber, with the problems of sealing, are, however, considerable and the press operation is complicated and expensive. The billet length that can be used is also severely limited by the length of the back pressure container.

2.5.4. Simple Hydrostatic Extrusion of Brittle Materials

The back pressure (differential pressure) method, although theoretically very suitable for the deformation of brittle materials, is not suitable for industrial application, because of the difficulties mentioned above. For this

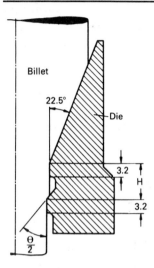

Fig. 2.38. Tandem extrusion die. H = Distance between the entries to the two die steps. Θ = Die angle of the second step. *(From Ref 27)*

reason, the Battelle Memorial Institute attempted to solve the problem of extruding low ductility metals by another approach (Ref 27). It was established that the cracks or fracture first developed in the rear section of the die, immediately before the exit plane, and that the surface cracking resulted from internal tensile stresses as the product left the die. The cracks observed are either longitudinal or transverse across the extruded product, depending on whether the predominating internal stresses are longitudinal or circumferential. This phenomenon had been noted much earlier by Bühler in rod and tube drawing (Ref 28). He discovered that it is possible to reverse the internal stresses at the surface to compressive stresses by a subsequent draw with a low reduction in area, less than 2%. This discovery led to the development of the tandem drawing die (Ref 28, 29), which was adopted for simple hydrostatic extrusion by Battelle. The tandem die used for the experiments — illustrated in Fig. 2.38 — is designed to give a 2% reduction in the second step. This method has been successfully applied to the extrusion of brittle materials, including beryllium and a molybdenum alloy TZM, without any cracking (Fig. 2.39). The lubricant used was PTFE (polytetrafluoroethylene), and the pressurizing fluid was castor oil. The results might be applicable to normal cold extrusion through a lubricated conical die (Ref 27).

2.5.5. Augmented Hydrostatic Extrusion

Displacement of the billet or of the extrusion can be improved by applying an additional axial load directly onto the billet or by pulling the extrusion. This simplifies the operation of the press.

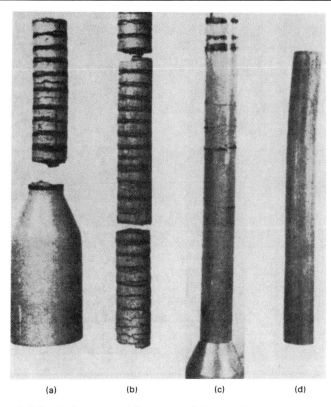

Fig. 2.39. Influence of the type of die on the surface cracking of beryllium in simple hydrostatic extrusion. **(a)** and **(b)** Standard die, R = 4. **(c)** Standard die, R = 3.3. **(d)** Tandem die, R = 4. (*From Ref 27*)

Methods of augmenting hydrostatic extrusion by axial pressure have been described by Slater and Green (Ref 30); the principle is illustrated in Fig. 2.40 and 2.41. In Fig. 2.40 the additional load is transmitted from the upper hydraulic cylinder onto the billet by a ram. The pressure in this cylinder is equal to the fluid pressure in the billet container. The pressure needed for extrusion is reduced approximately by the amount F/A_B, where F is the effective load on the billet of cross section A_B. A hollow stem is used to transmit the extra load to the billet (Fig. 2.41); a mechanical clamp connects the billet and the hollow stem. The long billet must be extruded step by step.

Pressure-augmented hydrostatic extrusion has the advantage of improving control over the process and avoids sudden decreases in pressure.

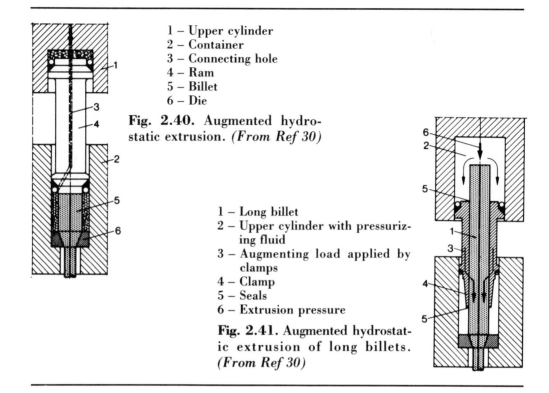

1 – Upper cylinder
2 – Container
3 – Connecting hole
4 – Ram
5 – Billet
6 – Die

Fig. 2.40. Augmented hydrostatic extrusion. *(From Ref 30)*

1 – Long billet
2 – Upper cylinder with pressurizing fluid
3 – Augmenting load applied by clamps
4 – Clamp
5 – Seals
6 – Extrusion pressure

Fig. 2.41. Augmented hydrostatic extrusion of long billets. *(From Ref 30)*

Pressurizing fluid is not lost from the open die, because it is displaced through a hole in the connecting cylinder during the extrusion stroke. A press working on this principle has been constructed by Fielding & Platt (Chap. 4 and Ref 26). The disadvantages of this design are the complexity of the system and the large number of high-pressure seals needed. This is not a problem if tensile augmentation is used, because the additional load is applied externally; it is used in extrusion of wire (Ref 31, 32). However, a sensitive control system is needed to coordinate the correct tensile load with the extrusion conditions.

2.5.6. Semicontinuous Hydrostatic Extrusion

The principle of semicontinuous extrusion is incorporated in progressive hydrostatic extrusion with pressure augmentation shown in Fig. 2.41 (Ref 19, 30). The operation, which has been used only in an experimental press, allows billets of any length to be extruded. The augmenting pressure is transmitted to the billet via a sealed clamping system, which, in combination with the high pressure in the container, allows the billet to be extruded pro-

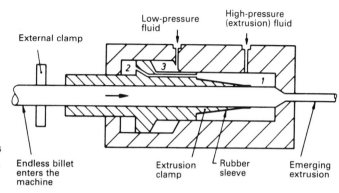

Fig. 2.42. Semicontinuous hydrostatic extrusion press. *(From Ref 19)*

gressively (Fig. 2.42). However, extrusion has to be interrupted at regular intervals when the clamping jaws have moved a specified distance towards the die. The press cycle then continues as follows (referring to Fig. 2.42):

(*a*) Container 1 is filled from the high-pressure system and pressurized, and the jaws close. At the same time, the rear chamber 2 is filled.

(*b*) The external clamp, which initially pushes the billet into the die, is released when the fluid pressure in container chamber 1 and 2 has reached a certain value. Extrusion starts when the extrusion pressure and the augmenting load produced in the chamber are reached.

(*c*) When the jaws have covered the maximum stroke, the external clamp is closed with the simultaneous release of the high fluid pressure. Extrusion then stops and the jaws are released.

(*d*) The jaws are moved back to the left-hand position by a low-pressure fluid applied to chamber 3, and a new cycle commences from phase (*a*), above.

2.5.7. Continuous Hydrostatic Extrusion

If the mechanically applied augmentation load, which can be applied only step by step (semicontinuous process), is replaced by a continuously applied load, the continuous hydrostatic extrusion of endless billets results (Ref 19, 34). This has been carried out experimentally by utilizing the dragging effect of a liquid with a high viscosity as it flows in a continuous current past the billet in the extrusion direction (Fig. 2.43). The cascade-type division of the dragging system prevents the high axial pressure over the working length from causing bending or yielding. The high hydrostatic pressure and the absence of tensile stresses make very high reduction possible in one step (up to 98% for copper wire); consequently, the number of dies required for the same reduction in area is much smaller than for conventional drawing in which the

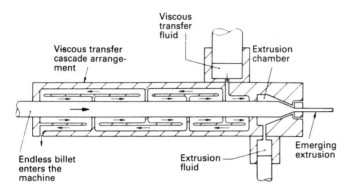

Fig. 2.43. Continuous hydrostatic extrusion. *(From Ref 19)*

maximum reduction is about 50%. Wire can be reduced to small diameters by having several of these presses in series. Systems of this kind have been built by Western Electric (Ref 34) and Sir James Farmer Norton & Co., Ltd. (Ref 35).

2.5.8. Hydrostatic Extrusion at High Temperatures

Originally, hydrostatic extrusion was used only for cold working—that is, the billet was not preheated. However, since the heat of deformation initiates recrystallization and softening when copper, α-brass or aluminum are extruded at high extrusion ratios, there is no reason — from the material property point of view — to use only cold deformation. The extrusion pressure can be reduced, or the maximum possible extrusion ratio increased, by preheating the billet to give a more economical production.

Experimental results in this field have been published for the hot extrusion of copper and Cu37Zn; the essential details are given in Fig. 2.44. An extrusion ratio of about 50 can be attained for copper at 20 °C and a pressure of 15 kbar; the ratio can be increased to over 1000 if the billet is heated to 350 °C. In these experiments only the billet and the die were preheated. The pressurizing fluid, insulated by the high-pressure seals, was introduced at room temperature.

Only low extrusion ratios can be used in the hydrostatic extrusion of steel with cold billets, and this provided an incentive for developing the hot deformation process to achieve deformations relevant to the needs of industry. Experiments were therefore carried out using quasi-fluids — that is, solids that are much softer than the billet at the deformation temperature — for hot hydrostatic extrusion. Examples of such quasi-fluids include NaCl, CaF_2 and

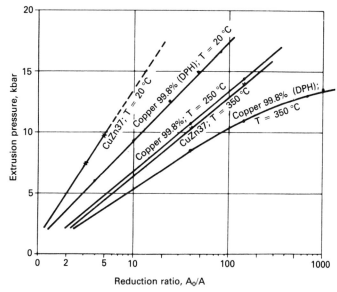

Fig. 2.44. Relationships between extrusion pressure and extrusion ratio. *(From Ref 36)*

glasses at just below their melting point (Ref 35). Extrusion ratios of 30 and 40 at pressures of 12 and 20 kbar, respectively, have been obtained by this method with a tool steel and a high-speed steel at 1000 °C. At room temperature the limit was a ratio of 3 (Ref 36-38). The principle of this process is very similar to that of the Séjournet method of lubrication used in conventional hot extrusion of steel.

2.5.9. Special Methods of Hydrostatic Extrusion

2.5.9.1. Thick-Film (Hydrafilm) Process

The method known as the Hydrafilm, or thick-film, process is characterized by a thick film of lubricant around the billet and by a relatively low volume of the pressurizing fluid (Fig. 2.45). This volume is adjusted to the amount needed to produce the required hydrostatic pressure using an extrusion ram sealed at the front end. Pressure has to be applied directly to the billet by the ram at the start of extrusion but not necessarily during extrusion, giving the advantages of inexpensive augmented extrusion. The lubricant applied to the billet before extrusion is a separate medium from the hydrostatic pressurizing fluid, which, if it is a thick fluid — for example, wax (especially beeswax), grease or a highly viscous fluid — can be applied before the

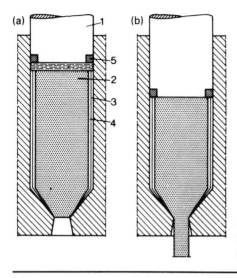

1 – Extrusion ram
2 – Billet
3 – Film of pressurizing fluid
4 – Separate film of lubricant
5 – Sealing ring

Fig. 2.45. Schematic diagram of the thick-film (Hydrafilm) process: **(a)** before extrusion; **(b)** during extrusion. *(From Ref 37)*

billet is loaded, because the volume required is low. The Hydrafilm process, therefore, has the following advantages (Ref 37):

(*a*) Hydrostatic extrusion can be carried out as simply as conventional extrusion.

(*b*) It is easier to replace conventional extrusion with this method because the volume of pressurizing fluid is minimal.

(*c*) The principle of hydrostatic extrusion can be realized on high-speed mechanical presses and with a high output.

(*d*) The process is especially suitable for hot hydrostatic extrusion because the pressurizing fluid has a minimum volume and does not have to be pumped. Extrusion temperatures of 800 °C and higher are possible. The hot hydrostatic extrusion of steel described in section 2.5.8 is very similar to the Hydrafilm process.

Experiments by Wallace, Kulkarni and Schey (Ref 49) have shown that there is an optimum die angle and lubricant viscosity. If the latter is too high, the stick-slip effect (bamboo rings) occurs; if it is too low, the lubricating film can break down completely.

2.5.9.2. The Hydrospin Process (Helical Extrusion)

The Hydrospin process consists of three stages and gives extremely high deformations (Ref 38, 39). In the first stage a tube is extruded by simple hydrostatic extrusion using a die and a stationary mandrel. In the second stage a rectangular strip is sheared off from the wall of the tube by a rotating tool containing a stepped cutting edge. This strip is then immediately

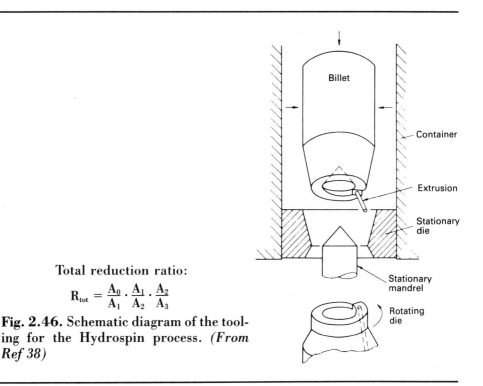

Total reduction ratio:

$$R_{tot} = \frac{A_0}{A_1} \cdot \frac{A_1}{A_2} \cdot \frac{A_2}{A_3}$$

Fig. 2.46. Schematic diagram of the tooling for the Hydrospin process. *(From Ref 38)*

extruded — the third stage — through a small opening in the vertical face of the step to give the desired shape to the product. The extrusion ratios of the three stages are multiplied together, and therefore the final ratio has a very high value without the use of particularly high fluid pressures. Consequently, this method is particularly suitable for the manufacture of thin wires or sections from soft materials such as copper and aluminum. Copper wire 0.5 mm in diameter has been produced with a total extrusion ratio of 15 000:1 on a machine built by Fielding & Platt (Ref 39). Tooling for the Hydrospin process is shown schematically in Fig. 2.46.

2.6. Cladding by Extrusion

Clad bar, wires, sections and tubes are required for some special purposes. Cladding by extrusion was developed for aluminum alloys, after the release of the Duraluminum patent rights (1927), to protect aircraft sections from corrosion. The high-strength but corrosion-sensitive base alloys were clad with pure aluminum. The realization that two metals can be joined together by cladding during extrusion has also gained special importance for heavy metals. The flow stresses of the two metals must be similar. Copper sections clad with silver for electrical contacts are produced in this way in a wide variety of shapes. The cladding of platinum-tungsten, copper-nickel alloys, and zirconium, titanium and copper has also received attention. Recently, the plating of copper onto aluminum has been developed. The cladding-by-extrusion process requires the clean and oxide-free contacting surfaces of the two metals forming the billet to be stretched (enlarged) during deformation and new surfaces formed. These weld together under the action of the pressure and temperature.

The technique of cladding has two primary aims:

(a) A defect-free bond.
(b) The ratio of the thickness of the cladding metal to that of the base metal has to be constant over the length of the extrusion.

In both cases, steady state extrusion (that is, constant deformation temperature and flow pattern) is required throughout the deformation. These conditions are fulfilled to varying extents by developments of the various extrusion methods. The results obtained by the different methods are described briefly below.

2.6.1. Cladding by Extrusion With a Shell

The billet, which consists of the core material surrounded by the cladding material, is extruded by the direct process without lubrication. The volume and shape of the cladding material must be matched to the particular nonuniform flow pattern associated with this method. The cladding is applied to the billet core in the form of a tube of nonuniform thickness. The diameter and length of the tube have to be calculated from the dimensions of the product. The thickness of the clad layer varies over the length of the product and cannot be predicted accurately.

2.6.2. Cladding by Extrusion With Reduced Friction at the Container Wall

The flow in lubricated direct extrusion is more homogeneous than that obtained in extrusion with a shell. Therefore, the ratio of the thicknesses of the two metals is significantly more uniform over the length of the extruded product, but it is not constant (Fig. 2.47).

Several more or less viable methods for completely uniform cladding over the total length of the product by this process can be found in the literature. The thickness of the cladding must lie within narrow tolerances. According to a patent held by the Erbslöh firm, a die holder, which can be

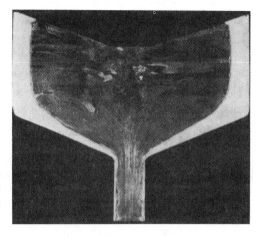

Fig. 2.47. Cladding copper with silver, produced on a 6.3 MN extrusion press (extruded without a shell; entry angle 24°). *(From Laue, unpublished)*

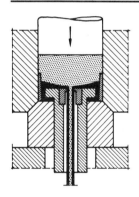

Fig. 2.48. Cladding by extrusion with a controlled die carrier (DBP 1053460).

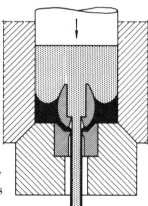

Fig. 2.49. Cladding by extrusion with two dies (DBP 1115686).

withdrawn in a controlled manner, in the container makes it possible to obtain uniform cladding. The die holder and the liner wall form an annular reservoir for the cladding material (Fig. 2.48).

Figure 2.49 shows an improved design for producing a clad extrusion by means of a stationary die fitted to the base of the container and a second die connected to the first by arms. The cladding material is extruded through the stationary die, which forms the external shape of the clad product. The core material is extruded through the second die. Accurate and expensive tooling is required, but a uniform cladding is obtained over the total length of the extrusion.

2.6.3. Cladding by Extrusion Without Container Friction

2.6.3.1. Hydrostatic Extrusion

Another recently developed process is cladding by hydrostatic extrusion. This is used for cladding aluminum wires and rods with copper for electrical conductors. Further details are given in section 2.5.2.2.

2.6.3.2. Indirect Extrusion

A uniform flow pattern is a characteristic of the indirect process, and therefore the process also can be used to extrude clad products.

2.6.4. Cladding After the Principle of Cable Sheathing

The principle used in cable sheathing (section 2.4) can also be used in uniformly cladding a preformed long extrusion.

Bibliographic References

1. Akeret, R.: Untersuchungen über das Strangpressen unter besonderer Berücksichtigung thermischer Vorgänge. Aluminium 44 (1968) p. 412/415.
2. Laue, K.: Strangpressen. Z. f. Metallkunde 50 (1959) p. 495/502.
3. Biswas, A., and Zilges, F. J.: Direktes, indirektes und hydrostatisches Strangpressen. Aluminium 49 (1973) p. 296/299 and 352/356.
4. Fister, W.: Beitrag zum Strangpreßproblem. Thesis TH Aachen (1966).
5. Petsch, E.: Neues Indirekt-Strangpreßverfahren für Metalldraht auf moderner ölhydraulischer Strangpresse und automatischer Haspelanlage. Z. f. Metallkunde 50 (1959) p. 629/634:
6. Akeret, R.: Sonderverfahren zum schnelleren Strangpressen von Aluminium-Hartlegierungen. Z. f. Metallkunde 64 (1973) p. 311/318.
7. Laue, K.: Isothermes Strangpressen. Z. f. Metallkunde 51 (1960) p. 491/495.
8. Lange, G.: Der Wärmehaushalt beim Strangpressen; Berechnung des isothermen Preßvorganges. Z. f. Metallkunde 62 (1971) p. 571/588.
9. Ziegler, W., and Siegert, K.: Indirektes Strangpressen von Leichtmetall. Z. f. Metallkunde 64 (1973) p. 224/229.
10. Siegert, K.: Temperaturführung beim direkten und indirekten Strangpressen von Leichtmetall. Vortrag Werkstoff-Kolloquium TU Berlin (1973) (DGM Technical Report).
11. French Patent No. 2.131.265, December 1972.
12. Siegert, K., and Ruppin, D.: German Patent 2263 997.
13. Robertson, J.: British Patent 19356 (January 1894).
14. Bridgman, P. W.: Studies in Large Plastic Flow and Fracture with Special Emphasis on the Effects of Hydrostatic Pressure. New York (1952), p. 362.
15. Pugh, H. L. D., and Low, A. H.: The Hydrostatic Extrusion of Difficult Metals. J. Inst. Metals 93 (1964) p. 201/217.

16. Anonymous: Hydrostatisches Strangpressen. Industrie-Anzeiger 86 (1964) p. 94/96.
17. Vater, M., and Rathjen, C.: Untersuchungen über die Größe der Stempelkraft und des Innendrucks im Aufnehmer beim Strangpressen von Metallen. Fortschr.-Ber. VDI-Z, Series 2, No. 9 (1966), p. 122.
18. Hydrostatic Extrusion. Fielding & Platt, Ltd., Gloucester, England.
19. Adie, J. F., and Harper, S.: Hydrostatisches Strangpressen. Z. f. Metallkunde 62 (1971) p. 343/350.
20. Johnsson, S.: Fortschritte beim hydrostatischen Strangpressen. Bänder-Bleche-Rohre 9 (1968) p. 317/321.
21. Pugh, H. L. D., and Ashcroft, K.: Das hydrostatische Strang- und Fließpressen von Metallen. Industrie-Anzeiger 86 (1964) p. 15/22.
22. Publication ASEA AQ 14-101T: Quintus, Hydrostatisches Strangpressen.
23. Hornmark, N.: Hydrostatisches Strangpressen von Stahl und NE-Metallen. ASEA-Zeitschrift 16 (1971) p. 65/70.
24. Low, A. H., and Donaldson, C. J. H.: NEL Report No. 289, The National Engineering Laboratory, East Kilbride, Scotland (1967).
25. Pugh, H. L. D.: Hydrostatic Extrusion of Steel. Iron and Steel 45 (1972) p. 39/44 and 49/51.
26. Anonymous: Hydrostatic Extrusion at the U. K. A. E. A. Installation of a 1600/80 ton press in the Springfield Works. Metal Forming (1968) p. 107/110.
27. Fiorentino, R. J., Richardson, B. D., and Sabroff, A. M.: Hydrostatic Extrusion of Brittle Materials. Role of Design and Residual Stress Formation. Metal Forming (1969) p. 243/252.
28. Bühler, H.: Austrian Patent No. 139.790 (December 1934) and British Patent 423.868 (February 1935).
29. Sims, C. E., and Landis, M. N.: Methods of Producing Steel Products and Articles. US Patent 2.589.881 (May 1952).
30. Slater, H. K., and Green, D.: Augmented Hydrostatic Extrusion of Continuous Bars. Proc. Inst. Mech. Eng., Part 3, C 183 (1967) p. 217 (also Fielding & Platt Ltd., "Semi-Continuous Hydrostatic Extrusion").
31. Pugh, H. L. D.: NEL Report No. 416, The National Engineering Laboratory, East Kilbride, Scotland (1969).
32. Richardson, B. D., Fiorentino, R. J., and Sabroff, A. M.: ASTM Report No. MF62-218, Philadelphia (1968).
33. Fiorentino, R. J., and Sabroff, A. M.: Shapes Get Bigger, More Complex with Hydro-static Extrusion. Iron Age 196 (1965) p. 106/108.
34. Fuchs, F. J.: High Pressure Continuous Wire Extrusion. Western Electric Co., Inc., Engineering Res. Center, Princeton, N. J.
35. Anonymous: High Temperature Hydrostatic Extrusion. Light Metal Age (1970) p. 22/23.
36. Svedberg, W., and Erbe, R.: Hydrostatisches Warm-Strangpressen. Z. f. Metallkunde 24 (1971) p. 534/537.
37. Fiorentino, R. J., Meyer, G. E., and Byrer, T. G.: Some Practical Considerations for Hydrostatic Extrusion. NEL/AIRAPT Conf. of Hydrostatic Extrusion, University of Stirling, Scotland (1973), Vol. 1.
38. Green, D.: "Hydrospin" — A New Concept of Extrusion. J. Inst. Metals 99 (1971) p. 76/80.
39. Marsh, D. J.: Helical Extrusion of Non Ferrous Metals. Z. f. Metallkunde 63 (1972) p. 697/701.
40. Ziehm, K. F.: The Rediscovered Concept of Inverted Extrusion. Light Metal Age (1970) p. 6/10.

41. Veltjens, D.: Preßprogramm "Block-auf-Block." Interne Mitteilung ("private communication"), Schloemann-Siemag.
42. Stüwe, H. P.: Fließspannung und Verformungsgeschwindigkeit beim Strangpressen. Z .f. Metallkunde 62 (1971) p. 697/701.
43. Vater, M.: Strangpressen. Ein Verfahren zur Formgebung fester Stoffe im plastischen Zustand. Bänder-Bleche-Rohre (1964) p. 145/149 and 158.
44. Stüwe, H. P.: Einige Abschätzungen zum Strangpressen. Metall 22 (1968) p. 1197/1200.
45. Richter, H.: Die Herstellung von Stangen, Rohren and Profilen durch Verbundstrangpressen. Z. f. Metallkunde 60 (1969) p. 619/622.
46. Kursetz, E.: Verbindung durch Strangpressen. Werkstatt und Betrieb 102 (1969) p. 609/610.
47. Pearson, C.E., and Parkins, R. N.: The Extrusion of Metals. 2nd ed. (1961).
48. Riemann, H.: Kabelmäntel ohne Haltestellen. Draht 19 (1968) p. 3/12.
49. Wallace, P. W., Kulkarni, K. M., and Schey, J. A.: Thick-film Lubrication in Model Extrusions with Low Extrusion Ratios. J. Inst. Metals 100 (1972) p. 78/85.

3. Special Technology for Extruding Various Materials

3.1. Workability of Metals in Extrusion

3.1.1. Working Properties of Metals and Alloys

Workability, in general, and extrudability, in particular, are complex parameters that are functions of the material and the deformation conditions. The term "workability" indicates the ease with which a metal can be deformed and the degree of deformation it can withstand. The ease of deformation is controlled by the flow stress k_f under the given conditions, and the degree of deformation by the ductility φ_{Fr}. Thus workability can be expressed as:

$$W \approx \frac{\varphi_{Fr}}{k_f} \tag{Eq 58}$$

The two deformation parameters φ_{Fr} and k_f are very difficult to measure in extrusion, and workability is usually determined by laboratory studies, the results of which cannot replace extrusion trials but merely complement them. Chapter 1 describes how the torsion test is the most suitable method of measuring the flow stress k_f and the ductility φ_{Fr} (deformation to fracture) in hot working.

Whereas k_f is almost independent of the type of loading, ductility is very dependent on the state of stress during deformation. This is illustrated in Fig.

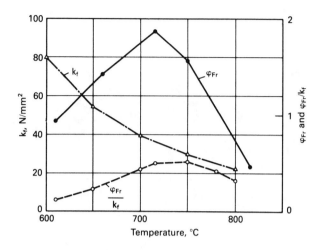

Fig. 3.1. Working characteristics of CuZn39Pb3 as a function of temperature (specimen dimensions in torsion tests: diameter, 10 mm; gage length, 50 mm). *(From Stenger)*

1.5, a and b. Hence, the deformation to fracture measured in torsion testing does not give the ductility in extrusion. In the latter case the measured values have to be recalculated for higher mean pressures — σ_m/k_f (Fig. 1.5., a and b) — to give φ_{Fr} values more suitable for extrusion. However, because quantitative conversion relationships are not available, the workability measured by torsion testing is used for comparisons — for example, to compare different materials, different material conditions, deformation temperatures, and the like.

Figure 3.1 illustrates one such comparison, in which the dependence of the material CuZn39Pb3 on the temperature is plotted and the graph gives the optimum hot working temperature. According to this diagram, the best workability is obtained at a temperature of about 740 °C, although the maximum ductility is obtained at 715 °C. The optimum hot working temperature in this case depends on whether, under the chosen extrusion conditions, the process is carried out close to the limit of ductility of the metal or close to the capacity of the extrusion press. Materials with a very low ductility fail in the torsion test after less than one revolution and the compression test is then more suitable for measuring the ductility, which is higher than in the torsion test because of the more favorable stress condition (Fig. 1.5a). The compression test is not suitable for measuring the ductility of materials with a good workability, because the maximum deformation is limited to 80% and ductility to failure is not attained.

Table 3.1 summarizes the deformation parameters of several metallic materials measured in hot torsion tests. The workability φ_{Fr}/k_f provides a relative value for the extrudability. The relationship between φ_{Fr}/k_f values

Table 3.1. Deformation Parameters of Various Alloys Measured in Torsion Tests (Compiled by Stenger)
(Specimens taken from longitudinal axis of the billet)

Material	Deformation temp, °C	k_f (N/mm²) at $\dot{\varphi} = 6$ s⁻¹	N_{Fr}	φ_{Fr}(a)	$\dfrac{\varphi_{Fr}}{k_f}$
CuZn39Pb3	700	40	5.5	1.7	0.43
CuZn37	750	52	6.5	2.1	0.4
CuZn30	800	62	5.5	1.7	0.27
CuZn35Ni	800	30	15.5	4.9	1.64
CuNi18Zn20	950	90	4.8	1.5	0.17
CuNi3Si	900	178	11.6	3.7	0.21
CuAl10Fe	800	52	25.0	7.9	1.52
X3CrNiMo1805	1100	125	9.0	2.8	0.22
X10CrNiMoTi1810	1150	173	9.0	2.8	0.16
X10NiCrAlTi3220	1150	178	19.0	6.0	0.34
CuNi10Fe	950	92	10.4	3.3	0.36
AlMgSi0.5	500	40	65.0	20.5	5.1
AlMgSi1	520	42	11.8	3.4	0.81
AlZnMg1	500	60	6.0	1.9	0.32
AlMg3	500	82	5.3	1.7	0.21
AlMg1	450	70	52.0	16.4	2.34
AlCuMgPb	380	129(b)	1.2	0.6	0.04
AlSi5	460	50(b)	13.3	6.6	1.32

(a) $\varphi_{Fr} = \dfrac{R \cdot \pi \cdot N_{Fr}}{L}$; R = 5 mm; L = 50 mm. (b) $\dot{\varphi}$ = s⁻¹.

and extrudability is not particularly accurate, but the following classifications serve as a practical guide:

$\dfrac{\varphi_{Fr}}{k_f}$ (N/mm₂)	Extrudability
< 2	Poor
2 to 4	Average
4 to 15	Good
> 15	Very good

It must be emphasized that this refers only to the extrudability of the material and does not indicate whether a certain section or tube can be produced from a material with a good extrudability. The extrusion parameters (e.g., extrusion ratio, billet length, temperature, etc.) can be so unfavorable that the press capacity available is insufficient. Higher temperatures then have to be used, particularly with the high-strength and high melting point alloys. However, extrudability decreases above an optimum temperature (Fig. 3.1) because of the tendency towards hot-shortness cracking transverse to the extrusion direction. Inhomogeneous materials with secondary phase precipitates or impurities at the grain boundaries that weaken the grain adhesion at high temperatures are particularly susceptible to this, because the material cannot withstand the tensile stresses developed at the surface of the extrusion by friction at the die.

The extrudability of many metals, including many aluminum and magnesium alloys, nickel alloys and high-strength steels, falls between narrow limits (see section 1.3.4). Extrudability in individual cases is assessed according to various parameters, including:

(*a*) Workability φ_{Fr}/k_f.
(*b*) Extrusion temperature.
(*c*) Permitted temperature range.
(*d*) Load or specific pressure required.
(*e*) Exit speed at a constant extrusion load.
(*f*) Maximum extrusion speed (to the onset of hot shortness).
(*g*) Maximum extrusion ratio.

Because the special techniques needed to extrude different materials are to a large extent dependent on the extrusion temperature, it is taken as the basis of the classification of the materials in Table 3.2.

3.1.2. Methods of Lubrication

The importance of lubrication for the material flow in the container and the extrusion load is discussed in Chap. 1, and the important point is made that lubrication can have a detrimental effect on the surface finish if the metal flow remains inhomogeneous (flow type B or C) — even though friction in the container has been reduced — and the lubricant is entrained in the extruded product. Therefore, container lubrication should be avoided as far as possible if flow type B or C cannot be definitely excluded when a lubricant is used. (Table 3.3). This is generally the case for aluminum alloys and for those copper alloys that are extruded without a shell and do not have a lubricating oxide skin. However, many materials are so difficult to extrude within the given temperature range that a lubricant has to be used to reduce the extrusion load or to protect the die (Table 3.3); in such cases, optimum lubrication and conical dies must be used to give as homogeneous a flow as possible without surface defects. Lubrication is advisable or necessary in the following cases:

(*a*) Cold extrusion or extrusion at relatively low temperatures (less than 300 °C).
(*b*) Extrusion of some difficult alloys — for example, copper alloys in the middle temperature range (600 to 1000 °C) — through conical dies.
(*c*) Extrusion of difficult alloys — for example, nickel alloys, steels, etc. — above 1000 °C; that is, in the temperature range suitable for glass lubrication. For these alloys, conical dies are also used.

Table 3.2 Classification of Extruded Materials on the Basis of Temperature

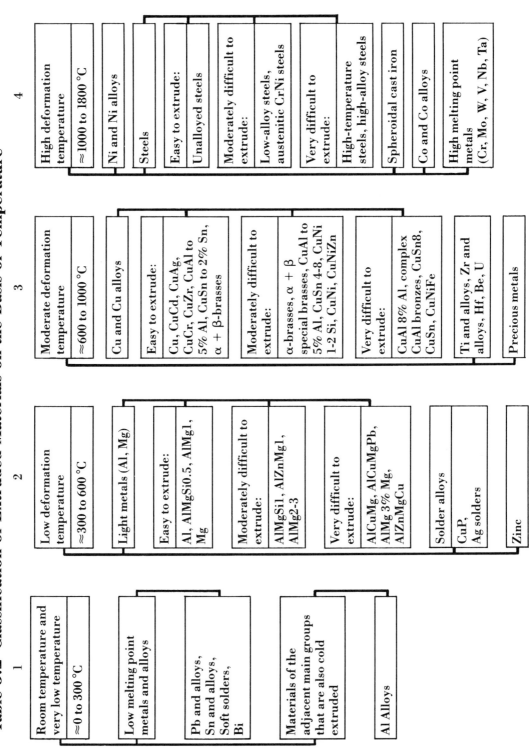

1	2	3	4
Room temperature and very low temperature	Low deformation temperature	Moderate deformation temperature	High deformation temperature
≈0 to 300 °C	≈300 to 600 °C	≈600 to 1000 °C	≈1000 to 1800 °C
Low melting point metals and alloys	Light metals (Al, Mg)	Cu and Cu alloys	Ni and Ni alloys
			Steels
Pb and alloys, Sn and alloys, Soft solders, Bi	Easy to extrude: Al, AlMgSi0.5, AlMg1, Mg	Easy to extrude: Cu, CuCd, CuAg, CuCr, CuZr, CuAl to 5% Al, CuSn to 2% Sn, α + β-brasses	Easy to extrude: Unalloyed steels
Materials of the adjacent main groups that are also cold extruded	Moderately difficult to extrude: AlMgSi1, AlZnMg1, AlMg2-3	Moderately difficult to extrude: α-brasses, α + β special brasses, CuAl to 5% Al, CuSn 4-8, CuNi 1-2 Si, CuNi, CuNiZn	Moderately difficult to extrude: Low-alloy steels, austenitic CrNi steels
	Very difficult to extrude: AlCuMg, AlCuMgPb, AlMg 3% Mg, AlZnMgCu	Very difficult to extrude: CuAl 8% Al, complex CuAl bronzes, CuSn8, CuSn, CuNiFe	Very difficult to extrude: High-temperature steels, high-alloy steels
Al Alloys	Solder alloys: CuP, Ag solders	Ti and alloys, Zr and alloys, Hf, Be, U	Spheroidal cast iron
			Co and Co alloys
	Zinc	Precious metals	High melting point metals (Cr, Mo, W, V, Nb, Ta)

Table 3.3. Summary of the Extrusion Methods Used for Different Materials

Method of extrusion		
Without lubrication, without shell	Without lubrication, with shell	With lubrication, without shell
Type of Material		
Materials with a lubricating oxide skin (e.g., Cu) and materials that flow according to type B and in which lubrication would lead to a poor quality surface finish (e.g., Al alloys).	Materials that flow according to type C (e.g., brass) and materials that readily adhere to the container wall (e.g., complex Al bronzes).	Materials with container flow characteristics that can be made similar to flow type A by using a lubricant and usually conical dies.
	Materials that rapidly oxidize during billet heating, i.e., those in which any flowing in of the oxide skin in type B flow must be prevented at all costs (low-alloy Cu materials such as CuCr, CuZr, etc.).	Materials that are worked by cold extrusion, including hydrostatic extrusion, as also alloys that are difficult to extrude, such as Ni alloys, steels and high melting point metals that cannot be extruded — or only uneconomically — without lubrication.

The nature and function of the lubricant change as the extrusion temperature increases. Lubrication at low temperatures (point a and, to some extent, point b in the list above) is used only to reduce friction. In the middle temperature range (point b) there is also some insulation between the hot billet and the tooling from the use of partly molten lubricants and vapor formation in addition to the lubrication effect. At temperatures above 1000 °C (point c) the thermal insulation of the tooling from overheating is of equal importance to the lubricating effect, particularly with the difficult-to-extrude alloys. The lubrication film can also hinder oxidation. Details about the different lubrication techniques used are given in the following sections according to the temperature range and material. The review of lubrication in metalworking by Schey is worth reading (Ref 69).

Lubricants can be classified into two groups according to temperature:

(a) Below 1000 °C: "grease" lubrication — grease, graphite, MoS_2, mica, talc, soap, bentonite, asphalt, and plastics (for example, high-temperature polyimides).
(b) Above 1000 °C: "glass" lubrication — glass, basalt, crystalline powder.

3.2. Extrusion Technology for Materials Extruded Between Room Temperature and 300 °C

3.2.1. Extrusion of Lead and Tin

3.2.1.1. Materials and Extruded Products

This group includes only lead and tin or alloys of the two elements with themselves or other elements, the most important of which are antimony, copper, silver and cadmium. These materials are used mainly for pipes, soft solder and cable sheathing. The soft solders are given in DIN 1707. Solders are extruded and drawn in the form of solid or hollow wire with a flux core in diameters ranging from 1 to 5 mm. Lead piping for chemical engineering or, in certain cases, for drinking-water pipes is produced from soft lead (pure lead, copper lead, commercial-purity lead) or from hard lead containing approximately 1% antimony (Table 3.4). The alloying additions of antimony, arsenic, tin, cadmium, etc., improve the creep or fatigue strength, which is usually inadequate for chemical equipment. Soft lead and PbSb or PbSn alloys are used for cable sheathing if aluminum sheathing, which — since the invention of the *Flexwall* — is frequently more suitable, is not selected. The most important lead alloys for cable sheathing — pure lead or lead alloys with antimony and tin — have been standardized in DIN 17640.

3.2.1.2. Extrudability and Metal Flow

Lead and tin recrystallize at temperatures as low as 0 °C after deformation — there is therefore no strain hardening at room temperature. This is clearly demonstrated by the stress-strain curves of soft primary lead, whereas tin exhibits traces of strain hardening (Fig. 3.2). The low flow stress, very low or nonexistent strain hardening, and high ductility give the soft materials a high plasticity. Solid-solution hardening is obtained by alloying, which increases the basic strength, the degree of work hardening, and the recrystallization temperature. Alloying additions naturally increase the extrusion load. According to Pearson and Smythe (Ref 1) the load at 240 °C increases above that required for pure lead as follows:

PbCu0.06	10%	PbSn0.4Cd0.15	59%
PbSb0.8	56%	PbSb0.5Cd0.25	75%

The higher flow stress of the alloys makes it necessary to reduce the extrusion ratio and to extrude at the highest temperature possible, for a good

Table 3.4. Soft and Hard Lead for Pipes

Name	Formula	Alloy composition, %	Permissible impurities, %	Extruded and drawn products
Soft lead(a) . . . . (DIN 1719)	Pb99.99	. .	0.01 max	Wire and tube for the chemical industry
	Pb99.985	. .	0.015 max	. .
Copper-bearing lead	Pb99.9Cu	0.04 to 0.08 Cu	others, 0.015 max	Tube for the sulfuric acid industry
Pig lead	Pb99.94	. .	0.06 max	Pressure pipes
	Pb99.9	. .	0.01 max	. .
Hard lead (DIN 17641)	R-Pb	0.75 to 1.25 Sb 0.02 to 0.05 As(b)	. .	Pressure pipes (drinking water)
	Pb(Sb)	0.2 to 0.3 Sb(b)	. .	Drainage pipes

(a) Chemical lead. (b) Rem, Pb.

output. The grain-boundary strength, especially of the alloys, is reduced as the melting point or solidus temperature is approached. The additional heat input from friction between the metal and the container and the die raises the temperature above the critical limit, and hot-shortness cracks form transverse to the extrusion direction. The critical temperature for PbSb1 is approximately 290 °C. Lead and tin alloys are usually extruded between room temperature and 300 °C, and the exit speed is governed by the temperature and the associated tendency to crack formation. The normal range of exit speeds varies from 10 to 60 m/min.

3.2.1.3. Extrusion of Lead Pipes

Although steel, copper and plastic pipes are now used for most gas and water installations, lead pipe is still of some importance in some countries (for example, England), and the production of lead pipes is dealt with in detail in English textbooks and has been summarized by Pearson and Parkins (Ref 2). Indirect extrusion on vertical hydraulic tube presses charged with molten

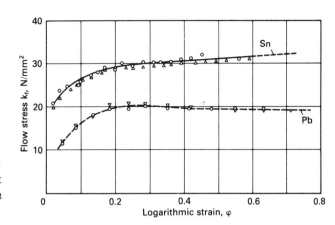

Fig. 3.2. Stress-strain curves of lead and tin at room temperature. *(From Ref 7)*

metal is the conventional method of production. The presses have direct drive without accumulators; their capacities range from about 5 MN, with a container charge of 250 kg maximum, to 15 MN, with 1800 kg maximum. The large charges in the container permit the extrusion of long pipes without welding.

After the slag has been removed, the container, which can be moved vertically by the main cylinder, is filled with molten lead ($\approx$400 °C) at its lowest position and moved upwards at low pressure against the fixed hollow stem containing the die. The slag removal prevents further oxidation and shrinkage. The mandrel is either securely located on the container axis, or fitted to a mandrel holder outside the container. This latter arrangement is used to extrude with a stationary mandrel relative to the die (Fig. 3.3). The mandrel itself is short, and small-bore tubes can be extruded to narrow tolerances. The extrusion stem and mandrel are lubricated with tallow every cycle. Extrusion is started when the solidified billet has been sufficiently cooled by steam or water to give an exit temperature between 200 and 250 °C. The tube emerges at the top of the press and is either coiled (up to about 50 mm diameter) or drawn into straight lengths.

Whereas a 25 mm thick discard is left in the container after extrusion with a mandrel fixed in the container, and is covered with the subsequent molten charge, it is possible to remove the discard from an externally located mandrel by lowering the container. For stripping, the mandrel can be lowered with the bottom cylinder. Small-bore tubes with a high degree of concentricity are also extruded with bridge dies (spider dies; see Chap. 5). Modern continuously operating cable sheathing presses are also used to produce lead piping (3.2.1.4).

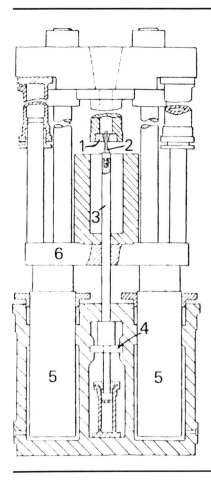

Fig. 3.3. Vertical lead pipe press. 1 – Die. 2 – Mandrel tip. 3 – Mandrel holder. 4 – Mandrel restraint. 5 – Main cylinder. 6 – Crosshead. *(From Ref 2)*

3.2.1.4. Extrusion of Lead Cable Sheathing

The sheathing of cables for carrying heavy currents or for communications is the most important application of lead extrusion. The processes used are described in Chap. 2, together with aluminum cable sheathing by extrusion. The most common method for lead is cable sheathing in vertical hydraulic presses that are charged with molten lead — in a manner similar to that for tube presses (section 3.2.1.3) — and extruded billet-to-billet in an endless strand. Extrusion is carried out through a welding chamber die after the lead has cooled to approximately 250 °C. The lead divides into two streams in the die, flows around the cable and then is rewelded to form a closed sheath (see Chap. 2, Fig. 2.2). The presses used for lead cable extrusion vary from 6 MN to 30 MN, with container capacities of 135 kg to 1000 kg of lead. The container diameter is selected to give a specific pressure of 390 to 440 N/mm^2. The specific pressure can, however, be higher during extrusion. Direct three-

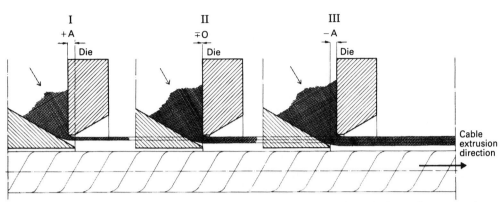

Fig. 3.4a. Varying the wall thickness of a cable sheath by adjusting the relative position of the die and mandrel. *(From DEMAG-Hydraulik)*

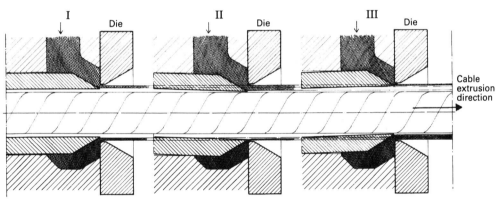

Fig. 3.4b. Varying the wall thickness by adjusting the angle of the mandrel. *(From DEMAG-Hydraulik)*

cylinder water pumps without any accumulator system are generally used.

In order to maintain a constant wall thickness, it is necessary to be able to adjust the relative positions of the die and hollow mandrel (Fig. 3.4a and b), and also to monitor the temperature of the die (temperature range between 160 and 200 °C) by means of built-in thermocouples. The axial and radial temperature profiles in the tool set can be varied by heating elements. It is of particular importance for the safe operation of oil-filled high-tension cables to prevent leaks forming at extrusion defects (see section 3.2.1.5) that would lead directly to failure of the cable. The cable manufacturer pays particular attention to the quality of the longitudinal weld and the junction between successive charges. Oxide and slag inclusions have a significant influence in this respect, and several methods have been developed to eliminate these defect sources. Pearson and Parkins (Ref 2) have described these problems in detail, but only the methods actually used in various plants are described below:

(*a*) Melting of the discard surface to obtain a clean metal-to-metal bond when the next charge is added (the oxide and impurities float to the surface); electrical arcs, acetylene torches, etc., are used.

(*b*) Protection of the molten lead surface during melting.

(*c*) Drawing off the slag and foam from the surface of the molten metal (skimming).

(*d*) Direct feeding of the molten metal through tubes to the bottom of the container; special nozzles — e.g., swirl nozzles (Ref 4) — are used to accelerate the floating of the oxide and impurities.

(*e*) Casting with a hot top, which is then sheared off at the top of the container with a special shear.

(*f*) Prevention of oxidation by an inert gas (e.g., CO_2) in the container, and by surrounding the metal jet with a hydrogen flame.

(*g*) Evacuating the container and casting under a vacuum.

(*h*) Optimizing the melting process.

(*i*) Avoiding the welding chamber die extrusion process by using special presses that, even with molten metal charges, extrude seamless sheathing (no longitudinal weld)— e.g., the Judge press (Chap. 2).

Almost all these difficulties can be avoided with the continuously operating screw-driven presses similar to those used by Pirelli or Kabelmetal and built by Hanson & Robertson or Pirelli (Ref 2). The molten lead is continuously extruded in the absence of air by the rotating screw to an endless tube without a longitudinal weld (details are given in Chap. 2).

The continuously operating screw-driven press is not universally applicable, because it is difficult to extrude higher-alloy-content lead cable sheaths. The future of lead-sheathed cables is also difficult to assess, and this discourages investment in new equipment. More attention, therefore, has been paid to improving the vertical extrusion process, and presses have been developed that can extrude continuous cable sheaths without stopmarks (bamboo rings) or the other defects described in the next section. Special designs allow for extrusion with lead or aluminum; Fig. 4.58 shows an example. This press uses molten lead charges or solid aluminum billets. The operating cycle is described in Chap. 2.

3.2.1.5. Extrusion Defects in Lead Pipe or Cable Sheath Extrusion

The most important defects are:

(*a*) Pipes with concentric oxide layers, caused by oxide skin formation on the discard.

(*b*) Irregular grain size around the periphery of the pipe, the result of critical cold working on one side during coiling followed by annealing.

(*c*) Oxide and slag inclusions and related defects at the junction between two charges.

(*d*) Oxide and slag inclusions in the longitudinal weld.

(*e*) Inadequate welding of the longitudinal weld as well as an inhomogeneous structure adjacent to the weld, because of incorrect extrusion conditions (temperature and pressure).

(*f*) Transverse cracks on the surface, caused by excessive extrusion temperature or speed, particularly with alloys (e.g., 0.85% Sb) in which friction at the die surface can result in the formation of liquid phases.

(*g*) Blisters on the surface of the extruded product, caused by extrusion with entrapped air or gas bubbles from the melt.

(*h*) Stopmarks around the periphery, formed when the press is stopped for recharging with lead. This defect can be minimized by careful stopping and restarting. In addition, bursting and other proved tests that approximate service conditions have shown that these marks are harmless (Ref 2). According to Radley (Ref 3), mechanical properties are not impaired by grain growth at the stopmark if the temperature at this point does not exceed 200 °C.

3.2.1.6. Extrusion of Solder

The solders used in Germany are given in DIN 1707, but a wide range of nonstandard alloys are also used — for example, SnCu3. Solder wire is generally extruded to diameters between 1 and 5 mm in small hydraulic extrusion presses of about 2.5 MN capacity. Depending on the alloy, both multihole and, in plants with modern handling equipment, single-hole extrusion are used. The latter method gives long extrusions that are more suitable for further processing (drawing). Billets are discontinuously cast to multiple lengths in water-cooled molds and the head shrinkage cavity sawn off.

Efficient solder presses are similar to larger extrusion presses in having automatic, integrated auxiliary equipment. Figure 3.5 shows a Collins 2.5 MN horizontal press fitted with a resistance-heated container for billets 72 mm diameter by 175 mm length. The container temperature is approximately 100 °C. The billets are fed as part of the press cycle from the magazine into the induction furnace and then rolled at 50 °C to the center line of the container. The billets are lubricated with a special grease that not only reduces container friction but also prevents a buildup of solder on the stem. The solder press in Fig. 3.5 is connected to four multiple drawing machines, the first of which receives the standard diameter product of 16 mm from the press. The three other drawing machines extend the range of diameters to 0.25 mm.

Some solder wire is produced with a flux core and the die used is very similar to that for cable sheathing but, instead of a cable, the flux is fed

Fig. 3.5. Extrusion installation for solder wire (from right to left: billet magazine, billet lift, billet heater, extrusion press). *(From Glyco-Metallwerke)*

through the hollow die (Fig. 3.6). Wire extruded from alloys that have a tendency to hot shortness and wire with special fluxes are sometimes quenched in water as they leave the die. Although solder wire is extruded with a lubricant, billet-to-billet extrusion is normally used.

3.2.2. Cold Extrusion

Cold extrusion is often considered a special process, even though it involves conventional direct or indirect extrusion. The only difference is that cold or only slightly warm billets are used. The term "cold extrusion" is used when the material being extruded has to be cold worked instead of hot extruded in the conventional manner. The technology of cold extrusion is not limited to certain materials, nor even to alloys with high flow stresses. Aluminum, copper, high-strength aluminum alloys, zirconium, titanium, molybdenum, beryllium, vanadium and niobium are extruded cold or at very low deformation temperatures. Stresses in the tooling are the limiting factor. The maximum stem pressure is normally 1400 N/mm^2.

Cold extrusion has several advantages over hot extrusion:

(*a*) No oxidation or gas/metal reactions.
(*b*) Higher mechanical properties are obtained by cold working (if the heat of deformation does not initiate recrystallization).

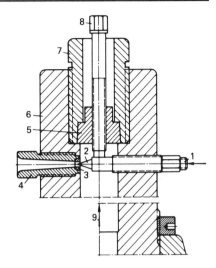

1 – Connection for flux feed
2 – Mandrel for flux feed
3 – Die
4 – Die holder
5 – Container seal plug
6 – Container
7 – Threaded container seal holder
8 – Adjusting screw for mandrel centering
9 – Ram movement

Fig. 3.6. Extrusion tooling for solder wire with a flux core. *(From Glyco-Metallwerke)*

(c) Narrow tolerances.
(d) Better surface finish if the optimum lubrication is used.
(e) Faster extrusion speeds with alloys susceptible to hot shortness.

The faster extrusion speeds that can be attained in spite of the higher flow stresses are possible only with effective lubrication and optimum die design. Willis and Bryant (Ref 5) carried out intensive investigations into the cold extrusion of aluminum alloys and concluded that the optimum die angle for surface finish and extrusion load was 120°. The investigations also demonstrated that a smooth, bright surface could be obtained only with the optimum thin film of lubricant. The surface quality of the billet increases in importance as the standard of finish required on the product is raised — that is, the billets must be turned or even lightly etched. Wax has proved to be a particularly good lubricant. Special attention has to be paid to the heat treatment of the billet (homogenizing), which can considerably reduce the flow stress of the cast material because of the high pressures needed for cold extrusion. Homogenizing and quenching heat treatable alloys (for example, AlMgSi0.5), followed by fast cold extrusion with all its advantages and then age hardening without solution heat treatment, offers interesting possibilities (see 3.3.1).

The work of Dangerfield and Gwyther (Ref 6) clearly explains why cold extrusion is not used more extensively in spite of the advantages described above. They investigated the limits of tube extrusion for several aluminum alloys on a 5 MN press and found that there were many restrictions on the practical mechanical properties and surface quality. A basic disadvantage of cold extrusion is that the heat of deformation and, hence, the temperature in the deformation zone increase as the flow stress of the alloy increases. The exit temperature can be several hundred degrees above the billet temperature, and at high extrusion ratios the heat developed may be sufficient to initiate partial or complete recrystallization and any work hardening will be removed. The increase in temperature can initiate the precipitation of a second phase in solution treated and quenched billets of heat treatable aluminum alloys and reduce or prevent any possible age hardening. The high-quality billet surface needed, which necessitates some machining, and the critical lubrication mean that it is very expensive to achieve a surface finish on the product by cold extrusion equivalent to that found on cold drawn bar. Thus, the real advantages of cold extrusion must always be critically assessed from an economic point of view.

3.3. Extrusion Technology for Materials Extruded Between 300 and 600 °C

3.3.1. Extrusion of Aluminum

3.3.1.1. Alloys and Extruded Products

All commercially available aluminum alloys can be extruded, and the most important extrusion alloys are standardized according to product group:

> DIN 1746: Aluminum Tubes
> DIN 1747: Aluminum Bar and Wire
> DIN 1748: Aluminum Extruded Sections

These standards cover a very extensive range of alloys, but not all of them are used in large volume. The main areas of application, including architecture, vehicle construction and small machined components, concentrate on selected alloys that are suitable for the final application and that also can be produced and worked at a reasonable cost. The following alloys are the most important for the different product groups in the standards mentioned above (they are given in order of volume importance):

> Tubes: AlMgSi1, AlMg3, AlCuMg1, AlCuMg2, AlMn, Al99.5.
> Bar: AlCuMgPb, AlMgSi1, AlMg3, AlMgSiPb.
> Wire: Al99.5 (electrical conductors), otherwise the same as bar.
> Sections: AlMgSi0.5, AlMgSi1, AlZnMg1.

In contrast to aluminum alloy sheet and strip, which are usually cold worked to obtain the desired mechanical properties, the heat treatable alloys of the AlMgSi, AlCuMg, AlZnMg and AlZnMgCu families are more important for extrusion, particularly for sections that cannot be finished by cold drawing, because of their complex shape. Age hardening is also utilized in the production of bar and tubes in high-strength alloys and alloys difficult to draw. Extruded semifinished products in the form of tubes, bar or wire, on the other hand, are cold drawn if close tolerances are called for, if non-heat-treatable materials (e.g., Al99.5 or AlMg3) are prescribed to prevent corrosion, or if small final cross sections are needed that cannot be extruded or are uneconomical to extrude (e.g., wire of less than 5 mm diameter). There are, therefore, two different extrusion procedures, depending on the material and the product:

(a) Non-heat-treatable alloys: the exit temperature and the cooling of the extrusion are not critical for the mechanical properties.

(b) Heat treatable alloys: if there is a separate solution heat treatment before aging, then the exit temperature and extrusion cooling are usually not critical; quenching immediately from the extrusion temperature (= solution temperature) without any subsequent solution heat treatment necessitates control of the quenching temperature and rate of cooling.

3.3.1.2. Extrudability

Round and, occasionally, flat continuously cast billets sawn from cast logs 4 to 7 m long provide the starting material for extruding aluminum alloys. The billet diameters are given, together with the most common container diameters, in a proposed standard drawn up by the extrusion working party of the DGM (Ref 8). The billet diameters range from 74 to 694 mm for press capacities of 5 to 125 MN.

The cast billets are usually homogenized before extrusion, because the as-cast condition gives a product of unsatisfactory quality and has a lower workability for the following reasons:

(a) Grain-boundary segregation, low melting point eutectics and brittle intermetallic compounds reduce the workability of the metal.

(b) Supersaturated solutions of finely dispersed precipitates of the alloying components (e.g., Al_6Mn, AlFeMn, Mg_2Si) increase the high-temperature flow stress and, thus, reduce the workability.

(c) Certain alloying elements, including manganese, iron and zirconium, either in solution or as finely dispersed precipitates, retard recrystallization. This effect is of particular significance in the extrusion of AlMgSi(Mn) alloys for color anodization, and also if the extrusion effect is to be utilized.

(d) Mg_2Si precipitated in AlMgSi alloys during cooling after continuous casting reduces the hardenability of the extruded sections and impairs the finish of bright-finish alloys.

(e) Grain-boundary segregation — i.e., variations in the concentration of dissolved alloying elements — results in a streaked texture after anodizing.

(f) Heterogeneous grain- and cell-boundary precipitation give structural markings and, in unfavorable dispersions, reduce the quality of the finish of bright-finish sections.

Table 3.5. Typical Values for Billet Heat Treatment and Extrusion of Aluminum Alloys

Material	Homogenizing temp, °C	Min holding time, h	Container temp, °C	Billet temp, °C	Exit speed(a), m/min
Al99.8 to 99.9	580 to 600	6	380	420	50 to 100
Al99.9Mg0.5 to 0.2	560 to 580	6	390	430	50 to 80
AlMn.	600 to 620	6	430	450 to 480	30 to 70
AlMg1	550 to 560	12	390	430	30 to 75
AlMg3	530 to 540	12	425	460	3 to 6
AlMg5	500 to 520	12	410	460	1.5 to 3
AlMgMn	550 to 560	12	420	450	6 to 15
AlMg4.5Mn	520 to 540	12	410	450	2 to 6
AlMgSi0.5.	560 to 580	6	410	460 to 480	35 to 80
AlMgSi1	560 to 570	6	430	450 to 500	5 to 30
AlMgSiPb	430 to 450	12	360	350 to 400	22 to 5
AlCuBiPb.	420 to 440	12	360	350 to 380	3 to 15
AlCuMgPb	430 to 450	12	360	350 to 420	1.5 to 3
AlCuMg1	480 to 490	12	400	420 to 450	1.5 to 3
AlZnMg1.	460 to 480	12	480	500 to 530	5 to 25
AlZnMgCu0.5 to 1.5. . . .	470 to 480	12	400	420 to 430	0.8 to 2

(a) Depending on the degree of difficulty.

These effects can be partly or completely eliminated by heat treatment of the cast billets. However, the purpose of the billet heat treatment varies according to quality and economic requirements and can involve dissolution, precipitation, or uniform distribution of the alloying components. The choice of homogenization, heterogenization or a combined heat treatment depends on each individual case. The process used for the different aluminum alloys is related to the extrusion technology of the material in question. Commercial heat treatments are given in Table 3.5. High-temperature heat treatment, which is not necessarily homogenization, is generally carried out at the aluminum smelter, where the billets are continuously cast. The homogenization furnaces are designed for the heat treatment of complete logs up to 7 m long. In the case of age-hardening materials (in particular, AlMgSi0.5 for bright-finish anodizing), rapid cooling from the heat treatment temperature is needed to suppress precipitation of the secondary phase, which impairs the quality of the bright finish. Quenching chambers with water sprays are very suitable because the cradles with the hot logs can be rapidly transported into them. The cradles provide a constant air gap between the logs, and the charge can be rapidly and uniformly cooled. The logs are most often cut into billets

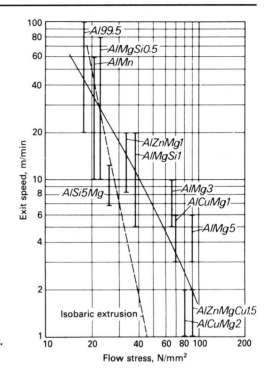

Fig. 3.7. Flow stress and extrudability. *(From Ref 10)*

but are sometimes hot sheared immediately after the billet furnace by the press to the length desired (see Chap. 4).

Not only is the high-temperature flow stress reduced by 10% or more by the billet heat treatment, but the solidus temperature — the maximum exit temperature, at which surface tearing starts — is, according to Akeret (Ref 9), raised by 15 to 30 °C (see section 1.3.4). The working range of the extrusion press for any particular alloy is therefore increased.

The extrudability of aluminum alloys (section 1.3.4) is determined by the temperature range between the upper limit for hot shortness and the lower temperature at which the flow stress is too high to maintain the billet in a plastic condition under the applied load. The implied relationship between exit speed and flow stress — given by Eq 9 — has been depicted graphically by Akeret (Fig. 3.7).

Aluminum alloys are classified into three groups according to their extrudability:

(*a*) Alloys easy to extrude: pure aluminum, AlMn, AlMg1, AlMgSi0.5, AlMgSi0.8.
(*b*) Moderately difficult alloys: AlMg2 to 3, AlMgSi1, AlZnMg1.
(*c*) Difficult alloys: AlCuMg, AlCuMgPb, AlZnMgCu, AlMg > 3% Mg.

Table 3.6. Relative Extrudabilities of Aluminum Alloys (From Ref 12 and 115)

	Easy to extrude:	Z = 50 to 150
Moderately difficult to extrude:	Z = 30 to 50
Difficult to extrude:	Z = <30

Alloy (AA designation)	Designation in chemical symbols	Relative extrudability Z		Alloy (AA designation)	Designation in chemical symbols	Relative extrudability Z	
		Ref 12	Ref 115			Ref 12	Ref 115
EC......Al99.5		150	160	5456 ....AlMg5MnCr		20	..
1060 ....Al99.6		150	125	6061 ....AlMgSilCuCr		60	60
1100 ....Al99Cu		150	125	6063 ....AlMgSi0.5		100	100
2011 ....AlCuBiPb		15	35	6066 ....AlMgSiCuMn		40	..
2014 ....AlCuSiMnMg		20	20	6101 ....AlMgSi(a)		100	..
2024 ....AlCuMg2Mn		15	15	6151 ....AlMgSiCr(b)		70	..
3003 ....AlMnCu		100	120	6463 ....AlMgSi0.8		100	..
5052 ....AlMg2.5Cr		80	..	7001 ....AlZnMgCu2.5Cr		7	..
5083 ....AlMg4.5MnCr		20	20	7075 ....AlZnMgCu1.5Cr		10	9
5086 ....AlMg4MnCr		25	25	7079 ....AlZnMgCu0.5MnCr		10	..
5154 ....AlMg3.5Cr		50	..	6351 ....AlMgSiMn		60	..
5254 ....AlMg3.5Cr		50	..	7178 ....AlZn7Mg2.7Cu2Cr		..	8
5454 ....AlMg2.7MnCr		50	..				

(a) Electrical conductor.   (b) Forging alloy.

In general, the billet temperature should be as low as possible to give the fastest possible extrusion speeds. Specific ram pressure values are frequently given as a measure of extrudability. However, the specific pressure is not very informative, because it depends on the extrusion ratio, and even the easily extruded alloys can require high pressures when low temperatures are used (see discussion below). The extrusion parameter of greatest economic interest is the exit speed (numerical values are given in Table 3.5). Exit speed is also technically relevant, because it depends on both the flow stress and the hot workability (resistance to hot shortness). However, because extrudability is governed not only by the extrusion speed but also by specific alloy properties, temperature range and extrusion ratio range, a scale of relative extrudabilities has been evolved from American practice (Table 3.6). It includes the relative extrudability factors of other aluminum alloys in reference to the most important alloy, AlMgSi0.5, which is given the dimensionless value of 100.

Extrudability also depends on the billet length. If the normal billet lengths given in Table 6.4 are used, the container diameter must be reduced and the specific pressure increased as the extrudability of the alloy decreases. In some cases, the maximum billet length given in Table 6.4 has to be reduced considerably to attain acceptable extrusion speeds.

The easily extruded alloys can be extruded at economically satisfactory speeds of up to 100 m/min or faster; in contrast, the speeds for the moderately difficult and very difficult alloys are very low. They cannot be increased significantly by hot extrusion technology because of the narrow interval between the extrusion load limiting lower temperature and the temperature for hot shortness (solidus temperature). Akeret (Ref 11), among others, has studied this problem and suggested that the temperature range of the press could be extended and the extrusion speed increased by cold or warm lubricated extrusion or by using the indirect process to reduce the extrusion load. The different processes available are based on reduction of the initial billet temperature by as much as possible. The increase in load is compensated for by reducing the friction or by lubrication. The initial billet temperature is selected to prevent the heat of deformation from raising the extrusion temperature above the maximum permissible. The large interval between the initial temperature and the upper temperature limit is completely available in the form of deformation energy, because the friction component is reduced or eliminated. Higher extrusion ratios or faster extrusion speeds are then possible, although this assumes that temperature equilibrium across the section and heat conduction in the tooling can take place rapidly enough. The special processes listed below overcome these problems and have been described by Akeret (Ref 11); their importance could well increase in the future:

(a) Direct extrusion without lubrication, using billets with the rear end colder than the front (see taper heating and isothermal extrusion, Chap. 1).
(b) Indirect extrusion (no friction between billet and container).
(c) Direct hot extrusion with lubrication (reduced friction).
(d) Direct cold extrusion with lubrication (large reduction in friction).
(e) Hydrostatic extrusion (no container friction and very little die friction).

The common feature of these processes is that the heat developed by friction at the surface of the billet is eliminated or compensated for and need not be dissipated through the die. Processes (b) to (e) require high-quality machined billet surfaces because the surface of the billet forms the surface of the extruded product in lubricated extrusion. Other factors limiting the practical exploitation of these processes include optimum quality and quantity of the lubricant, the limited extrusion ratio, the stresses placed on the die by the extrusion load, and the need to use conical dies, which are difficult to produce. The strong dependence of the exit temperature on the extrusion ratio and the differing tendency to recrystallization can also present problems in cold extrusion. At high extrusion ratios the material softens spontaneously and the increase in strength from cold working is lost. The metallurgical aspects of the heat treatable alloys have been discussed in section 3.2.2.

3.3.1.3. Metal Flow and Lubrication

The usual method of hot extrusion of aluminum alloys through flat (not conical) dies is characterized by the strong tendency of aluminum to adhere to steel at high temperatures. This tendency cannot be entirely eliminated by lubrication. As the billet is pushed through the container, the billet surface adheres to the steel and a shell is cut by the pressure pad, which also pushes it together. This results in nonuniform flow in the container, generally of type B or C (Chap. 1). The billet and container are not lubricated, because lubrication does not significantly alter the flow behavior and there is the danger that the lubricant will be drawn along the shear zone into the extrusion to produce pores and blisters. Unfortunately, the sticking of the aluminum to the die or, in tube extrusion, to the mandrel can in many cases reduce the quality of the surface finish because the adhering particles cause scratches. The surface finish can be improved and die cleaning reduced by slight lubrication of the die or front end of the billet. The lubricants used include: special grease, graphite with cylinder oil for supersaturated steam, colloidal graphite in water or alcohol (liquid or spray for lubricating the end of the billet), and molybdenum disulfide in oil. Soft soap or beeswax is successfully used with some alloys to lubricate the mandrel in tube extrusion. Phosphating the billet before extrusion is one method of increasing the smearing effect of soap and, in particular, of hindering the formation of deposits in the die bearing (Ref 13). Chemically bonded lubricants used for die lubrication are claimed to reduce oxide deposits, double the number of extrusions between die cleanings, improve the surface finish, and increase the extrusion speed.

The billet is sometimes lubricated at both ends to prevent it from sticking to the pressure pad and to simplify discard separation.

3.3.1.4. Extrusion of Aluminum Alloy Sections

Most aluminum sections are produced from the heat treatable alloys AlMgSi0.5, AlMgSil and AlZnMg1. The non-heat-treatable alloys such as AlMg3 play only a minor role in section extrusion. The good extrudability of the alloys mentioned above, together with their mechanical properties, decorative appearance and corrosion resistance, have secured a prominent position for extruded aluminum sections in comparison with other extruded products and materials. Conversely, extrusion technology has been furthered by continuing demands for new sections and improved product quality. Consequently, the extrusion of aluminum sections represents the most advanced extrusion technology in terms of tooling, press design and, above all, die design.

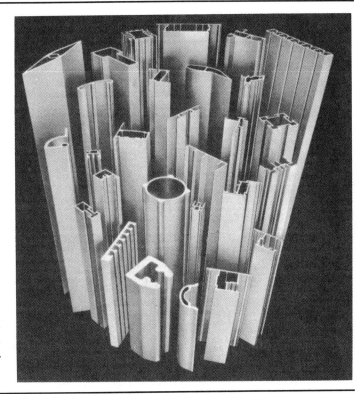

Fig. 3.8. Extruded aluminum sections. *(From Aluminium-werke Wutöschingen)*

The extrusion of sections represents a special problem area for die design — namely, the determination of the correct die orifice in relation to shrinkage allowances and the bearing lengths required. This subject is discussed in Chap. 5. There is virtually no shape that cannot be produced with the easily extruded alloys; some examples are shown in Fig. 3.8. Diverse sections are naturally associated with varying degrees of difficulty in extrusion and die manufacture, and they have been systematically classified according to their shape. They have also been given a numerical factor representing the degree of difficulty. DIN 1748, page 3, differentiates between solid, semihollow and hollow sections. However, a more detailed classification is needed in practice, and it has been found necessary to use a criterion similar to that used in Fig. 3.9 to assess the extrudability (minimum wall thickness) and the cost of die production (Ref 15). Certain guidelines have to be followed for complex sections in spite of the extremely wide range of shapes produced in order to determine the optimum form for the finished product and its economical production (Ref 18, 26, 44).

An important, internationally used dimension to describe the size of any section is the diameter of the circumscribing circle. The larger the circum-

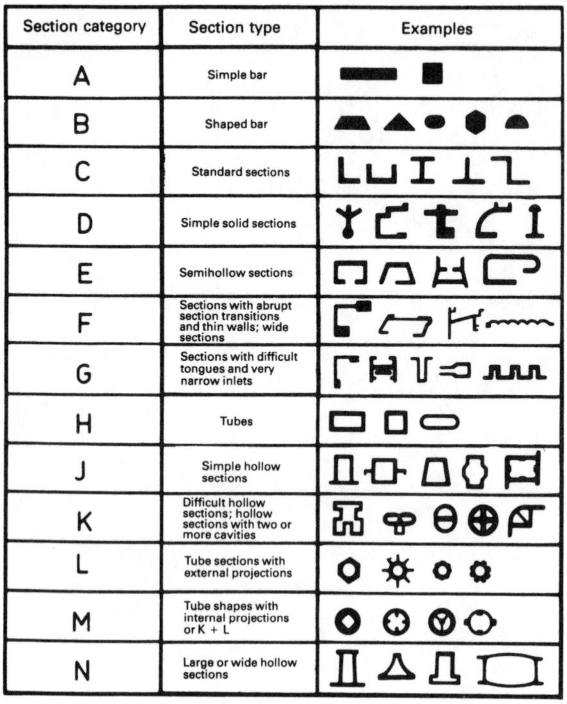

Section category	Section type	Examples
A	Simple bar	
B	Shaped bar	
C	Standard sections	
D	Simple solid sections	
E	Semihollow sections	
F	Sections with abrupt section transitions and thin walls; wide sections	
G	Sections with difficult tongues and very narrow inlets	
H	Tubes	
J	Simple hollow sections	
K	Difficult hollow sections; hollow sections with two or more cavities	
L	Tube sections with external projections	
M	Tube shapes with internal projections or K + L	
N	Large or wide hollow sections	

Fig. 3.9. Classification of aluminum extruded sections according to the degree of difficulty. *(From Ref 16)*

scribing circle, the bigger the press required. The extrusion pressure increases as the wall thickness of the section is reduced. Table 3.7 and Fig. 3.10 give the minimum wall thicknesses that can be extruded as a function of the press size and circumscribing circle diameter. Containers with flat bores are used to extrude wide sections in presses over 50 MN. For example, a flat container 660 by 240 mm (rectangle with rounded ends) in a 72 MN press can extrude a maximum section size of 600 by 180 mm. The shape factor is used as a measure of the degree of difficulty in England and the United States, regardless of the classification into the different types of sections:

$$\text{Shape factor} = \frac{\text{Periphery of the section}}{\text{Weight per unit length}} \left[\frac{\text{Inches}}{\text{Pounds per foot}} \right]$$

The shape factor increases with the complexity of the section and the reduction of wall thickness.

The form factor is a measure of the section and is obtained from the data given in Table 3.7 and Fig. 3.9:

$$\text{Form factor} = \frac{\text{Diameter of the circumscribing circle}}{\text{Minimum wall thickness}}$$

Table 3.7. Minimum Wall Thicknesses for Extrusion Presses Between 10 and 80 MN

Alloy	Section type(a)	Circumscribing circle diam of section, mm										
		<25	<50	<75	<100	<150	<200	<250	<300	<350	<400	<450
		Min wall thickness, mm										
Al99 to 99.9 ..	A	0.8	1	1.2	1.5	2	2.5	2.5	3	4	4	5
AlMgSi0.5	B	0.8	1	1.2	1.5	2	2.5	2.5	3	4	4	5
AlMg1	C	1	1	1.5	2	2.5	2.5	2.5	4	5	5	6
AlMn	C	1	1	1.5	2	2.5	2.5	2.5	4	5	5	6
AlMgSi1	A	1	1.2	1.2	1.5	2	2.5	3	4	4	5	6
AlSi5Mg......	B	1	1.2	1.5	2	2	2.5	3	4	4	5	6
AlZnMg1	B	1	1.2	1.5	2	2	2.5	3	4	4	5	6
	C	2	1.5	2	2	3	4	4	5	5	6	6
AlMg3	A	1	1	1.2	1.5	2	2.5	3	4	4	5	6
AlMg5	A	1	1	1.2	1.5	2	2.5	3	4	4	5	6
AlCuMg1	A	1.2	1.2	1.2	1.5	2	3	5	5	6	7	8
AlCuMg2	A	1.2	1.2	1.2	1.5	2	3	5	5	6	7	8
AlCuMg2(b)...	B	2	2	3	4	5	5	6	8	10	10	12
AlZn5MgCu...	A	2	2	2.5	3	3	5	6	8	12	12	14
Extrusion press range:		to 10 MN		to 25 MN				to 50 MN			to 80 MN	
					to 35 MN							

(a) A = solid and semihollow sections; B = hollow sections with uniform wall thickness (including tube); C = hollow sections with varying wall thickness (one or more cavities in the section).

(b) Extruded over the mandrel.

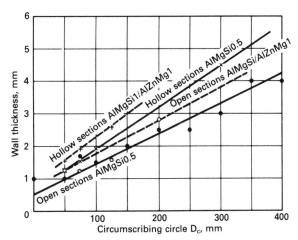

Fig. 3.10. Minimum wall thickness of AlMgSi0.5, AlMgSi1 and AlZnMg1 as a function of the circumscribing circle diameter. *(From Laue and Stenger)*

Köblitz (Ref 19) gave a different form factor for the degree of difficulty of a section and the associated ease of production and price determination:

$$f_{form} = \frac{10A}{D_u \cdot \log A \ \sqrt{U_0 + a \cdot U_i}} \qquad \text{(Eq 59)}$$

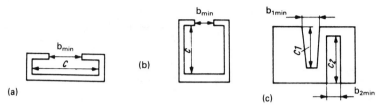

Fig. 3.11. Example of section inlets for shape-factor determination. See text. *(From Ref 19, Köblitz)*

where A is the cross sectional area of the section (mm^2), D_u is the circumscribing circle diameter (mm), U_0 is the outside periphery of the section (mm), and U_i is the inside periphery (mm) of semihollow and hollow sections.

The factor a_f expresses the difficulty of semihollow and hollow sections. For hollow sections, $a_f = 2$; for semihollow sections and a minimum gap width $b \geq 1.5$ mm (Fig. 3.11):

$$a_f = \sqrt{\frac{c}{b_{min}}} \qquad \text{(Eq 60)}$$

for c: $b_{min} < 1.5$:$a_f = 1$.

If there are several inlets or semihollow areas in the section, the square root term in the equation is given by:

$$\sqrt{U_o + a_1 U_{i1} + a_2 U_{i2} + \ldots + a_n U_{in}} \qquad \text{(Eq 61)}$$

A lower shape factor implies a higher degree of difficulty.

3.3.1.4.1. Extrusion of AlMgSiO.5 to 0.8 Sections

Large quantities of sections in these alloys based on Al99.5 are used for metal fabrication and architectural purposes; the quality must meet the following requirements:

(*a*) Minimum strength in the age-hardened condition of $R_m = 220$ to 250 N/mm^2.
(*b*) Good surface finish (few die lines).
(*c*) Good decorative anodizing properties — e.g., with the direct current sulfuric acid process or a color anodizing process.
(*d*) Narrow dimensional tolerances.

The continuously cast billets or logs are homogenized at 560 to 580 °C, to give uniform anodizing properties. The controlling phase for the age-hardening process, Mg_2Si, is almost completely dissolved during homogenization. Some of the Mg_2Si forms very fine precipitates during the customary air cooling of the logs, but this only slightly reduces the mechanical properties of the finished product. On the other hand, this partial Mg₂Si precipitation improves the extrudability, because the high-temperature flow stress is lower than for the fully solution treated condition (up to 10%) (Ref 17, 25). The as-cast surface of the log is so good that the billets can be extruded without any surface treatment. The thin skin of the billet is sheared in the container and removed with the discard. The billet temperature is kept as low as possible to give the maximum extrusion speed, although the heat produced by deformation will be correspondingly higher (Chap. 1).

This requirement places the billet temperature in the temperature range for the precipitation of Mg₂Si (T < 500 °C) and, accordingly, the billets must be rapidly heated to the working temperature to minimize the time available for precipitation. This is the reason for using high-speed furnaces (gas or induction furnaces; Chap. 4). The billet temperature and exit speed are coordinated to heat the material in the deformation zone above the solution temperature (≈520 °C; Fig. 3.12) and to redissolve the fine dispersions of Mg₂Si precipitates. The critical cooling speed of the alloy AlMgSi0.5 is such that the

Fig. 3.12. AlMgSi equilibrium diagram with the 540, 520, 500, 480 and 160 °C isotherms. *(From Ref 111 and 112)*

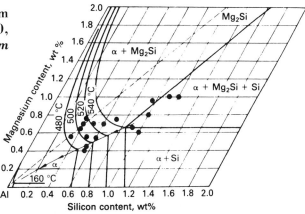

section need not be quenched in water, which can result in warping, but can be cooled in air. Cooling with forced air convection on the runout table from the exit temperature (520 to 540 °C) to approximately 200 °C suffices for the subsequent age hardening to the desired mechanical properties (Ref 21, 42, 43). The time-temperature-precipitation diagram for AlMgSi0.5 in Fig. 3.13 summarizes the solid solution or precipitation state at different cooling rates (Ref 21).

The extruded length of the AlMgSi0.5 section depends on the press size, but can extend to 50 m. Up to four strands are extruded, depending on the

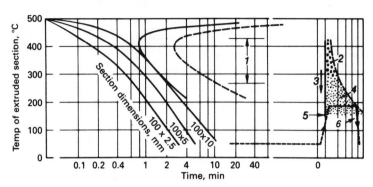

The temperature range 1 is the preferred range for Mg_2Si precipitation and must be traversed rapidly during cooling of the extrusion. Mg_2Si precipitation is suppressed during cooling if the cooling curves (shown for three sections with air cooling of 5 m/s) are to the left of the solid parabolic limiting curve. To the right of the diagram, 2 to 5 trace the age-hardening process: 2 = coarse Mg_2Si precipitates; 3 = tendency for increasing strength; 4 = fine Mg_2Si precipitates; 5 = no age hardening (start); 6 = 100% age hardening (end).

Fig. 3.13. Time-temperature-precipitation diagram for AlMgSi0.5. *(From Ref 21 and 43)*

section size, but more strands are used in some cases. The sections can be guided along the runout table with pullers that grip automatically. After the sections have been transported transversely from the press axis they are straightened by stretching 1 to 3%. Extruded sections of AlMgSi0.5 or the easily extruded aluminum alloys can usually be brought to within the required dimensional tolerances (DIN 1748, page 4) by stretching — given the correct die shape. This is not always possible with complicated sections or very large sections, and correction on a roll-correction machine or by hand might be needed after stretching.

AlMgSi0.5 has a tensile strength of $R_m \geq 140$ N/mm^2 in the as-extruded temper. The tensile strength is increased to more than 220 N/mm^2 by aging the sections after rapid cooling to room temperature. The aging process lasts for several hours at 170 to 180 ° C, during which time precipitation processes occur. The changes in mechanical properties after aging at different temperatures are depicted in Fig. 3.14.

3.3.1.4.2. Extrusion of AlMgSi0.5 Bright Trim Material

Sections of AlMgSi0.5 and sometimes AlZnMg bright trim alloys were used extensively in the past for automobile window frames. The chemically polished and anodized sections are also used as trim for automobiles, house-

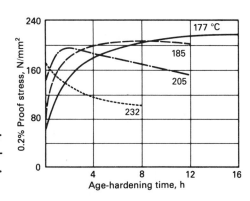

Fig. 3.14. Age-hardening curves for AlMgSi0.5 at different temperatures (age-hardening time = time at temperature). *(From Ref 41)*

hold appliances and furniture (Ref 23). The alloy AlMgSi0.5 based on Al99.75 is used for normal quality, and a base of Al99.9 for the best quality bright finish. The requirement of maximum brightness is particularly difficult to meet with age-hardening alloys because there is the danger of the heterogeneous precipitation of the Mg_2Si phase during different stages in production, resulting in a dull anodized surface. Therefore, the complete production sequence is arranged to avoid the precipitation of Mg_2Si. However, the bright finish can also be dulled by secondary solidified AlFeSi phases, and both sources of defects must be considered in the production.

The first preventive measure taken is to control the casting process to produce a fine distribution of the solidified residual melt (AlFeSi) at the cell and grain boundaries and a small cell size. These heterogeneous precipitates are almost insoluble in commercially practical heat treatments even at high homogenizing temperatures. If initially they are too large they are retained after heat treatment, broken down during extrusion and impair the bright finish. Prolonged billet heat treatment at 580 °C leads to partial dissolution and coagulation of the precipitates and an associated improvement of the bright finish on the extruded section. Electron microscopic investigations positively identified these precipitates as the Mg-free AlFeSi phase (Ref 17, 42). The Mg_2Si phase needed for age hardening is completely dissolved by the high homogenization temperature used for AlMgSi0.5 bright finish billets. Then it is necessary only to retain this solid solution condition by rapid billet cooling with water. The bright finish is impaired when the particle size exceeds a certain value that can be measured in the microscope. It is extremely important that only fine precipitates of Mg_2Si form during billet cooling and reheating to the extrusion temperature so that they are completely redissolved in a few seconds as they pass through the deformation zone at about 500 °C. Rapid cooling of extrusions with water behind the die is needed to retain the solid solution produced by the heat of deformation.

Attempts to cool thin-wall but complicated sections by forced air convection to avoid the problems of dimensional changes with water quenching produced unacceptable dull areas in the bright finish. Tension-controlled pullers have been successfully used to avoid warping of smaller sections (Chap. 4). Bright finish alloy billets are usually machined to remove surface segregation and impurities that impair the bright finish.

3.3.1.4.3. Extrusion of AlMgSi1 Sections

Extruded sections of the alloy AlMgSi1 with manganese additions are used for high-strength (R_m = 280 to 320 N/mm^2) structural sections and color anodized architectural components. Although the main requirement in the first case is the high mechanical properties, uniform color anodizing is more important in the second application. The extrusion conditions for these two applications are therefore different.

Structural Sections

Compared with AlMgSi0.5, the higher alloy content of AlMgSi1 necessitates a faster rate of cooling for structural sections to obtain the maximum hardenability. The maximum strength of $R_m \geq 320$ N/mm^2 can be guaranteed only when the section is quenched in water from the exit temperature (which must exceed the solid solution temperature). This applies in particular to wall thicknesses over 4 mm. Quenching the section with water behind the die always results in uncontrolled twisting of the section, which, because of the size of the extrusion, cannot be prevented by using a puller. This means that the water-quenched sections must undergo expensive, usually uneconomical correction before heat treatment. The tensile strength is, therefore, limited to 280 to 300 N/mm^2, and AlMgSi1 sections are cooled in air similar to AlMgSi0.5 sections to finish in the region of partly precipitated Mg$_2$Si (Fig. 3.13). Metallurgical investigations have concentrated on finding an optimum alloy composition with a critical cooling rate equal to that given by forced air cooling to be able to guarantee the desired strength and notch impact toughness (Ref 20).

Sections are heat treated for 8 hours at 160 to 170 °C. If the time before heat treatment is increased, extensive natural aging can take place and the mechanical properties after the full precipitation heat treatment are reduced. Consequently, the interval between extrusion and aging should be short or the sections should be stabilized at 80 °C (or given a shock heat treatment at 200 °C to stop the natural aging).

Architectural Sections for Color Anodizing

The gray to black color preferred for commercial siding can be produced with the alloy AlMgSi(Mn) by color anodization (Ref 23). This material is

Fig. 3.15. Streaking and coarse grain revealed after gray anodization of a hollow AlMgSi(Mn) section. *(From Ref 17)*

easier to extrude than the alloy AlSi5 previously used. However, problems do arise if partial recrystallization takes place in spite of the addition of manganese to raise the recrystallization temperature (Chap. 1). The peripheral regions of the extrusion are subjected to higher strains than the core material because of the shearing that takes place in the container. If a critical strain is reached in the peripheral zones, the heat of deformation can initiate spontaneous recrystallization. In the hollow section in Fig. 3.15, the internal zones — that is, the material on the internal wall and close to the axis — have not spontaneously recrystallized under the deformation conditions, whereas the external regions that form the surface of the section have recrystallized with a coarse-grain structure.

This tendency to coarse-grain recrystallization in the surface layer poses considerable problems in production. The different temperature-flow stress conditions around the circumference of the section — particularly at irregularities such as corners, junctions and increases in thickness — can fall within the critical deformation zone and initiate spontaneous recrystallization. The critical deformation is, by contrast, not reached in neighboring zones, recrystallization does not occur, and the fine-fibrous extruded surface is retained. Not all structures react in the same way to color anodizing, and clearly visible shade and color variations form as streaks over the total length of the extrusion (Fig. 3.15). Recrystallized areas appear darker than unrecrystallized areas. Streaking is also seen even if recrystallization has not formed excessively coarse grains.

Two approaches have been used to avoid this undesirable formation of a recrystallized or coarse-grain structure on an extrusion surface. One method is to completely suppress recrystallization, but this is possible only if the recrystallization-retarding action of dissolved or finely dispersed precipitates of manganese is at a maximum. The extrudability of the alloy is then too poor for complicated sections. Moreover, it is not possible to completely exclude the very thin coarse-grain layer on the section surface in spite of the recrystallization retardation. Therefore the second method adopted is to produce a completely fine-grain recrystallized structure by exceeding the critical deformation as much as possible. Based on knowledge of the relationship between the dispersion of the precipitated phase and the rate of nucleation, which has been described by Scharf (Ref 24), the billets are heat treated at 560 to 580 °C to produce coarse manganese precipitates, which accelerate the rate of nucleation and promote recrystallization. Extrusion tests have shown that sections can be produced with a uniformly recrystallized structure free of coarse grains and streaks after color anodizing by using the highest possible billet heat treatment temperature (560 to 580 °C, 24 h). The Mg_2Si particle size after the billet heat treatment also plays a role and can be controlled by the rate of billet cooling and a relatively low extrusion temperature to give fine-grain recrystallization.

An advantageous by-product of the increased recrystallization tendency of AlMgSi(Mn) caused by coarse precipitates is a reduction in the flow stress. Hot torsion tests recorded a flow stress after billet heat treatment at 580 °C of about 10% less than that after heat treatment at 520 °C (Ref 17, 25). One disadvantage is the reduction in the age-hardening potential associated with the partially coarse Mg_2Si precipitates, although this is not so critical for construction sections. Sections of AlMgSi(Mn) for color anodization are, consequently, usually offered with the same strength as AlMgSi0.5 sections of $R_m = 220 \, N/mm^2$, even though the alloy is capable of much higher mechanical properties.

3.3.1.4.4. Extrusion of AlZnMg1 Sections

The copper-free heat treatable alloy AlZnMg1 has three outstanding properties that have secured for the extruded sections of these alloys an increasingly important role in the automobile, machine-construction and engineering industries. These properties are:

(a) Low quench sensitivity, making it possible to attain the full age-hardening characteristics by air cooling from the solution temperature (= extrusion exit temperature).

(b) High tensile strength in the region of $R_m = 340$ to 400 N/mm^2 after age hardening.

(c) Good welding characteristics with spontaneous natural aging of the weld (to a tensile strength of approximately 280 N/mm^2) because of the low quench sensitivity.

In the past the use of this alloy, which is similar to AlMgSil in many respects, was treated with caution because it was susceptible to stress-corrosion cracking if the production parameters were not controlled. Recent investigations have determined the parameters that must be maintained during heat treatment and extrusion to produce sections that are almost totally insusceptible to stress-corrosion cracking. These parameters are intended to suppress crack formation and crack propagation under the influence of tensile stresses by the controlled dispersion of heterogeneities and precipitates. The most important parameters are:

(a) Homogenization of the billets at relatively low temperatures (e.g., 460 °C for a maximum of 12 h).

(b) Retention of an unrecrystallized structure or suppression of recrystallization by the addition of recrystallization-retarding elements (e.g., zirconium, manganese and chromium), and the avoidance of deformation conditions that would promote recrystallization, by using the lowest possible extrusion ratios, low billet homogenization temperatures and low extrusion temperatures (Fig. 3.16 and 3.17).

(c) Cooling in air from the extrusion or solution heat treatment temperature.

(d) Age hardening at 120 to 130 °C, 12 to 24 h, or two-step aging (Ref 27).

The alloy AlZnMg1 is very suitable for thick-wall sections because the solution temperature above 350 ° C is not critical and the rate of cooling needed for age hardening is low. The sections never have to be quenched in water and, consequently, do not twist to any significant degree. The subsequent correction treatment remains within acceptable limits. The maximum mechanical properties are obtained by the two-step aging treatment. The hardening curves are depicted in Fig. 3.18.

3.3.1.4.5. Recent Developments in AlZnMg1 Extrusion

Extensive investigations have demonstrated that the alloy AlZnMg1, by optimization of its manganese, zirconium and magnesium content and using a suitable homogenization, can be modified to such an extent that its extrudability is similar to that of AlMgSi0.8. It has been shown experimentally that chromium — and, to a limited extent, manganese — has a deleterious effect on most of the parameters investigated. The chromium content of the alloy can, hence, be reduced to virtually zero without impairing its mechanical, physical and corrosion-resistant properties.

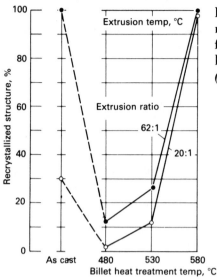

Fig. 3.16. Percentage of recrystallized structure as a function of the AlZnMg billet heat treatment temperature. *(From Ref 27)*

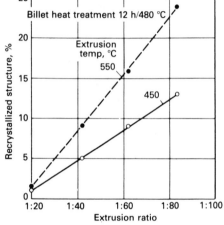

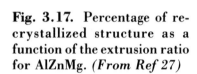

Fig. 3.17. Percentage of recrystallized structure as a function of the extrusion ratio for AlZnMg. *(From Ref 27)*

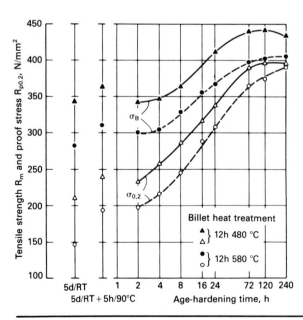

Fig. 3.18. Two-step age hardening at 90/120 °C for AlZnMg1 as a function of the billet heat treatment. *(From Ref 27)*

Hollow sections with wall thicknesses as thin as 0.9 mm can now readily be extruded in this new alloy. Its stress-corrosion cracking resistance exceeds all existing standards and its tensile strength varies from 360 to 420 N/mm^2, depending on the magnesium content.

The usual three-step heat treatment for this alloy is given below and must be followed to obtain the desired properties:

(a) Cooling in air or with fans (depending on the section size) at the press.
(b) Aging 3 to 5 days at room temperature (nucleation).
(c) Heating 4 to 16 h at 90 to 110 °C, followed by 12 to 24 h at 135 to 145 °C (Fig. 3.18A).

For some applications, over-aging (at 150 to 160 °C) might be useful.

The third aging step and the choice of temperature are critical for resistance to stress-corrosion cracking. Figure 3.18B gives an example of the relationship between the stress-corrosion cracking life (tension = 100% of $R_{p0.2}$ proof test) and the temperature of the third step for solution treated and quenched sheet specimens.

3.3.1.5. Extrusion of Hollow Sections

Hollow sections in alloys that easily reweld together (Table 3.8) are extruded from solid billets with bridge or welding chamber dies, which are described in Chap. 5. In comparison with the extrusion of solid sections, the division of metal flow in the die by the mandrel support and the rewelding to form the closed hollow section present several technical peculiarities:

(a) Extrusion loads are higher because of the metal division in the die and the increased friction.
(b) The temperature must exceed 500 °C for the divided metal streams to reweld in the welding chamber. In order to guarantee this with thick-wall sections, the container temperature should be relatively high and not less than 50 to 70 °C below the billet temperature—i.e., 450 to 470 °C (Ref 29).
(c) Longitudinal welds produced in the welding chamber process can appear lighter than the rest of the section after anodizing, because of metallurgical influences. Care is, therefore, required in the design to ensure that the welds occur on non-visible surfaces in the finished product or at the corners (Fig. 3.19).
(d) Small hollow sections are produced with multihole welding chamber dies similar to solid sections, but the number of strands is limited to four.

Hollow sections in alloys that do not easily reweld (Table 3.8) are extruded with a stationary (relative to the die) mandrel (over the mandrel tip) from hollow billets. Wall thickness tolerances are not so narrow as with the welding chamber process because the mandrel has a tendency to bend to the side.

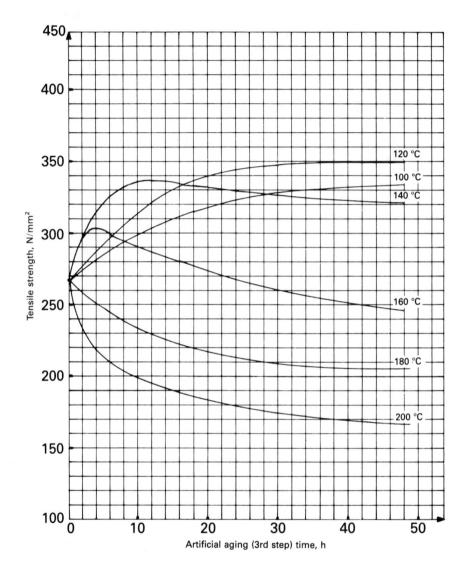

Fig. 3.18A. Influence of the third-step artificial aging temperature on the mechanical properties of an AlZnMg1 solid section fan cooled after extrusion. First and second steps were 5 days of aging at room temperature followed by 4 hours of artificial aging at 100 °C. *(From Lang, unpublished)*

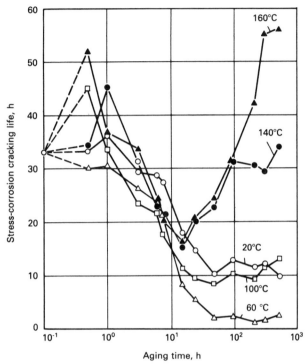

Fig. 3.18B. Relationship between stress-corrosion cracking life and the aging temperature of solution heat treated and quenched sheet specimens (similar to values obtained with press quenched sections); 30 min at 480 °C, water-quenched, immediately aged artificially (one-step aging). *(From Ref 118)*

Table 3.8. Welding Properties of Various Aluminum Alloys in Hot Extrusion With Special Dies for the Production of Tubes and Hollow Sections (From Ref 29)

Alloy	Welding properties	Alloy	Welding properties
Pure Al	Very good(a)	AlMg3	Very limited(a)
AlMn	Very good(a)	AlMgSiPb	Very limited(a)
AlMg1	Very good(a)	AlCuMg	Very poor(b)
AlMgSi0.5	Good to very good(a)	AlZnMgCu	Very poor(b)
AlMgSi1	Good to very good(a)	AlCuMgPb	Very poor(b)
AlZnMg1	Good(a)	AlMgPb	Very poor(b)
AlMgSi0.8	Good to very good(a)	AlMg5	Very poor(b)
AlMg2	Limited(a)		

(a) Depending on the thickness of the form and the wall. (b) In practice, not extruded in hot working presses with special dies.

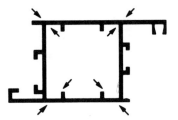

Fig. 3.19. Possible location of the welding regions in an aluminum hollow section extruded through a welding chamber die. *(From Aluminiumwerke Wutöschingen)*

3.3.1.6. Extrusion of Tubes

The following methods are used to extrude tubes:

(a) Solid billets are pierced in the press and extruded over a moving mandrel that is slightly tapered; extrusion over a stationary mandrel is used less frequently (excessive tool wear).
(b) Hollow billets are extruded with a moving or stationary mandrel.
(c) Solid billets are extruded with a welding chamber die.

The last method is being used to an increasing extent for tubes in the easily welded alloys (Table 3.8). The same tooling with replaceable mandrel and die can be used for a wide range of dimensions. The extrusion conditions used are similar to those for hollow sections. Tubes capable of being coiled are extruded by the billet-to-billet method (Chap. 2, extrusion processes) in a continuous operation. The standard method for aluminum tube extrusion is method A. The die and mandrel are slightly lubricated; in many cases, special attention has to be given to the lubrication of the mandrel, sometimes with a special lubricant (section 3.3.1.3), to prevent severe scoring of the inner surface of the tube or complete tearing. The mandrel is externally cooled with water after extrusion. If a moving mandrel is used, the slight taper results in a variation in the wall thickness of the tube with the thinnest section at the rear end. The taper is 0.3 to 0.5 mm. This variation in wall thickness is eliminated in the subsequent cold drawing operation.

Method A is uneconomical for tubes with an inside diameter less than 20 mm because the mandrel length should not exceed 7 to 8 times the diameter and the billets would be too short. Small diameter tubes are, therefore, extruded over the stepped mandrel tip of a stationary mandrel, the shank of which is thick enough to withstand the stresses of extrusion and piercing. In some cases hollow billets can be used (method B) to avoid the piercing operation and to allow larger billets to be extruded or to extrude tubes with a large inside diameter. The economic advantage is, from practical experience, more than outweighed by the costs of a boring operation, which is usually associated with billet machining for the required concentricity, and the swarf losses. Consequently, aluminum tubes are produced mainly by method A, with unmachined cast billets.

Extruded aluminum alloy tubes are usually cold drawn to meet narrow tolerances, to reduce the wall thickness, or to give a degree of work hardening in the case of non-heat-treatable alloys. The difference between the extruded tube diameter and the finished tube diameter depends on the cold drawing capability of the material (Table 3.9). One point that must always be considered is that the press output (extrusion speed) increases with increasing tube wall thickness, but the amount of drawing required is also increased. Thus, there is always an optimum tube dimension at which the extrusion costs and the drawing costs are at a minimum.

The final heat treatment of tubes — for example, stress relieving or solution heat treatment and age hardening — takes place after cold drawing, with the exception of tubes extruded to the finished size (e.g., in AlMgSi0.5), which are delivered as standard sections. The wall thicknesses and dimensional tolerances of extruded and drawn tubes are given in DIN 9107 and 1795 (extruded tube wall thicknesses are given in Table 3.10) (Ref 30). Extruded tubes in the high-strength alloys or free-cutting alloys are produced using techniques similar to rod extrusion in these alloys (section 3.3.1.8).

3.3.1.7. Extrusion of Aluminum Cable Sheathing

The aluminum cable sheathing process using Al99.5 is described in Chap. 2. The extrusion conditions correspond to those for billet-to-billet extrusion of hollow sections and tubes with welding chamber dies. Again one of the main requirements is to maintain a temperature of at least 500 °C in the die for rewelding. The billets are heated to give a temperature of approximately 500 °C at the front end and 400 °C at the back. Billet upsetting at the start of extrusion then takes place in a controlled way from the die end and the air is removed from the back. This removal of air from the container is very important for cable sheathing. The die is water-cooled at the cable entrance to prevent the cable insulation from burning. As soon as the aluminum has surrounded the cable core, it is cooled directly behind the die with water spray rings to avoid damage to the cable insulation. These cooling measures are sufficient to avoid any overheating of the cable during the break of 25 to 30 seconds in every press cycle for billet loading (Ref 31, 32, 33).

3.3.1.8. Extrusion of Bar and Wire

The term "bar" covers round, square, hexagonal and flat cross sections that are extruded in straight lengths. Wires are products that are small enough to be coiled. The maximum diameter or cross section for coiling is 20 mm in the

Table 3.9. Relative Cold Drawing Properties of Aluminum Alloys

Cold drawing properties	Non-heat-treatable (extruded or annealed)	Heat treatable (annealed)
Easy	Al99.5 to 99.85 AlMn AlMg0.5	AlMgSi0.5 to 1 AlMgSiCu AlCuSiMn
Moderate	AlMg1 to 2	AlZnMg1 AlCuMg1 to 2 AlCuBiPb AlMgSiPb
Difficult	AlMgMn AlMg2.5Cr AlMg3 to 5 AlMg4.5Mn	AlZnMgCu0.5 to 1.5 AlCuMgPb

Table 3.10. Wall Thicknesses of Extruded Aluminum Tubes (From DIN 9107)

OD, mm	Wall thickness, mm — Relative extrudability		
	Easy	Moderate	Difficult
10 to 18	1 to 4	1.5 to 4	2 to 4
18 to 30	1 to 7.5	1.5 to 7.5	2 to 7.5
30 to 50	1 to 15	1.5 to 15	2 to 15
50 to 80	2 to 25	2.5 to 25	3 to 25
80 to 120	4 to 30	4 to 30	4 to 30
120 to 200	7.5 to 35	7.5 to 35	7.5 to 35
200 to 315	10 to 35	10 to 35	10 to 35

soft alloys. The important applications and materials in this product sector are listed in Table 3.11. The range of alloys and products is best divided into three groups with different production characteristics.

Bar

The extrusion of bar from pure aluminum — e.g., for bus bars — poses no problems, but the production of bars in the more highly alloyed materials is associated with narrow temperature and speed ranges because the tendency to hot shortness increases rapidly with higher alloy content (Ref 34). The extrudability of free-cutting alloys is not inferior to that of the high-alloy lead-free alloys in spite of the lead content of about 1%. One possible

Table 3.11. Aluminum Alloy Bar and Wire

Application	Type of semifinished product	Main alloys
Drop forged components	Bar	AlMgSi AlMgSiCu AlCuMg1 to 2 AlZnMgCu0.5 to 1.5
Cold forged components.	Bar and wire	Al99 to 99.5 AlMg1 to 3
Cold impact extruded components	. .	AlMgSi (AlCuMg1) (AlZnMg1)
Machined small components	Bar and wire	AlMgSi AlMg5 AlMgSiPb(a) AlCuMgPb(a) AlMgBiPb(a)
Jewelry	Wire	Al99.9 Al99.9Mg0.5 Al99.9Mg1 Al99.9MgSi0.5
Electric cable and conductors	Wire	E-Al E-AlMgSi

(a) For machining on automatic lathes.

explanation is that aluminum is only slightly wetted by lead and this prevents the lead from forming at the grain boundaries and weakening the bonding (Ref 35).

The lowest extrusion temperature possible has to be used with these alloys to minimize the risk of hot shortness. This increases the flow stress and bar less than approximately 60 mm (depending on the extrusion ratio) is extruded through a multihole die to reduce the extrusion load. The load can also be reduced by billet heat treatment. In the case of alloys containing manganese, heating the billets to temperatures above 500 °C gives a heterogeneous structure, that is, precipitation of the supersaturated manganese as a coarse dispersion, with a lower flow stress.

Unfortunately, the recrystallization-retarding effect of manganese or other elements is reduced as the degree of heterogeneity increases and the press effect no longer occurs (Ref 24, 36-38). The mechanical properties of the finished product are then reduced. A further consequence of the reduction in the recrystallization temperature is coarse-grain recrystallization, particular-

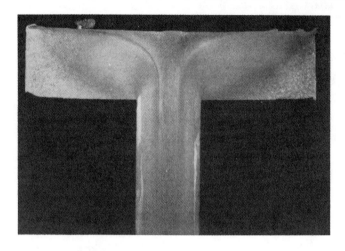

Fig. 3.20. Coarse-grain recrystallization on the extrusion surface. *(From Stenger)*

ly at the surface of the extrusion where the greatest shear deformation occurs (Fig. 3.20). This undesirable coarse-grain formation takes place either spontaneously during extrusion or in the emerging product during the subsequent solution heat treatment, or during heating for further hot working (forging).

Coarse-grain formation is particularly undesirable if the extruded material is for forging bar stock and, in this case, the optimum billet heat treatment temperature (430 to 480 °C) is selected to develop finely dispersed precipitates. This gives the maximum recrystallization-retarding effect and the best conditions for retaining the unrecrystallized extruded fibrous structure (Ref 36, 37). Allowance must be made for the relatively high flow stress. It is also possible to obtain the necessary conditions for preventing coarse-grain recrystallization in billets that have not undergone the high-temperature heat treatment because the elements that can precipitate (e.g., manganese) are still supersaturated and thus retard the recrystallization process. Bar from AlMgSi1, for example, can therefore be extruded with a fine-fibrous structure with no billet heat treatment. Studies of AlCuSiMn, however, have proved that a low-temperature billet heat treatment gives the most favorable structure for avoiding coarse-grain formation (Ref 41). The coarse-grain structure in the surface layer increases towards the end of the extrusion because the sheared area occupies a larger cross sectional area (Chap. 1).

A compromise has to be made between the susceptibility to hot shortness and coarse-grain recrystallization when selecting the optimum billet temperature. A low temperature is desirable to avoid hot shortness but, frequently, a relatively high temperature has to be selected to reduce the tendency to coarse-grain formation: no coarse precipitates of the recrystallization-retarding elements form at high billet temperatures and, consequently, no recrystallization takes place (Ref 24, 36). The reduction in percentage of recrystallization of AlCuMg1 as the billet temperature is raised is given in Fig. 3.21. The solution heat treatment temperatures of the high-strength alloys are, therefore, above the optimum extrusion temperature and a separate solution heat treatment is necessary before age hardening.

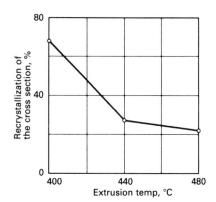

Fig. 3.21. Influence of the extrusion temperature on the recrystallization of AlCuMg1 bar. *(From Ref 37)*

Wire in High-Alloy Materials

The same basic problems occur in the extrusion of wire in the high-strength alloys as in the production of bar. There is also the added difficulty of the high extrusion ratio that makes it necessary to increase the number of strands as the flow stress increases and the wire diameter is reduced. Up to 20 strands are used in practice, which gives correspondingly low coil weights even with large billets. This naturally reflects on the efficiency of the subsequent wire drawing operation if the coils cannot be butt jointed together. If welding is not possible, the number of strands should be as small as possible with the optimum billet weight, because of the efficiency factor. Extruded wire usually has a diameter between 8 and 14 mm; typical exit speeds are given in Table 3.5.

Coiling of the alloys difficult to extrude presents problems. The wire coilers used in practice have a maximum of four take-up spools and simultaneous coiling of more strands is rarely considered. The problem is sometimes overcome by extruding the strands as straight lengths and then coiling them. The wire strands can easily stick together when they are hot and the surface finish is damaged. Water-cooling immediately after the die helps prevent this. Heat treatable alloys are not normally quenched at the press because natural aging would seriously impair the cold drawing capability.

Wire in the Easily Extruded Aluminum Alloys

The soft alloys, like Al99.5, and the low-alloy materials AlMg1 and AlMgSi0.5 can usually be extruded at the speeds given in Table 3.5 to wire through single-hole or through multihole dies with a maximum of four openings to give acceptable coil weights. These materials easily weld together, and any size of coil can be produced by billet-to-billet extrusion (Chap. 2 and Ref 39). Feed stock for wire drawing is also produced in pure aluminum or the low-alloy aluminum materials by hot rolling for large orders. More recently this feed stock has been produced more economically by continuous casting — e.g., the Properzi process. Although these processes are more efficient than extrusion for small diameters and large volumes, the undeniable advantage of wire extrusion is the ability to economically produce small quantities of wire in a very wide range of diameters with relatively low tooling costs, even in alloys that cannot be produced by continuous casting and rolling or by conventional rolling (Ref 40).

3.3.2. Extrusion of Magnesium

3.3.2.1. Alloys and Extruded Products

Magnesium alloys have a very favorable specific weight-to-strength ratio and are used in aircraft and spacecraft as well as the nuclear industry. They also have very good machining properties. The alloys MgMn2, MgAl3Zn, MgAl6Zn MgAl8Zn and MgZn6Zr are standardized in DIN 9715 and 1729/1. Other alloys used outside Germany include MgZn2Zr and MgZn3Zr (England, USA), and MgAl1 to MgAl7 (USSR). The alloys MgAl8Zn and MgZn6Zr are also age hardened with mechanical properties about 10% higher than the as-extruded temper. Magnesium alloys are not drawn to increase the mechanical properties, but to attain closer dimensional tolerances. The press sizes and the dimensions of the semifinished products are similar to those encountered in aluminum extrusion.

3.3.2.2. Extrudability and Flow Behavior

Magnesium and its alloys have a hexagonal lattice and, therefore, a lower cold workability than aluminum. When it is heated its workability ranges from moderate to good but does have some peculiarities. Billet homogenization reduces the flow stress (Table 3.12) but a lengthy heating period before extrusion is still necessary to obtain a uniform temperature throughout the billet and extensive dissolution of heterogeneous components, including the Mg_4Al_3 phase, to give good extrudability. A rule of thumb for the heating period is approximately 1 h per 50 mm billet diameter (Ref 46). Billet temperatures and possible extrusion speeds are given in Table 3.13. The

Table 3.12. Specific Pressures for MgAl3 Tube Extrusion as a Function of Billet Heating (From Ref 45)

(Billet dimensions: 98 by 42 by 150 mm; tube size: 44 by 1.5 mm)

Heat treatment of billets prior to heating at the press	Heating prior to extrusion Temp, °C	Time, h	Specific pressure (N/mm²)
Not heat treated	380 to 350	1	250 to 300
Not heat treated	380 to 350	3	210 to 260
Not heat treated	380 to 350	6	180 to 220
Not heat treated	340 to 300	1	320 to 400
Not heat treated	340 to 300	3	250 to 300
Not heat treated	340 to 300	6	200 to 250
350 °C, 12 h	340 to 300	1	190 to 250
350 °C, 12 h	340 to 300	3	170 to 200
350 °C, 12 h	340 to 300	6	150 to 180
350 °C, 24 h	340 to 300	1	170 to 220
350 °C, 24 h	340 to 300	3	160 to 200
350 °C, 24 h	340 to 300	6	130 to 170

Table 3.13. Billet Temperatures and Extrusion Speeds for Magnesium Alloys

Material	Billet temp, °C	Extrusion speed, m/min according to: Zolobov(a)	Pearson(b)	Harris(c)
Mg	250 to 450 (d)	. .	. .	. .
MgMn.	350 to 440 (d)	. .	. .	6 to 30
MgMn2.	250 to 350 (d)	. .	15 to 30	. .
MgAl1Zn	300 to 420	9 to 30	. .	. .
MgAl2Zn	300 to 400	6 to 15	. .	. .
MgAl3Zn	300 to 400	2 to 6	. .	5 to 12
MgAl5Zn	280 to 360	1 to 2.5	. .	. .
MgAl6Zn	350 to 400	. .	4 to 6	2 to 6
MgAl7Zn	300 to 350	6 to 15	. .	. .
MgAl8Zn	300 to 420	9 to 30	. .	1 to 2
MgZn2Zr	300 to 400	. .	2 to 5	. .
	300 to 400	. .	0.3 to 1(e)	. .
MgZn3Zr	300 to 400	. .	2 to 5	. .
	300 to 400	. .	0.3 to 1(e)	. .

(a) Ref 45. (b) Ref 2. (c) Ref 46. (d) Smooth surfaces at high speeds. (e) High strength, $R_m > 300$ N/mm², obtained at low temperatures and low speeds.

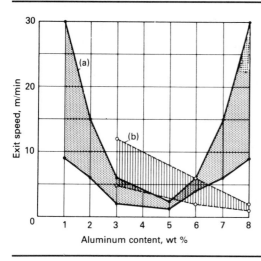

Fig. 3.22. Extrusion speeds of MgAl alloys. *(From Ref 45 [a] and 46 [b])*

surface starts to tear if a critical limit is exceeded. According to the literature the extrusion speed is lowest and the range of speeds the narrowest for an alloy with an average aluminum content of 5% (Fig. 3.22) although the eutectic formed above approximately 6% aluminum at 435 °C must limit the exit speed of the more highly alloyed material to a low value of approximately 3.5 m/min (Ref 2). The flow in the container is more uniform than that of aluminum — possibly the result of the lower shear stress.

3.3.2.3. Extrusion of Bar, Section and Tube

The extrusion of magnesium alloys not only produces the desired change in shape but also gives the equally important modification of the as-cast brittle coarse-grain structure. Continuously cast billets are used for the starting material, usually without machining, and gas furnaces are used for the necessarily long billet heating before extrusion. The technology of bar, section and tube production is similar to that of aluminum extrusion but the dies for sections are manufactured with shorter bearing lengths and smaller inlet radii. Welding chamber dies are used for tubes and hollow shapes in the alloys MgMn2 and MgZn2Zr to MgZn6Zr, which reweld together without any difficulty, and billet-to-billet extrusion can be used. The MgAl alloys, which have poor rewelding characteristics, have to be extruded over a mandrel and solid billets are pierced in the press for tube production. In contrast to the normal material, MgMn2 has the property of forming good, smooth as-extruded surfaces at high extrusion speeds but cracking at low exit speeds (Ref 2). Recrystallization can be retarded and a texture developed in the zinc-containing alloys MgZn2Zr and MgZn3Zr to give the highest mechanical properties (Ref 2, 46) by extruding at a low temperature and low speed (Table 3.13). Discards as short as 5% of the billet length can be used in magnesium extrusion without any funnel defect forming because of the relatively uniform material flow in the container.

3.3.3. Extrusion of Zinc

Unlike rolled semifinished products, extruded zinc tube, wire and bar have only a minor role as a replacement material for copper alloys. The commercial zinc alloys contain aluminum, copper and magnesium. Zinc has a hexagonal structure similar to magnesium and, accordingly, only a moderate workability. The optimum extrusion temperature varies from 200 to 350 °C depending on the alloy (Table 3.14). The exit speeds are low because of the relatively high specific pressure needed and the low ductility, and fall in the range 3 to 6 m/min. Superplastic ZnAl alloys — for example, ZnAl22 (with a 99.99% base) — are extruded at 250 °C to provide the starting material for cold working (Ref 47).

3.3.4. Extrusion of Low Melting Point Brazing Alloys

Brazing alloys based on CuP8 (hard eutectic brazing alloy with low surface tension) and silver-containing alloys based on CuZnAg or CuAgCdZn, with brazing temperatures between 610 and 960 °C, are mainly sold as extruded and sometimes drawn wire, according to DIN 8513, pages 1 to 3, in the form of cut-to-length rods with diameters of 1, 1.5, 2 and 3 mm. The alloys that are difficult to draw (for example, the brittle CuP8) have to be extruded to their finished diameter. This is possible only if a large number of strands are extruded — up to 30 on a horizontal press, up to 100 on a vertical press. The most important extrusion data are given in Table 3.15. Wire reduced by cold drawing is cold coiled.

Table 3.14. Extrusion Temperatures for Zinc Alloys (From Ref 2 and 45)

Material	Extrusion temp, °C
Zn	170 to 200
ZnCu	200 to 240
ZnAl	250 to 300
ZnAlCu	300 to 350

Table 3.15. Extrusion Parameters for Brazing Alloys

(Direct extrusion without a shell, with a flat die [180°] lubricated with graphite/oil)

Material	Extrusion temp, °C	Extrusion speed, mm/s
CuP	520	2
CuAgP	520	2
Silver solder	450 to 680	1

NOTE: Container temperature, 400 to 450 °C; maximum extrusion ratio, 100:1.

3.4. Extrusion Technology for Materials With Extrusion Temperatures Between 600 and 1000 °C

3.4.1. Copper Alloys

3.4.1.1. Materials and Extruded Products

There are very many copper alloys, the majority of which are extruded in some form or other to intermediate or finished products. DIN standards list 82 alloys:

Alloy group		No. of standardized alloys
DIN 1787	Copper..	6
DIN 17666	Wrought copper alloys, low-alloy content	22
DIN 17660	Copper-zinc alloys (brass, special brass)	30
DIN 17662	Copper-zinc alloys (tin, bronze)......................	4
DIN 17665	Copper-aluminum-alloys (aluminum bronze)............	8
DIN 17664	Copper-nickel alloys	6
DIN 17663	Copper-nickel-zinc alloys (German silver)	6

The properties and application of the extruded products cannot be discussed in detail here. Information can always be obtained from materials handbooks and appropriate standards (Ref 54, 56, 57, 64). For the extrusion technician, the most important thing is to know which alloys are best for which products. This information is summarized in Table 3.16 (note that extruded sections are not so important for copper as for aluminum alloys). The majority of extruded semifinished products in pure copper and low-alloy copper materials are drawn to give the required dimensional tolerances and mechanical properties. In these cases usually only simple shapes and tubes suitable for drawing are extruded. Drawing extruded sections is difficult and requires considerable experience, especially in the design of the drawing die. Easily extruded alloys — for example, $(\alpha + \beta)$-brasses — can be extruded to a wide range of shapes (Fig. 3.26a).

3.4.1.2. Extrudability

As in other materials, the extrudability of copper alloys is governed by the flow stress, the associated minimum billet temperature, and the temperature at which hot shortness occurs. The nature of this defect varies with alloy composition and extrusion parameters, from slight transverse surface cracks

Table 3.16. Summary of Extruded Copper Alloy Semifinished Products (Compiled by Laue/Stenger)

Alloy	Predominant semifinished product			Finished product
	Bar/wire	Section	Tube	
E-Cu X	X	X	. .	Electrical conductors
SF-Cu		. .	X	Apparatus components, refrigerator tubes, water pipe
Low-alloy Cu:				
Not heat treatable X	X	. .	. .	Electrical conductors
Heat treatable:				
CuCr, CuCrZr X	X	, .	. .	Welding electrodes
CuNiSi................ X	X	X	X	Bolts, electrical connectors
CuZn:				
α-brasses(a) X	X	. .	X	Cold formed components, heat exchanger tubes
β-brasses(b) X	X	X	. .	Machined components, drop forged components
α special brasses(c) X	X	. .	X	Apparatus construction
β special brasses(d) X	X	X	. .	Higher-strength drop forged components, engineering and bearing components
CuSn2 to 6 X	X	. .	. .	Apparatus components
CuSn8 X	X	. .	X	Bearing components
CuAl5 X	X	. .	. .	Tubes for chemical engineering, damper bars (electrical motors)
CuAl8 X	X	. .	X	Acid-resistant apparatus components, welding wire
Complex Al bronzes.......... X	X	. .	X	Gear and worm wheels, corrosion-resistant bearing elements, nuts and bolts
CuNi5Fe		. .	X	Seawater pipes
CuNi10Fe.................... .		. .	X	Seawater pipes
CuNi20Fe		. .	X	Condenser tubes
CuNi25 X	X	. .	. .	Coin material
CuNi30Fe.................... .		. .	X	Condenser tubes
CuNi30Mn.................... X	X	. .	. .	Electrical resistance wire
CuNi44 X	X	. .	. .	Electrical resistance wire
CuNiZn(e)................ X	X	. .	. .	Apparatus components, cutlery, instruments, armatures

(a) CuZn5 to CuZn40.   (b) Zn ≥ 40%, Pb to 3.3%.   (c) Zn to 39%.   (d) Zn ≥ 39%.   (e) German silver.

Fig. 3.23. Effect of an excessive extrusion temperature: **(a)** extruded CuSn5Al bar, 20 mm diam; **(b)** outside surface of an extruded CuZn37Si tube. *(From VDM Frankfurt)*

to the breakup of the extruded product in the form of a fir tree (fir tree defect, Fig. 3.23). The extrudability range extends from the easily extruded materials — β-brasses — to the very difficult (that is, high specific pressure) alloys — high-alloy-content aluminum bronzes — and the very poor alloys susceptible to hot shortness — leaded German silver. Extrusion speeds are generally higher than those encountered in aluminum extrusion and hydraulic accumulator drive is generally used. High-speed extrusion is used to minimize the fall in temperature of the billet during the cycle. Billet temperatures are usually between 600 and 1000 °C although the container temperature cannot exceed 500 °C, which results in a large heat loss and undesirable cooling towards the end of extrusion. The heat losses can only be compensated for by the heat of deformation if high extrusion speeds and relatively low initial billet temperatures are used to give a temperature increase towards the end of extrusion (e.g., brass extrusion).

The extrusion temperatures used in practice are given in Table 3.17 for different copper alloys. Exit speeds exceeding 300 m/min cannot be coped with by the runout equipment and this limits the use of the maximum possible extrusion speeds with the high extrusion speed alloys.

3.4.1.3. Flow Behavior and Lubrication

In addition to the extrusion load, the wide variations in hot working characteristics among the copper alloys and the different flow behavior also account for the differences in metal flow in the container, which is governed by the severity of the friction at the container wall. The following types occur in practice:

Table 3.17. Extrusion Data for Copper Alloys (Compiled by Boden)

Material	Melting range(a), °C	Billet temp, °C	Max extrusion ratio	Max extrusion speed, m/min
E-Cu	1080 to 1083	780 to 950	≈ 250	≈ 300
Low-alloy Cu:				
CuZr	965	850 to 920	100	150
CuCr	1075	900 to 1020	100	150
CuNi1.5Si	1040 to 1070	750 to 900	75	100
CuNi2Si...............	1040 to 1070	750 to 900	75	100
CuNi3Si...............	1030 to 1050	850 to 950	50	75
CuZn:				
α-brass	. .	700 to 825	≈ 100	≈ 60
(α + β)-brass	. .	675 to 800	≈ 700	≈ 250
β-brass	. .	650 to 750	≈ 700	≈ 360
CuZn10	1015 to 1035	825 to 875	150	100
CuZn28	915 to 945	750 to 850	60	100
CuZn33	905 to 935	750 to 850	150	150
CuZn37	900 to 915	725 to 825	200	150
CuZn40	880 to 890	700 to 800	300	300
CuZn40Pb............	875 to 885	650 to 750	300	300
CuZn38Pb1...........	880 to 900	650 to 750	250	250
CuZn40Mn	880 to 890	650 to 700	250	250
CuZn35Ni	880 to 890	700 to 800	200	300
CuZn20Al	960 to 1010	750 to 850	75	100
CuZn40Al2	880 to 890	550 to 700	250	250
CuZn31Si	930 to 950	720 to 760	150	150
CuSn:				
CuSn2	1020 to 1070	800 to 900	100	150
CuSn6	910 to 1040	650 to 740	100	50
CuSn8	860 to 1015	650 to 740	80	30
CuAl:				
CuAl5	1050 to 1060	750 to 850	75	150
CuAl8Fe	1030 to 1035	740 to 780	100	150
CuAl10Fe	1030 to 1050	750 to 900	100	200
CuAl10Ni	≈ 1050	750 to 900	50	100
CuNi:				
CuNi10Fe	1100 to 1145	850 to 950	80	50
CuNi20Fe	1130 to 1190	850 to 950	. .	. .
CuNi30Fe	1180 to 1240	900 to 1000	80	50
CuNi30Mn............	1180 to 1240	. .	. .	. .
CuNiZn:				
CuNi10Zn42Pb........	925	600 to 800(a)	. .	. .
CuNi12Zn24	1020	900 to 950(a)	. .	. .
CuNi12Zn30Pb........	1010	. .	. .	. .
CuNi18Zn20	1055	940 to 990(a)	. .	. .
CuNi18Zn19Pb........	1050	. .	. .	. .
CuNi25Zn15	1105	1000(a)	. .	. .

(a) From *VDM-Handbuch*.

Unlubricated extrusion with a shell (flow type C, Chap. 1): $(\alpha + \beta)$-brasses, complex Al-bronzes. There is little scaling on these alloys and, consequently, considerable sticking between the metal and the container. A good surface quality is obtained only by extruding with a shell.

"Dry" extrusion without a shell and with a flat die (flow type B, Chap. 1): copper, low-alloy copper materials including CuCr, CuNiSi, CuNi and CuNiZn alloys, α-brass, binary CuAl alloys, CuSn up to 6% tin. The alloys in this group have to be extruded at high temperatures because of the high extrusion ratios used, and the billets rapidly develop an oxide film that acts as a lubricant between the billet and the container. This lubricating effect is often undesirable, because it can spoil the surface quality of the extrusion. A billet temperature between 550 and 660 °C would be the optimum for copper extrusion but would require specific pressures of approximately 1000 N/mm^2 (Ref 45).

Flat dies are used to develop a dead metal zone that retards oxide on the billet surface (Ref 45). Although it would be preferable to extrude copper, CuZr, CuCr and other metals with a shell, it is precluded by the lubricating effect of the oxide, except in particular cases (for example, with very high extrusion ratios) when the normal pressure between the billet and the container wall and the friction are high enough to develop the shear loads needed to cut a shell. As described in Chap. 1, the flow in the container has a decisive influence on the formation of certain extrusion defects, including peeling and blister formation (flow type B) and pipe (flow type C). The choice of discard length also has to take these effects into account. The defects first occur in approximately the last third of the extrusion and generally can only be avoided by not extruding to the full extent of the press capacity. Table 3.18 gives the usual discard lengths for copper alloy extrusion.

Lubricated extrusion without a shell, with a conical die (flow type B or A): difficult (that is, high specific pressure) alloys, including complex Al-bronze, CuSn8, CuNi30Fe, etc. The flow of these alloys is eased — that is, the load is reduced — by lubrication and the simultaneous exclusion of the dead metal zone by using conical dies. The term "impact extrusion" is often met with in practice here, although it usually refers to an entirely different method of metal working.

3.4.1.4. Production and Treatment of Extrusion Billets

In the 1960's round extrusion billets were still cast exclusively in vertical cast iron and steel molds. The molds for brass and bronze were water-cooled. More recently, semicontinuous vertical machines have been developed, in which 3 to 4 logs of copper 7 to 8 m long are cast, using graphite molds. Brass is cast in water-cooled copper molds. Modern horizontal continuous casting can

Table 3.18. Discard Lengths Depending on the Alloy, Method of Extrusion and Container Diameter in the Extrusion of Solid Sections (From Ref 61)

Alloy	Type	Extrusion method	Container diam, mm				
			160	180	200	315	400
			Discard length, mm				
Cu, α-brasses, e.g., CuZn5 CuZn33 CuZn28Sn, tin bronzes up to CuSn6, Al alloys	Alloys easily to moderately difficult to extrude; flow type B	Without lubricant, without shell	20-25	25-30	25-30	35-40	35-40
(α + β)-brasses, e.g., CuZn37 CuZn39Sn CuZn40 CuZn35Ni CuZn30Al, etc.	Alloys easily to moderately difficult to extrude; flow type C	Without lubricant, with shell	30-35	35-40	35-40	40-50	50-60
CuAl10Fe, CuAl10Ni, i.e., complex Al bronzes	Alloys difficult to extrude; flow type C	Without lubricant	40-45	50-55	50-60	60-70	70-80

be carried out in fully continuous casting installations suitable for copper, brass, aluminum-bronze, copper-nickel and other alloys (Fig. 3.24). Round billets up to 250 mm in diameter can be cast as three strands; billets 250 to 350 mm in diameter are cast as two strands. The maximum log diameter produced by vertical or horizontal continuous casting suitable for extrusion is 400 mm. However, there are installations for tube and solid materials up to 1500 mm diameter.

Homogenization of the cast logs or cut billets is usually not required for copper alloys, although the extrudability of difficult alloys (for example, CuSn8), can be improved by it. The as-cast billet surface must normally be machined to obtain a good surface quality, and this reduces the billet diameter by 3 to 4 mm. This applies, in particular, to materials of flow type A or B extruded without a shell. Machining is not needed for extrusion with a shell.

Tubes are extruded from solid billets that are pierced in the press. This prevents oxide formation on the inside surface of the tube, which can result in defects. Billets for tubes in the difficult alloys (for example, CuNi or complex Al-bronzes) frequently have to be prebored to a diameter approximately 1 mm more than the mandrel diameter because of the high piercing and extrusion

Fig. 3.24. Horizontal casting plant.
(From Technica, Würzburg)

loads. The mandrel must always be lubricated to prevent perforations and tears on the inside surface of the tube. Induction heating is very suitable for billet heating if severe oxidation is to be avoided. Holding times of several hours at temperature, however, are desirable or even unavoidable for high-alloy materials because the resultant homogenization can significantly improve the extrudability.

3.4.1.5. Extrusion of Copper

The most important extruded semifinished products are tubes and sections (Table 3.16).

3.4.1.5.1. Copper Tubes

Extruded copper tubes are the starting material for drawn copper pipe. Several modern copper plants producing only copper tube have been built to meet the demand for this product. The installations consist of an extrusion press, a cold Pilger tube-reducing machine and an extensively automated

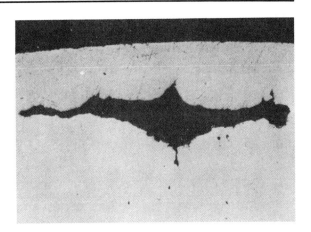

Fig. 3.25. Blister on the outside surface of an SF-Cu tube after annealing in an H_2 protective atmosphere; extruded tube (ID, 55×5.5 mm) after four draws, 42×1.9 mm. (*From Ref 117*)

coil-drawing machine. Copper can easily be cold worked, and intermediate annealing between draws is not needed. There is, therefore, no recrystallization and the extruded tube used to produce drawn hard tubes must already have a suitable fine-grain structure, which is obtained by extruding the copper tubes directly into a water bath. This interrupts the secondary grain growth in the product as it leaves the die at 1000 °C.

A further consequence of water-quenching is the absence of oxidation on the tube, and pickling before drawing is not necessary. Any water present inside the tube would lead to complications. Therefore, the tube is kept closed at both ends to protect the inside surface, which is difficult to clean, from oxidation. The front end is sealed by not completely piercing the solid billet. At the end of extrusion the mandrel is withdrawn and the final part of the billet extruded as a solid rod. Copper tubes in standard dimensions are usually extruded to approximately 40 m long. The range of sizes available extends from 55 to 250 mm in diameter with wall thicknesses in the range of 2.5 to 20 mm.

Oxide can flow into the surface of the tube towards the end of extrusion when heavily oxidized and long billets are used, resulting in peeling or blistering (Fig. 3.25). The lowest possible billet temperature, the shortest heating time, minimum billet length, a sufficient discard length (Table 3.18), an enclosed billet loader tray and the maximum possible extrusion ratio have to be used to avoid these defects. Removal of the oxidized surface by hot scalping (Ref 52) or blasting the scale with water as the billet passes from the furnace to the container are further means of obtaining clean, defect-free product surfaces. Mention must be made of the work by Blazey *et al.* (Ref 50) and Koltzenburg (Ref 51) on the relationship between the flow in the container

Fig. 3.26a. Extruded copper and copper alloy sections. *(From Revere Copper and Brass, Inc., New York)*

and the structural properties in tube extrusion. The lubricating effect of the oxide skin can be improved by additional lubrication with graphite to increase the possible extrusion ratio in copper tube extrusion. Conical dies can then be used to give so-called impact extrusion.

3.4.1.5.2. Copper Sections

Small volumes of copper bar and sections (Fig. 3.26, a and b) are delivered in the soft temper but the majority are cold worked. By carefully matching the cross section of the extrusion to that of the finished product it is possible to obtain the desired mechanical properties in a single draw, which can vary from 10 to 50%, depending on the strength required. This is not difficult with large sections but is limited with bar dimensions less than 10 mm or flat bar and sections less than 5 mm thick, because the extrusion load needed for such small sections exceeds the capacity of normal presses. Thus, very small final dimensions, assuming an optimum section from the point of

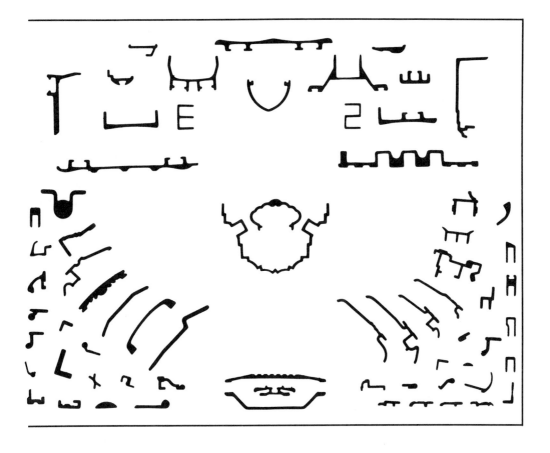

Fig. 3.26b. Examples of extruded copper hollow sections. *(From Metallgesellschaft Frankfurt)*

view of extrusion technology, can be produced only by several cold working operations with intermediate annealing. This naturally has a considerable effect on the production costs.

Small bar and sections can be produced by passing the extrusion through a water trough and then coiling the cold product immediately. Universal extrusion plants are equipped with these coilers by the runout trough, and they can be either lowered or removed if needed. The coils of round or flat copper — and occasionally sections — are cold drawn on drum drawing machines (rough drawing) sometimes with intermediate annealing to a predetermined size usually followed by a final anneal. The coiled material is given its final draw on straight draw benches and cut to production or finished lengths. Hollow copper sections for water-cooled bus bars in electrical engineering are extruded over the mandrel tip (stationary mandrel) from hollow billets. Figure 3.26b shows some examples of extruded hollow copper sections. The shape and location of the hollow chamber and the tolerances are determined by the shape of the mandrel tip and its exact location relative to the die. Plastic deformation of tool steel softened by the high extrusion temperature can cause considerable problems. The use of bridge dies, similar to those for aluminum extrusion, is increasing for the extrusion of these hollow sections because of the considerable difficulties encountered in holding dimensional tolerances.

3.4.1.6. Extrusion of Low-Alloy Copper Materials

The low-alloy content copper materials, of which the most important for extrusion are CuAg up to 0.25% silver, CuCd1, CuCr, CuZr and CuNiSi1.5 to 3, flow in a manner similar to copper—that is, the oxide formed by heating to a relatively high deformation temperature acts as a lubricant. These low-alloy content materials are also pressed with a shell, similar to copper tube extrusion, to avoid peeling and blistering in the product from the oxide of the billet surface associated with flow type B. This danger is more pronounced in these alloys than in copper because of the internal oxidation of the easily oxidized alloying elements. The increase in the hot flow stress associated with the presence of the alloying elements is important because it increases the extrusion load, and either the maximum extrusion ratio has to be reduced or higher billet temperatures used. This latter measure is avoided as much as possible because of oxide formation and its related defects.

In some cases the extrusion load for these alloys can be reduced by careful lubrication of the container (for example, with graphite) and the use of conical dies. However, this is not often done, because of the danger of peeling or blistering except with extremely low billet temperatures, short billets and the maximum possible extrusion ratio. The heat treatable copper alloys CuZr,

CuCr, CuNiSi, and the like, have to be age-hardened after solution heat treatment and subjected to a subsequent cold working operation to attain the mechanical properties and electrical conductivity given in DIN 17671, 17672 and 17674 (Ref 54, 56). The separate solution heat treatment can be eliminated by selecting an extrusion temperature well above the solubility limit of the second phase and by quenching directly into water from the exit temperature; this also prevents, or at least reduces, oxidation of the extruded product. In practice, the precipitated second phase in the as-cast structure does not completely dissolve during the customary induction heating, which reduces billet oxidation. The desired effect is then not always obtained by quenching at the press and the separate solution heat treatment before drawing is still required. However, if the cross section is small (for example, wire), quenching from the extrusion temperature is more advantageous because the cooling between the furnace and the quenching bath takes place too rapidly when separate solution heat treatment is used. Wire and small sections in CuZr, CuCr and occasionally CuNiSi1.5 and 2 are, therefore, extruded into water if the high extrusion temperatures do not result in the extrusion defects mentioned above.

3.4.1.7. Extrusion of CuZn Alloys (Brass)

The commercial CuZn alloys have zinc contents varying between 5 and 40%. Three types of alloy can be distinguished on the equilibrium diagram (Fig. 3.27) for working at 700 °C with the following solid solutions:

> Zinc content 5 to 33%: α-brass; face-centered crystal lattice.
> Zinc content 33 to 40%: (α + β)-brass.
> Zinc content over 40%: β-brass; body-centered crystal lattice.

The α-brasses have a crystal structure that can readily be cold worked. They also have good ductility in hot working but relatively high flow stresses (Fig. 3.28). In contrast, the β-brasses have good hot working characteristics with a lower flow stress (Fig. 3.29) but are not suitable for cold working after hot extrusion. Brasses with an (α + β) structure have correspondingly mixed working properties, and the dependence of the structure on the temperature has to be considered carefully, using the equilibrium diagram. Additions of up to 3.5% lead to improve the machinability (free-cutting alloys) can be made to the (α + β)- and β-brasses without impairing the extrudability, but the hot workability of the copper-rich α-brasses is severely affected. Lead additions are, therefore, limited to 0.05% for copper contents over 65%. The reason for this difference between the effect of lead on the hot working characteristics of the β- and α-brasses is that the surface energy at the lead boundaries in β-brasses is less severely reduced than in the α-brasses (or, for example, German silver).

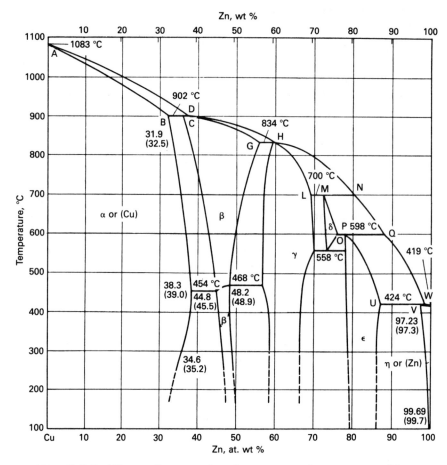

Fig. 3.27. Phase diagram for the copper-zinc system. *(From Ref 108)*

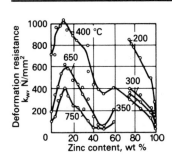

Fig. 3.28. Variations in the deformation resistance of CuZn alloys as a function of composition and temperature. *(From Ref 58)*

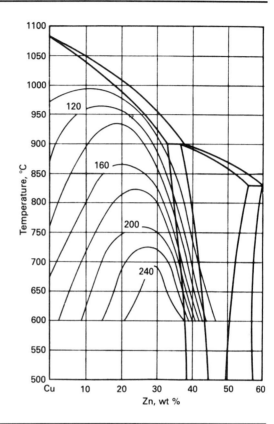

Fig. 3.29. Temperature dependence of the mean deformation resistance k_{wm} in N/mm^2 (240, 200, 160, 120) of CuZn alloys in compression by a drop hammer. *(From Ref 54)*

The techniques used in brass extrusion are related to the characteristic deformation properties of the two types of crystal. The α-brasses are mostly extruded to semifinished products that are cold drawn to the desired final dimensions and cold worked temper. Thin-wall tubes with a wall thickness less than 2 mm and thin bar with cross sections below 100 mm^2 are produced in the α-brasses by drawing. If the final dimensions can be obtained directly by extrusion, it is better to use the ($\alpha + \beta$)- or β-brasses with their better hot working properties. The low cold working ductility is sufficient for the low percentage caliber draw needed to attain the dimensional tolerances, at least for the ($\alpha + \beta$)-brasses. An upsetting draw without a mandrel is used for tube. This light caliber draw also straightens the extruded product. Round bar and tubes can, in addition, be straightened on roll correcting machines. The ($\alpha + \beta$)- and β-brasses are much more suitable than the α-brasses for the extrusion of complicated sections because of the lower extrusion temperature (Table 3.17 and Fig. 3.28) and the much lower extrusion loads, which reduce the mechanical and thermal stresses. Hollow sections are extruded over the mandrel tip, similar to copper sections, starting with hollow billets.

The fraction of the β solid solution in the brass structure has a significant influence on the extrudability and can be controlled by additions of the following alloying elements:

Alloying element	β component	Zinc equivalent(a)	Extrudability
Silicon.......... Increases		10	Improved
Aluminum....... Increases		6	Improved
Tin .... Increases		2	Improved
Manganese ...... Increases		0.5	Improved
Nickel.......... Decreases		-0.9 to -1.5	Impaired

(a) Related to an identical structure (Ref 109): 1% of the alloying effect has the same effect on the structure as the percentage of zinc given as the zinc equivalent.

For a given press capacity and extrusion ratio, the extrusion temperature has to be increased as the β content of the alloy is reduced. The temperatures needed to overcome the deformation resistance of the very difficult α-brasses are so high that coarse grains can form by secondary recrystallization; in extreme cases, hot shortness can develop. Hot shortness results in transverse cracks on the surface and can be prevented only by lowering the extrusion speed, or by reducing the extrusion ratio and extruding at a lower temperature. Coarse-grain formation and hot shortness are avoided in brass extrusion in the same way as in other metals: extruding with the lowest temperature permitted by the other extrusion parameters.

During heating in air, the oxide formed on CuZn alloys containing more than 80% copper is copper oxide; if the copper content is less than 80%, zinc oxide forms (Ref 57), which has no lubricating properties. This explains why the copper-rich brasses up to CuZn20 are extruded with quasi-lubricated containers — that is, without a shell (see section 3.4.1.3). There is sufficient adhesion between the billet and container when extruding the low copper content α-brasses to produce a shell. The decrease in the thermal conductivity of brass as the zinc content increases also has to be considered. The peripheral cooling of the billet in the container is no longer compensated for at high zinc contents and a hard shell is formed. The necessary conditions for extrusion with a shell are then fulfilled (Chap. 1). Nevertheless, there is still a considerable danger that parts of the billet surface will be torn away, resulting in peeling and blisters on the surface of the extruded product — particularly if thin-wall tubes have to be extruded with a thin shell for symmetrical mandrel guiding.

Extrusion with a shell is, by contrast, easier with the $(\alpha + \beta)$-alloys and this is standard practice. The mechanism and requirements for extruding these alloys with a shell are discussed in Chap. 1 and 2. The danger that the material flow will lead to pipe formation necessitates a large discard in direct extrusion. Indirect extrusion avoids this problem of the extrusion defect and is used extensively in France. However, methods are available for avoiding the defect and its associated losses in direct extrusion. They involve control over the following requirements (Ref 59, 61):

(a) The difference between the container diameter and the billet diameter should be as small as possible, to prevent the billet surface from folding when the billet is upset.

(b) Any residue from the shell of the previous extrusion must be completely removed.

(c) The container liner must be in a good condition to prevent the retention of shell residues and other impurities.

(d) The billet surface should be smooth and free from defects.

The $(\alpha + \beta)$- and β-brasses are very soft at the extrusion exit temperature and very susceptible to mechanical damage. Therefore, good guiding from the die and careful handling on the runout table are needed to prevent surface damage. Occasionally, zinc spots are formed when the metal boils off from the new surface as it leaves the die. The zinc condenses on the cooler tooling in the form of fine drops that collect together and are drawn off by the next extrusion. The zinc then alloys with the hot extrusion to form a zinc-rich brittle phase that can result in surface defects by drawing. Some brasses (for example, CuZn40Pb2) are very brittle in the temperature range from 250 to 500 °C, and care must be taken in handling the product as it cools through this range to avoid mechanical or thermal stresses and crack formation (Ref 60). Significant increases in the hardness of $(\alpha + \beta)$-brasses — up to 150% above the extruded temper — can be achieved by quenching from the exit temperature and heat treating at 200 °C.

3.4.1.8. Extrusion of CuSn Alloys (Tin Bronze)

Only CuSn alloys up to approximately 8% tin are suitable for extrusion. Cast bronzes with a tin content up to 6% consist of a homogeneous α-solid solution, whereas higher alloy contents contain the α-solid solution and also the $(\alpha + \delta)$-eutectoid; this reduces the workability, which, however, can be avoided by heat treatment (Ref 54, 63).

An excess of phosphorus is added as an oxidizing agent to prevent SnO_2 from forming because of inadequate oxidation of the melt. Hence, the most

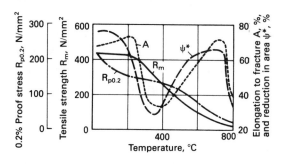

Fig. 3.30. Tensile strength, 0.2% proof stress, elongation to fracture, and reduction in area of the soft tin bronze CuSn8 between room temperature and 800 °C. *(From Ref 63)*

important CuSn extrusion alloy — CuSn8 — contains some phosphorus. Alloys with a tin content above 9% have such a low workability at both room temperature and high temperature that they cannot be extruded without special treatment. Nevertheless, there have been many attempts to improve the extrudability of CuSn alloys with tin contents as high as 32% by treatment of the melt (degassing) and heat treatment followed by slow cooling (Ref 62, 64).

CuSn wrought alloys are commercially extruded at temperatures between 700 and 750 °C (Table 3.17), which has been substantiated by hot tensile tests (e.g., Fig. 3.30) in which the maximum reduction in area to fracture occurred at 750 °C. In contrast, the workability is very limited at 350 °C. Figure 3.31 shows that the flow stress measured in dynamic compression tests increases as the tin content is raised. Bronzes up to 6% tin are considered moderately difficult to extrude, whereas CuSn8 is not only difficult to extrude but is also extremely difficult to work because of its susceptibility to cracking. This crack susceptibility, which frequently results in longitudinal cracks at the front end of the extrusion, derives mainly from internal stresses developed by extruding insufficiently homogeneous cast billets containing some segregation. CuSn8 billets should, therefore, be homogenized at 650 °C or higher for many hours, especially if the extrusion press is fitted with an induction furnace. If the extrusion temperature is raised to the upper limit to reduce the flow stress, hot shortness develops (fir tree defect) and the severity of this defect increases with temperature.

Tin bronzes with less than 6% tin are generally extruded without any container lubrication or shell; the oxide layer has some lubricating effect. The flow is, therefore, similar to type B. It is necessary to provide additional lubrication when extruding the alloy CuSn8, especially at high extrusion ratios. Flat dies are most suitable because conical dies can result in cladding and blisters (Ref 51). The billets have to be turned to guarantee a good surface

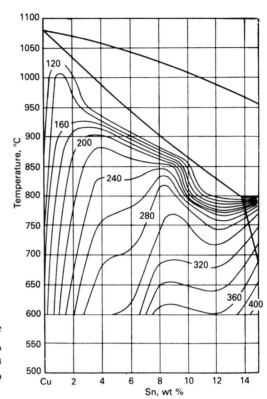

Fig. 3.31. Temperature dependence of the mean deformation resistance k_{wm} in N/mm^2 (400, 360, 320, etc.) of CuSn alloys in compression by a drop hammer. *(From Ref 54)*

finish. The large solidification range of CuSn alloys gives rise to segregation; tin sweat can occur on the billet surface by inverse segregation. Solid billets are generally used for tube extrusion and are pierced in the press. Tin bronzes less than 8% tin can readily be cold worked; the optimum dimensions for the extruded product can be selected according to the extrudability, and the final dimensions obtained by drawing. Small bar, not less than 20 mm in diameter, is extruded as one or two strands and coiled after air cooling for further processing on coil drawing machines. Cold working of the extruded materials can be significantly improved by homogenization at 700 °C.

3.4.1.9. Extrusion of CuAl Alloys (Aluminum Bronze)

The CuAl alloys include a wide range of materials with very different mechanical properties and working characteristics. In order to understand

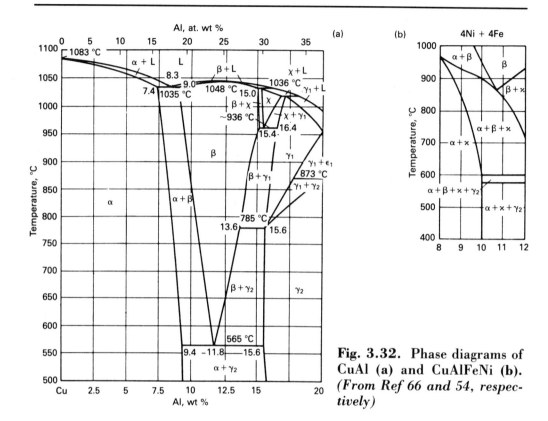

Fig. 3.32. Phase diagrams of CuAl (a) and CuAlFeNi (b). *(From Ref 66 and 54, respectively)*

these differences it is necessary to study the equilibrium diagram (Fig. 3.32). The CuAl alloys can be divided into two groups with the following main alloys:

Binary CuAl alloys:	CuAl5
	CuAl8
Complex CuAl alloys:	CuAl8Fe
	CuAl8Si
	CuAl9Mn
	CuAl10Fe
	CuAl10Ni

3.4.1.9.1. Binary CuAl Alloys

Binary CuAl alloys below approximately 5% aluminum consist entirely of the α phase and have a relatively high high-temperature flow stress, depending on the aluminum content, and tolerable cold working properties. Alloys with 8% aluminum are on the α/β boundary and those with 10% fall into the $(\alpha + \beta)$ region. The β phase is easier to work but the ductility at room

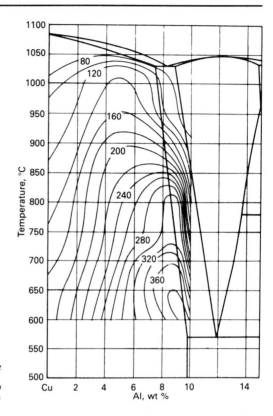

Fig. 3.33. Temperature dependence of the mean deformation resistance k_{wm} in N/mm² of CuAl alloys. *(From Ref 54)*

temperature is too low for cold working. Because even aluminum bronzes with 8% Al have an $(\alpha + \beta)$ structure after normal cooling from the exit temperature, the degree of cold working that can be applied to CuAl8 and CuAl10 to meet dimensional tolerances or to raise the mechanical properties is very slight. Consequently, only CuAl alloys below 5% Al can be considered for drawing down to smaller cross sections. The increase in the flow stress and high-temperature mechanical properties with increased Al content is shown in Fig. 3.33. The maximum flow stress at any given temperature occurs at the α/β boundary. This is reached by CuAl alloys with approximately 9% aluminum content; alloys with 8 to 9% aluminum are difficult to extrude. As the β component increases above 9% aluminum, the flow stress at constant temperature rapidly decreases.

The oxidized billet surface does not have the lubricating effect of copper oxide and the friction is so high that extrusion with a shell is the standard practice. The billet should be machined to avoid surface defects. The nonuniform flow (type B/C) is likely to lead to pipe formation towards the end of the extrusion but the danger can be avoided by using a suitably long discard. Lubrication of the container — that is, extrusion without a shell — might be necessary when extruding CuAl8 or CuAl10 at high extrusion ratios to reduce the load. Although CuAl5 always retains only an α structure after cooling from the exit temperature, semifinished products in CuAl8 contain residual β components after rapid cooling or in sections that can cool quickly because of the transformation inertia and this renders cold working more difficult. If the temperature changes during extrusion, the α : β ratio varies along the length of the extruded product with different α phase morphologies depending on whether they were formed by cooling from the β or (α + β) regions, and the mechanical properties will also vary (Ref 54).

3.4.1.9.2. CuAl Multiphase Alloys (Complex Aluminum Bronzes)

The complex aluminum bronzes belong to one of the most metallurgically interesting and the most difficult to extrude group of copper alloys. The alloying elements, chiefly iron, nickel, manganese and silicon, have the greatest effect on the mechanical, physical and chemical properties of the aluminum bronzes in the (α + β) group. Consequently, the complex CuAl bronzes have a higher aluminum content: between 6.5 and 12.5%. The aluminum bronzes containing iron, manganese and silicon have, according to Fig. 3.34, lower flow stresses at the extrusion temperature of 750 °C than does CuAl8, which has the highest k_w value of the binary CuAl alloys. CuAl10Ni, in contrast, has an extremely high high-temperature flow stress, approximately 70% higher than that for CuAl8 at 750 °C.

The plasticity behavior shown in Fig. 3.34 indicates that only CuAl8 is difficult to work and, among the complex bronzes, only CuAl10Ni very difficult to extrude. The other alloys should be relatively easy to work. These data, however, cannot be directly related to extrusion. The complex aluminum bronzes have a strong tendency to stick to the container wall and the β − α transformation takes place as the billet surface cools to form a hard peripheral shell — the low thermal conductivity of this alloy group furthers this effect. The requirements for extrusion with a shell, as with the (α + β)-brasses, are fulfilled but the shear forces needed to cut the shell at the prevailing temperature of 600 °C are very high compared with those encountered in brass extrusion. The shearing component of the extrusion load, therefore, is much higher than the pure deformation component (Chap. 1) in the complex aluminum bronzes, and this explains the low extrudability of the complex CuAl alloys. If small sections have to be extruded, often the only solution is to use a lubricated container.

The lubricant used in practice — cylinder oil for superheated steam with graphite — reduces so well the tendency of the metal to stick to steel that it is

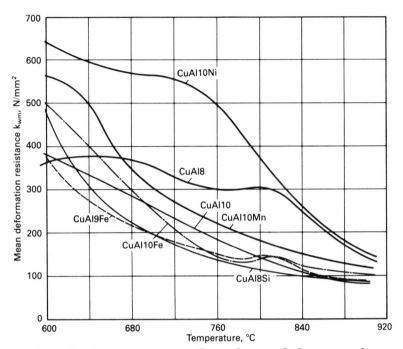

Fig. 3.34. Temperature dependence of the mean deformation resistance k_{wm} of complex CuAl alloys. *(From Ref 54)*

possible to extrude without a shell. Conical dies also help in reducing extrusion loads to more practical levels.

Adhesion of the complex aluminum bronzes to the tooling poses some problems in tube extrusion if the mandrel lubrication or conicity is insufficient and a torn or peeling internal surface forms. Another typical defect found with complex CuAl alloys is the wood fiber fracture, resulting from excessive gas porosity in the billet or inclusions of the aluminum oxide film. This defect is most common when extruding with a shell, with the very inhomogeneous metal flow type C. In extreme cases it can result in pipe formation, and a large discard has to be used to avoid this defect.

Complex aluminum bronze bar and tube are usually cooled in stationary air from the extrusion exit temperature to give tensile strengths from 600 to 800 N/mm^2 with CuAl10Fe, and from 700 to 900 N/mm^2 with CuAl10Ni, depending on the cross section (Ref 65). Higher mechanical properties, in particular an increase in the $R_{p0.2}$ limit and the hardness, are obtained by heat treatment. The extruded products are solution heat treated in the (α + β) or

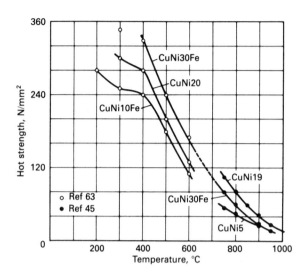

Fig. 3.35. Hot strength of different CuNi alloys. *(From Ref 63 and Ref 45)*

(α + β + κ) region (Fig. 3.32) and quenched to form the harder β′$_{MBz}$-martensite. It is also possible to quench directly from the extrusion temperature, although the separate heat treatment after extrusion gives better properties (Ref 65). The second part of the heat treatment consists of tempering between 500 and 650 °C, which increases the elongation to fracture by the partial decomposition of the β′$_{MBz}$-martensite and, in the nickel-containing alloys, the coagulation of the κ phase. With the exception of the alloys containing nickel, the complex CuAl alloys can be cold drawn after extrusion — not enough to give a useful reduction in area but enough to reduce the dimensional tolerances and to improve slightly the mechanical properties.

3.4.1.10. Extrusion of CuNi Alloys

Nickel forms with copper a continuous solid solution with a face-centered cubic lattice. This lattice structure is associated with good hot and cold working properties. However, the flow stress increases considerably as the nickel or other alloying content is raised, and very high temperatures have to be used for the extrusion of alloys with a high nickel content to obtain realistic loads. The extrusion temperatures normally used are between 850 and 1050 °C. The flow stresses of the CuNi alloys are not particularly high (Ref 45) at these temperatures (Fig. 3.35) but the high-temperature strength and service life of the tooling are more important in the assessment of the extrudability. The most important CuNi alloys are given in DIN 17664 and

Table 3.16. CuNi alloys have a nickel content varying from 5 to 44% with additions of up to 1.8% iron and 2% manganese. Both additives further increase the high-temperature flow stress and also raise the recrystallization temperature (Ref 63). These alloying elements improve the corrosion and erosion resistance of the CuNi alloys, with the retention of good mechanical and working properties. These properties make the CuNiFe alloys very suitable for seawater pipes, condensers, and the like. The most important alloy is CuNi30Fe.

Hydrogen solubility increases with the nickel content and care must be taken in casting the billets into water-cooled molds or in continuous casting to avoid gas porosity in the cast block. Careful treatment of the melt is necessary. Although there is no homogeneous solid solution in the as-cast billet — crystals with large variations in concentration — the CuNi alloys can be extruded without homogenization.

Extrusion from an unlubricated container with or without a shell can be used. In the first method the billet surface must be clean — that is, machined — to avoid peeling or blisters. Extrusion with a shell provides the greatest safeguard against blisters and peeling defects, and CuNi30Fe tubes are chiefly extruded by this method. Solid billets are used in horizontal presses and are pierced in the press, although high piercing loads are needed. The dimensions of the extruded tube, bar or wire are not governed by the size of the finished product, because of the good drawing properties of these alloys, and can be selected to give the most economical extrusion.

3.4.1.11. Extrusion of CuNiZn Alloys (German Silver)

The following six CuNiZn alloys are given in DIN 17663:

Alloy	Solid solution (see Fig. 3.36)	Workability	
		Hot	Cold
CuNi10Zn42Pb	$\alpha + \beta$	Good	Poor
CuNi12Zn24.	α	Average	Very good
CuNi12Zn30Pb	α	Poor	Average
CuNi18Zn20.	α	Average	Very good
CuNi18Zn19Pb	α	Poor	Average
CuNi25Zn15.	α	Average	Very good

The addition of 0.5 to 2% lead in the $(\alpha + \beta)$-German silver to improve the machinability does not impair the hot workability but does have a deleterious effect in the α alloys. The extrusion temperatures are given in Table 3.17 and the hot working characteristics of $(\alpha + \beta)$-German silver and lead-free α-German silver are depicted in Fig. 3.37. In both cases there is a concentrated maximum in the workability in a narrow temperature band between

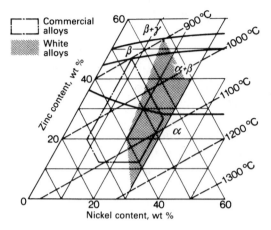

Fig. 3.36. Composition range of technical CuNiZn alloys in the ternary system. *(From Ref 63)*

600 and 700 °C. In principle the lowest temperature possible should be used to minimize oxidation and the susceptibility to hot shortness, and to control the grain size. Extrusion is done without a shell, with flat dies and no container lubrication. Therefore, particular care has to be given to the billet surface and billet heating to obtain defect-free surfaces on the extrusion.

3.4.2. Extrusion of Titanium and Titanium Alloys

Titanium has a high melting point (1668 °C) and, below 882 °C, a hexagonal lattice structure (α), which changes to a body-centered cubic structure (β) above this temperature. Pure titanium and its alloys have a good resistance to corrosion and a favorable strength-to-density ratio. Section, tube and bar are the major extruded products. The most important commercial titanium alloys contain aluminum to increase the strength, and vanadium, chromium, manganese, molybdenum or copper to depress the α/β transformation temperature (Table 3.19).

The decreasing solubility of the alloying elements, for example, copper, with decreasing temperature results in the retention of the β phase by undercooling, and special heat treatments can be used to give interesting hardening and tempering possibilities. The transformation kinetics of these (α + β) alloys is frequently complex and is depicted on time-temperature-transformation diagrams similar to those used for steel (Ref 66). The β-phase temperature range is preferred for extrusion. The flow stresses of titanium alloys in hot working are higher than those of steel (Fig. 3.38) and the alloys are, thus, difficult to extrude. Extrusion temperatures above 1000 °C are, however, not

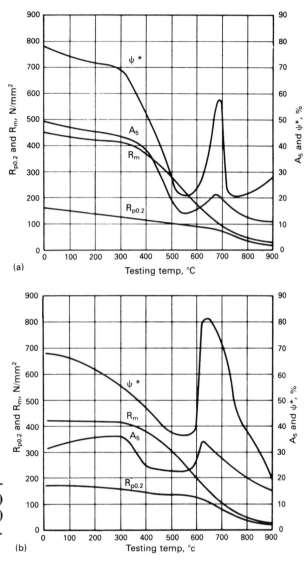

Fig. 3.37. Mechanical properties of an α-CuNiZn alloy (a) and an (α + β)-CuNiZn alloy (b) as a function of temperature. *(From Ref 66)*

used, because of the danger of gas absorption (hydrogen, oxygen, nitrogen) and embrittlement. Titanium alloys also oxidize very rapidly above 700 °C and rapid billet heating must be used—that is, induction heating or a furnace with a protective atmosphere. In comparison with steel, the high-temperature flow stress of titanium alloys increases very rapidly with increasing strain rate (Fig. 3.39 and Ref 68). This further detracts from the extrudability of the titanium alloys, which have to be extruded at high speeds to avoid excessive

Table 3.19. Extrusion Data for Titanium Alloys(a)

Material	Billet temp, °C	Material	Billet temp, °C
Ti99.5	700 to 900	α-alloys:	
(α + β) - alloys:		TiAlSn2.5.	840 to 1040
TiAl6V4.	900 to 1150	TiAl8Mo1V1.	930 to 1010
TiAl7Mo4	850 to 950		
TiAl6V6Sn2	800 to 1040	(a) Container temperature, ≈540 °C;	
TiAl6Zr4Sn2Mo2	800 to 950	maximum press speed, 30 to 350 m/min; maximum extrusion ratio, 100:1.	

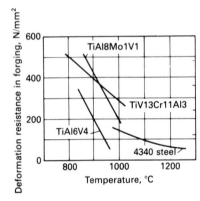

Fig. 3.38. Influence of the deformation temperature on the deformation resistance in forging three titanium alloys and AISI 4340 steel. *(From Ref 110)*

cooling and freezing of the billet in the container. Consequently, titanium alloys always have to be extruded with a lubricant, and conical dies (2α = 130°) with a large inlet radius are always used (Ref 45, 70).

Two types of lubricant are used: grease and glass. The first is used when narrow tolerances and a good surface finish are needed. Glass lubrication, on the other hand, acts as an insulator and protects the tooling; it is particularly suitable for extruding tubes or long, thin solid sections. Various, usually secret, mixtures of oil and grease with additions of MoS_2, graphite, mica, talc, soap, bentonite, asphalt, and the like, are used for "grease" lubrication. The glass lubricant is applied as in steel extrusion but the glasses have a lower softening temperature. Enamels and salts are also used as lubricants (Ref 45, 69).

A special technique is the extrusion of titanium billets in a copper skirt. The billets are surrounded by a thin copper sheet, sometimes with a steel plate as an intermediate layer (Ref 69), and extruded with a "grease" lubricant. This reduces the severe friction between the titanium and the tooling, as well as their tendency to weld together even in the presence of a lubricant,

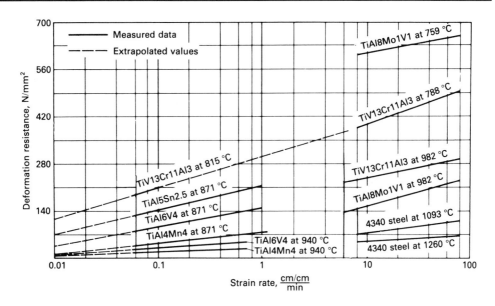

Fig. 3.39. Influence of the strain rate on the deformation resistance in forging different titanium alloys and AISI 4340 steel at different deformation temperatures (deformation resistance determined at 10% upset reduction). *(From Ref 110)*

and long lengths of uniform quality can be extruded (Ref 45, 69). The die life is also improved — similar to steel extrusion — from the usual one or two extrusions.

Friction between the titanium and the container is severe enough, even with a lubricant, to give inhomogeneous flow in the container, which can result in pipe formation, especially if flat dies are used. Conical dies are, therefore, preferred, to give a more uniform flow.

Following standard lubricated extrusion practice, titanium billets must be machined to achieve a good surface quality. Induction heating under a protective gas or in a salt bath is used to prevent oxidation and exclude the possibility of foliation. Argon shielding is also sometimes used during extrusion. Billets for tube extrusion are pierced outside the press either on a special vertical piercing press for diameters above 50 mm (Ref 70) or by drilling for bores less than 50 mm diameter. Piercing in the extrusion press would not only require high piercing loads but there would also be an excessive drop in temperature. Titanium extrusion is of considerable importance in the USA for the fabrication of thin-wall aircraft sections with wall thicknesses as low as

1 mm. Standard extrusion sections have a minimum wall thickness of 3 mm, although 2 mm can be extruded in special cases. The smaller wall thicknesses needed for aircraft sections are obtained by hot drawing through section drawing dies, because titanium alloys are very difficult to cold work.

The die shape and correct choice of die material is very important in titanium and titanium alloy extrusion. One-piece dies in materials with excellent mechanical properties at high temperatures and good resistance to wear are suitable for extruding sections with wall thicknesses above 3 mm. A ceramic-aluminum oxide coating is necessary for wall thicknesses below 3 mm to protect the die from overheating and washout. This coating has to be applied perpendicular to the wearing surface to improve the bonding, and dies for small sections have to be constructed in three segments. Long thin-wall sections can be extruded with a good surface quality by this combination of ceramic coating and glass lubrication.

3.4.3. Extrusion of Zirconium

Pure zirconium and, in particular, zirconium alloys with tin (ZrSn1.5 = Zircaloy) and niobium (ZrNb1) are important for nuclear reactor construction and fuel sheathing because of the low absorption of thermal neutrons, good corrosion resistance, and high-temperature strength. Pure zirconium has a hexagonal α lattice below 862 °C that transforms into the body-centered cubic β lattice above this temperature. The $(\alpha + \beta)$ phase region is found over a temperature range of varying extent in alloys or even if impurities are present.

The β phase has the best hot working properties and the optimum temperature range for hot working would be 800 to 1100 °C because the flow stress of zirconium is then very low. The high-temperature proof stress, which is approximately the same as the flow stress, is 45 N/mm^2 for ZrSn3 at 800 °C (Ref 45, 66). However, extrusion temperatures of 730 to 800 °C are preferred because the metal tends to absorb oxygen, hydrogen and nitrogen at high temperatures, which severely impairs the properties, especially the toughness, of the semifinished product. Zirconium — like titanium — welds very easily to the tooling during deformation and good lubrication is always required. The best method of lubrication, according to the development work in zirconium extrusion, is extrusion in a "skirt." The cast billets are usually surrounded with a sheathe of copper or brass, sometimes with an intermediate layer of iron or a soft steel sheet, and heated in a flame or electric furnace but not in an induction furnace. The sheathing hinders or prevents gas absorption and long lengths can be extruded with a good surface finish when conical dies (2α = 90 to 140°) and additional lubrication (e.g., oil-graphite) are used. The sheath is removed from the extruded product either mechanically or by dissolving in nitric acid. Another method of lubrication is initially to heat the zirconium billets in a salt bath and then coat them with a glass film. Temperatures of 1000 to 1100 °C are used (Ref 71, 72). This method of billet heating can detract from the surface quality of the product because of the detrimental effect of the salt (Ref 73).

In the indirect extrusion of thick-wall tubes of Zircaloy it is sufficient to place a copper disc between the billet and the extrusion stem to obtain a smooth internal surface. The high-temperature flow stress of most zirconium alloys is not very high and, consequently, a wide range of extrusion speeds can be used. The lower speed limit is relatively slow because there is only a slight danger that the billet will stick. The upper limit for the exit speed is taken to be approximately 60 m/min (Ref 45).

3.4.4. Extrusion of Beryllium

Beryllium has a high thermal capacity and heat resistance combined with good corrosion resistance and high mechanical properties. It is used in nuclear engineering and space technology. It has not been possible to avoid a coarse-grain structure in the cast billet, which gives a brittle material susceptible to cracking, by casting techniques, and the metal is fabricated chiefly by powder metallurgical processes, although there is extensive research into processing cast billets (Ref 74, 75). The extrusion billets are produced by cold compacting the powder and sintering in a protective atmosphere. The powder can also be directly hot extruded in an enclosed steel canister (Ref 45, 61).

Beryllium exhibits a maximum in ductility at 400 °C and also at 800 °C (Fig. 3.40). Accordingly, extrusion is classified into warm extrusion with billet temperatures between 400 and 500 °C, and hot extrusion between 900 and 1065 °C. Warm extrusion with graphite or MoS_2 lubrication requires high loads but allows for extruded products with narrow dimensional tolerances. This is important for the smaller cross sections. Hot extrusion is more common

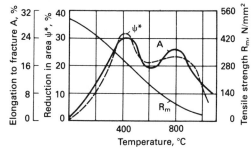

Fig. 3.40. Ductility and mechanical properties of compacted beryllium as a function of temperature. *(From Ref 76)*

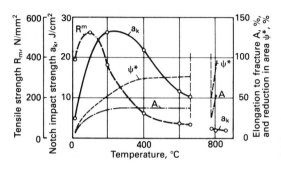

Fig. 3.41. Ductility and mechanical properties of uranium as a function of temperature. *(From Ref 79)*

with the lower resistance to deformation (Fig. 3.40). The billet is enclosed in a 1.5 to 3 mm thick soft steel sheet and extruded in a "skirt." The sheath protects the contents from oxidation during billet heating and when the extruded product leaves the die. Friction is further reduced by giving the steel sheath a galvanic coating of copper. Special lubricants containing mica or asbestos (Ref 69) are also used, together with conical dies. The extrusion speed must be as high as possible in hot extrusion to avoid billet freezing. The extrusion speed is between 6 to 15 m/min (Ref 45).

3.4.5. Extrusion of Uranium

Uranium has a rhombic (α phase) lattice below 668 °C. Above this temperature the structure consists of a tetragonal (β) lattice that transforms at 774 °C to the body-centered cubic γ phase. The β phase has a low ductility and temperatures between 650 and 790 °C have to be avoided. The α temperature range between 300 and 650 °C and the γ range of 800 to 1000 °C are used for extrusion. The advantage of the low flow stress at high temperature (Fig. 3.41) is outweighed by the tendency of uranium to rapidly form compounds with iron, nickel and other metals above 735 °C. Tool wear is then excessive. If the γ range is selected for extrusion, there are two alternatives: either to extrude in a "skirt" — for example, copper cladding the billet and lubricating with graphite or MoS_2 (Ref 69) — or to use chromium-plated steel dies with a tungsten carbide coating. In the latter case the container and other tooling that can come into contact with the uranium also have to be protected (Ref 45, 69). Barium chloride or glass can also be used as a lubricant.

Special techniques have been developed to avoid the dangerous oxidation the uranium billet. The billet is, for example, heated in a stainless steel shell under a protective argon atmosphere at 1000 to 1100 °C and then extruded (Ref 76). The difficulties mentioned above in extruding in the γ phase temperature range frequently necessitate extrusion in the α region, although this is associated with much higher flow stresses. Normal grease/graphite lubricants can be used. Kaufman (Ref 76) has described in detail the extrusion of uranium alloys with zirconium, niobium, chromium, molybdenum and silicon. The temperature of the β/γ phase boundary is lowered by alloying additives, and extrusion in the γ region is simplified.

3.5. Extrusion Technology for Materials With Extrusion Temperatures Above 1000 °C

3.5.1. Extrusion of Nickel and Nickel Alloys

3.5.1.1. Alloys and Extruded Products

Semifinished products in nickel alloys have many different applications in mechanical engineering, chemical engineering, electrical engineering, electronics (electrodes, resistance wire, heating elements), power stations and nuclear technology. Tube, wire and bar stock for turning, forging or impact extrusion blanks are extruded. The commercial alloys are summarized in Table 3.20.

3.5.1.2. Extrudability

Nickel and the most important nickel alloys have a face-centered cubic lattice and, accordingly, good ductility in hot and cold working but, depending on the alloy, very high flow stresses. This is true, in particular, of the heating element alloys. The flow stresses are generally higher than those of carbon steels, and nickel alloys are classified as very difficult to extrude. Figures 3.42 to 3.45 give the mechanical properties and reduction in area as a function of temperature. The flow stress of pure nickel is low enough for extrusion below 1000 °C. The soft nickel alloys with a copper or chromium content up to 20% also have a relatively wide temperature range for hot working. The more complex alloys, especially those containing molybdenum and the high-temperature NiCr alloys, on the other hand, must be worked in a narrow temperature range to avoid crack formation. Alloying additions to improve the mechanical properties of the NiCrCo alloys (Nimonic) both reduce the liquidus temperature and increase the flow stress. With these narrow working ranges of the extrusion process, there is always the danger of freezing because of heat losses to the container and die in spite of optimum billet heating

Table 3.20.   Nickel Alloys (From Ref 49)

Alloy	Name	Application	Semifinished product			Approx extrusion temp, °C
			Bar	Wire	Tube	
Pure Ni (DIN 17740)	. .	. .	X	X	X	1050 to 1200
Low Ni content alloys (DIN 17741): NiMn, NiBe, NiAl	. .	Chemical apparatus, electronic valves	X	X	X	1100 to 1200
NiCrMo alloys (DIN 17742)	Nimonic Inconel Hastelloy	Thermocouples, heating wire, chemical apparatus	. .	X	X	1120 to 1210
NiCu30Fe, NiCu30Al (DIN 17743)	Monel Nicorros	Chemical apparatus, engineering components	X	X	X	1050 to 1150
NiFe alloys (DIN 17745)	. .	Soft magnetic materials, soft glass welding and sealing	. .	(X)	. .	1050 to 1150

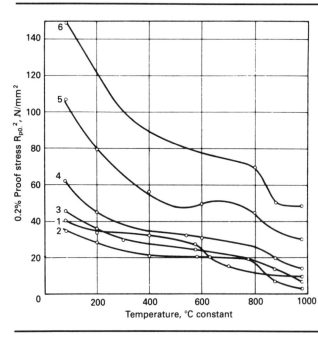

1 = Pure Ni
2 = Ni with 0.025% Al
3 = Ni with 0.08% Al
4 = Ni with 0.5% Al
5 = Ni with 1.5% Al
6 = Ni with 2.9% Al

Fig. 3.42. 0.2% proof stress $R_{p0.2}$ of pure nickel and nickel with small additions of aluminum as a function of temperature. *(From Ref 113)*

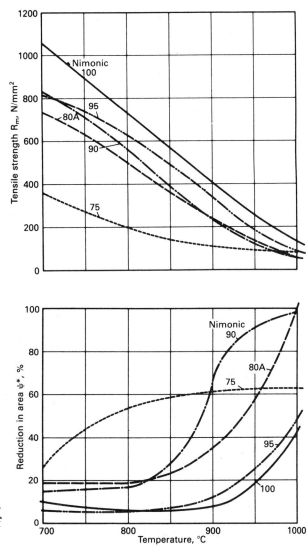

Fig. 3.43. Tensile strength and reduction in area of Nimonic alloys as a function of temperature. *(From Ref 81)*

(Ref 80). Table 3.20 gives the extrusion temperature ranges of the different alloy groups. Billet production, heating and lubrication are decisive factors in addition to the temperature.

3.5.1.3. Billet Production

In the 1930's nickel alloy products were extruded from forged or rolled billets (Ref 80). This feed stock is frequently preferred today because it is easier to extrude than to cast material, and extrusion gives a better surface

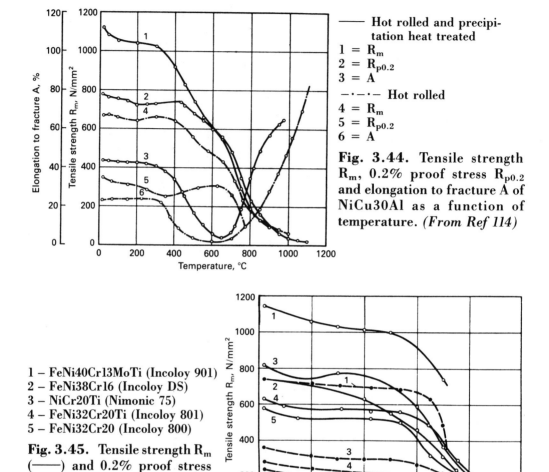

Fig. 3.44. Tensile strength R_m, 0.2% proof stress $R_{p0.2}$ and elongation to fracture A of NiCu30Al as a function of temperature. *(From Ref 114)*

1 – FeNi40Cr13MoTi (Incoloy 901)
2 – FeNi38Cr16 (Incoloy DS)
3 – NiCr20Ti (Nimonic 75)
4 – FeNi32Cr20Ti (Incoloy 801)
5 – FeNi32Cr20 (Incoloy 800)

Fig. 3.45. Tensile strength R_m (——) and 0.2% proof stress (– – –) of heat-resistant wrought alloys with a nickel-chromium base as a function of temperature. *(From Ref 66)*

finish. The forged or rolled billets can also be produced in long lengths and economically cut to billet lengths. The better surface quality of the products extruded from forged or rolled material arises from the structural orientation in the axial direction during the working of the feed stock. In contrast, cast billets from conventional cast iron molds crystallize perpendicular to the axis (i.e., radial columnar crystallization) and the structure has to be rotated in the flow direction for extrusion. This can result in grain-boundary tearing, which results in a poor surface finish. However, cast billets can be produced by the Durville process, in which the columnar crystals largely follow the extrusion direction (Ref 80). Good quality extruded products can be produced from these billets without machining the cast surface. Usually, the surface finish requirements are so high that the billets must be turned, particularly if the product is to be used in the as-extruded condition—for example, tube.

3.5.1.4. Billet Heating

Nickel and its alloys are very susceptible to sulphur and the billets must be heated in a low sulphur-content atmosphere. The rate of heating is also important, at least for cast billets, because the superimposition of residual stresses and thermal stresses can result in cracking if the heating is too rapid. Some NiCrCo alloys (Nimonic) cannot be charged directly into a hot furnace but must be slowly heated ($\approx$80 °C/h) from a low furnace temperature to the extrusion temperature to give a low-temperature gradient in all phases of the heating (Ref 80). Gas heated (e.g., butane gas) pusher-type or chamber furnaces are used for slow heating. Some nickel alloys—for example, nickel-iron and nickel-copper alloys—oxidize severely at high temperatures. The oxide layer formed impairs the effect of the lubricant (see 3.5.1.5) and produces an inferior surface finish. Consequently, these alloys must be heated in a reducing atmosphere as rapidly as possible. The resultant temperature gradients in the billet are less important. The oxide is also removed from the billet between the furnace and the extrusion press (Ref 80).

3.5.1.5. Lubrication

Nickel alloys must be extruded with a lubricant to overcome the high flow stresses. Before glass lubrication was used, the container, die and mandrel, if used, were lubricated with a mixture of stearine and graphite. This gave a good surface finish but limited the extrusion ratio to 25:1. Qualitatively good extrusions could only be produced at higher extrusion ratios and with less tool wear by using the glass lubrication process discovered by Séjournet (Ref 82). Boron silicate fiber glass was used at first but was later replaced by the better and cheaper lubricant milled basalt with an addition of Pyrex glass Ref 53, 80). Extrusion in a "skirt" is very suitable for the Nimonic alloys with very narrow extrusion temperature ranges. An easily worked NiCr alloy (e.g., Nimonic 80 A) or soft steel is used for the sheath material. Glass lubrication is also used to extrude nickel alloy billets formed by powder metallurgy (Ref 84).

The extrusion speed of the complex nickel alloys is very critical. If it is too slow, the film of lubricant breaks down to give a rough surface finish or the extrusion "freezes." The exit temperature increases rapidly if the exit speed is too high and transverse hot-shortness cracks are formed. Therefore, it is necessary to control the speed in order to maintain the temperature between the two limits. This applies, in particular, to the complex Nimonic alloys extruded at slow speeds (ram speeds of 5 to 7.5 mm/s) and implies isothermal extrusion. An extrusion plant for nickel has been built in England, in which the presses, using experience gained in aluminum extrusion, are fitted with an electro-mechanical speed control (Ref 80). An oil hydraulic press with direct pumping is used for extrusion at slow speeds.

Slow extrusion speeds are also associated with long contact times between the hot metal and the tooling. The contact time for most nickel alloys is 10 to 15 seconds, but frequently 20 to 30 seconds. At these high temperatures dies of high hot strength steels have a very limited life. Dies of Nimonic 90 — that is, made from one of the materials to be extruded — last almost twice as long. The high-temperature hardness of age-hardened Nimonic 90 is higher than that of a 9.5% tungsten steel above 700 °C (Ref 80). Higher specific pressures up to 1350 N/mm^2 and short stem lengths have recently been used to overcome the high resistance to deformation in the extrusion of Nimonic alloys. An age-hardened maraging steel (martensitic age-hardening steel) is used for the stem material.

3.5.2. Steel Extrusion

3.5.2.1. Material and Extruded Products

Economical extrusion of steel was frustrated for a long time by excessive wear of the tooling because of the very high working temperatures and oxidation. These problems were largely overcome by the discovery of the Ugine-Séjournet glass lubrication process (3.2.1 and 3.5.2.3) and the door opened to the economical production of certain semifinished products. Steel extrusion has made its mark in the production of the following:

(a) Small quantities of steel sections that could be rolled but where the installation of existing rollers or the production of new rollers would be too expensive (Ref 85).
(b) Steel sections that could be rolled only with difficulty, if at all (Ref 85).
(c) Hollow steel sections (Ref 85, 87).
(d) Semifinished products in special alloys that would be very difficult to produce by any other means (Ref 87).
(e) Small-bore standard tubes (Ref 87).
(f) Prototypes of sections that will later be rolled (Ref 88).

Steel sections (Fig. 3.46) and mass-produced tubes are mainly extruded in plain carbon steels, such as St 37, St 42 (AISI C, C1, C1026) and St 52. Some high-alloy steels are also extruded because of the usually small volumes required — for example, sections in the corrosion- and acid-resistant

Fig. 3.46. Extruded solid and hollow steel sections. *(From Fielding Plant Design)*

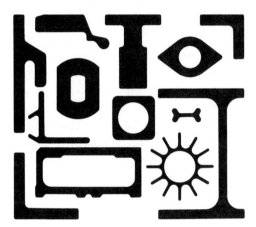

Fig. 3.47. Extruded sections of corrosion- and acid-resistant steels. *(From Hoesch, Schwerte)*

steels (Fig. 3.47) for chemical engineering, finned tubes in 15Mo3, 13CrMo44, 10CrMo910, and other special alloys for boiler construction. Table 3.21 summarizes data about the steels that are extruded.

3.5.2.2. Extrudability

Steels fall into the same category of difficult-to-extrude as do the nickel alloys. The flow stresses are relatively high and temperatures between 1000 and 1300 °C have to be used to keep the extrusion loads within tolerable limits. These high temperatures are associated with tooling and wear problems, which are discussed elsewhere.

The flow stresses of steels are given in Table 3.21, Fig. 1.41 and Fig. 3.48. The resistance to deformation decreases with increasing temperature, and it is advantageous, considering the load, to extrude at the highest possible temper-

Table 3.21. Extruded Iron Base Materials (Glass Lubrication) in Common Commercial Use Arranged According to Increasing Flow Stress

Alloy	Extrusion temp, °C	Mean flow stress (N/mm²)	Composition, % (rem, Fe)									
			C	Mn	Mg	Si	Cr	Ni	Mo	W	V	Ti
Carbon steels	1200 ± 100	150	0.1 to 1	0.3 to 1.5	.	<0.1	.	.	.	.	.	.
Low-alloy steels	1200 ± 70	130	0.2 to 0.6	0.3 to 1	.	.	0 to 1.7	0 to 3.7	0 to 0.3	.	.	.
Corrosion- and acid-resistant steels	1175 ± 25	180	<0.15	<1	.	<0.5	11 to 13	.	.	.	.	.
	1175 ± 25	190	<0.15	<1	.	.	11.5 to 13	.	.	.	.	.
	1180 ± 30	200	0.03 to 0.1	<2	.	.	18 to 20	8 to 12	.	.	.	.
	1180 ± 30	230	<0.08	<2	.	.	17 to 19	9 to 12	.	.	.	.
	1170 ± 20	240	<0.25	<2	.	<1.5	24 to 26	10 to 12	.	.	.	.
	1160 ± 20	250	0.03 to 0.08	<2	.	.	16 to 18	10 to 14	2 to 3	.	.	<0.4
High-speed steels	1140 ± 80	300	2	0.3	0.3	.	12	.	.	.	0.9	.
	1110 ± 20	..	0.7	.	.	.	4	.	.	18	1	.
Spheroidal cast iron	1050 ± 25	220	3.1 to 3.5	0.3 to 0.5	0.04 to 0.09	2.4 to 3	.	1.1 to 1.8	.	.	.	.

ature. However, the structure of the steel at the working temperature is just as important in the choice of extrusion temperature. The ductility can be seriously reduced if the structure is not a single homogeneous phase (usually face-centered cubic γ solid solution) but contains other phases, for example, α-ferrite, δ-ferrite in austenitic CrNi steels, or grain-boundary precipitates (Ref 92, 94, 96). The troublesome effect of secondary phases is most clearly shown in comparative torsion tests, in which the number of turns to fracture is measured at different temperatures (section 1.4.2.2). The ductility increases uniformly with temperature in steels with a homogeneous structure (Fig. 3.49), but decreases rapidly in the case of the two CrNi steels in Fig. 3.50 after a maximum at 1200 °C when δ-ferrite starts to form (Ref 92). Transverse or edge cracking can occur in the extruded material at a ferrite content above approximately 2%, depending on the extrusion ratio, section profile and other parameters. High extrusion temperatures are associated not only with extreme thermal stresses in the tooling but also with rapid heat losses that can result in a "sticker." The contact time between the billet and the tooling should, therefore, be as short as possible and steels

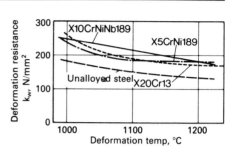

Fig. 3.48. Deformation resistance of steels as a function of temperature. *(From Ref 92)*

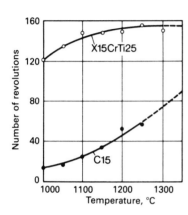

Fig. 3.49. Temperature dependence of the ductility of steels with a homogeneous structure. *(From Ref 92)*

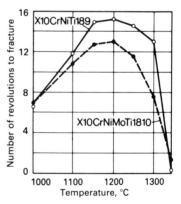

Fig. 3.50. Temperature dependence of the ductility of ferrite-containing austenitic steels. *(From Ref 92)*

must be extruded at fast speeds — usually at an exit speed of 4 to 10 m/s for unalloyed and low-alloy steels, and 1 to 2 m/s for the more highly alloyed steels (Ref 45, 88, 89). The extrusion process lasts only a few seconds and specific pressures between 1000 and 1200 N/mm^2 are needed to extrude at these high speeds.

The extrudability of a steel section depends on the extrusion ratio as well as the flow stress and ductility. Table 3.22 attempts to relate the extrudability

Table 3.22. Production Program of Presses According to Size (from Ref 91)(a)

Production factor	Press size, MN											
	10				20				30			
	Extrudability											
	Easy	Moderately difficult	Difficult	Very difficult	Easy	Moderately difficult	Difficult	Very difficult	Easy	Moderately difficult	Difficult	Very difficult
	Standard circumscribing circle measurement of product											
	135	115	95	75	200	180	155	130	260	220	195	195
Extrusion												
Max billet length, mm.....	560	460	350	250	800	650	500	370	1000	800	600	450
Max product length, m(b)	24	18	12	8	28	24	18	12	30	26	20	14
Tube Extrusion												
Min ID, mm.............	35	30	30	25	50	45	40	35	60	55	50	45
Max ID, mm.............	125	80	65	50	155	110	90	70	200	135	110	85
Max billet length, mm.....	370	310	230	200	520	410	330	270	630	500	410	330
Standard commercial length of extruded tube, m	14	12	8	3	18	16	12	8	22	18	14	10
Standard min wall thickness, mm	2.5	2.5	3	3	2.5	3	3	3.5	3	3.5	3.5	4.5

Production factor	Press size, MN							
	40				50			
	Extrudability							
	Easy	Moderately difficult	Difficult	Very difficult	Easy	Moderately difficult	Difficult	Very difficult
	Standard circumscribing circle measurement of product							
	305	260	230	200	350	300	260	230
Extrusion								
Max billet length, mm	1100	900	700	500	1250	1000	750	550
Max product length, m(b)	32	28	24	16	35	30	24	18
Tube Extrusion								
Min ID, mm	70	65	60	55	80	70	65	60
Max ID, mm	240	155	125	100	270	170	140	110
Max billet length, mm	720	580	470	380	810	650	520	420
Standard commercial length of extruded tube, m	24	20	16	12	28	24	18	12
Standard min wall thickness, mm	3.5	4	4.5	5	4	4.5	4.5	5.5

(a) This table presents only a general survey. In practice, production programing must take into consideration the particular alloy, the tube and section dimensions, and the production run. (b) In certain instances, the absolute maximum length limit is not given, because it depends on the lubricant and the cost of tooling and transportation at the press and during subsequent processing. In practice, some of the maximum lengths given in the table are not produced, for the same reasons.

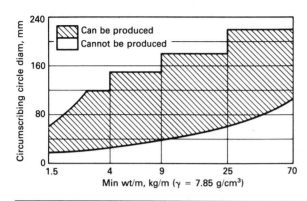

Fig. 3.51. Production of carbon steel sections in an 18 MN extrusion press. *(From Ref 88)*

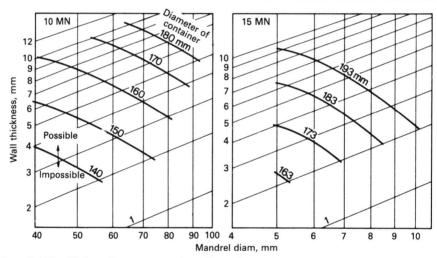

Fig. 3.52. Tube dimensions (unalloyed steels) that can be extruded in mechanical presses with press capacities from 10 to 15 MN. *(From Ref 87)*

of a section according to its circumscribing circle for different press capacities (Ref 91). The data are based on many years of practical experience but can be used only as approximate guidelines (Ref 92). Similar results have been given by the American extrusion industry. Figure 3.51 depicts the limits set by the press capacity for the production of carbon steel sections on an 18 MN extrusion press as a function of the weight per metre (Ref 89). The range of tube sizes that can be produced is given in Fig. 3.52. Groos (Ref 116) has drawn an output diagram for carbon steel tubes; it includes the parameters of tube dimensions and press capacity, and can be used to determine the output (Fig. 3.53). The usual range of extrusion ratios in tube and section extrusion is between 10 and 100, but approximately 20 to 25 is more often set as the limit

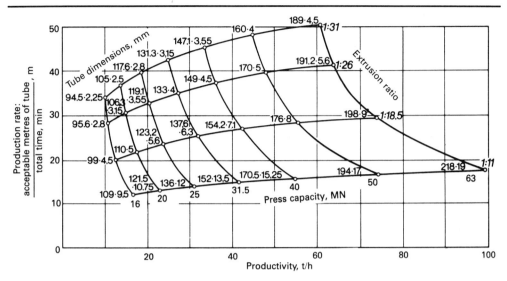

Fig. 3.53. Productivity diagram of C-steel tubes. *(From Ref 116)*

by the maximum length that can be extruded without the breakdown of the film of lubricant. This length depends on the section but is between 15 and 25 m (Ref 89, 91).

3.5.2.3. Lubrication

The development of lubrication technology was an important step in bringing the extrusion of very difficult materials to its present economically viable position (Ref 69, 88, 89, 92, 93). The lubricant has to reduce the load required and fulfill a number of other complex functions, all of which are critical for economical production and good quality. The following requirements have to be met by the lubricant (Ref 92):

(a) The lubricant should have good sliding properties in the form of a closed film of lubricant that does not break down even as it passes through the die, to reduce friction, die wear and the extrusion load.

(b) It should act as thermal insulation between the billet at 1000 to 1300 °C and the tooling, to increase the effective tool life.

(c) It should have a low thermal conductivity, to give and maintain thermal insulation and to prevent overheating of the tooling.

(d) It is applied to the billet surface immediately after heating and should form a thick coating to protect the billet and the extruded product from oxidation.

(e) Previously formed thin oxide layers should be dissolved or absorbed by the lubricant.

(f) Volume contraction upon solidification and cooling of glass-based lubricants

Table 3.23. Types of Glass Used as Lubricant in Steel Extrusion

No.	Composition, %					
	SiO_2	Al_2O_3	CaO	Na_2O	BaO	Other oxides, total
1(a).................	60	5	14	14	. .	7
2(a).................	72	4	8	13	. .	5
3(a).................	65	4	14	8	. .	9
4	71.5	2.7	0.8	7.5	13	4.5

(a) From Ref 82.

should be greater than that of steel; it then breaks away automatically from the cooling extrusion.

(g) The lubricant must not react chemically with the extruded metal or the tooling.

There is no lubricant that meets all of these requirements. When steel extrusion commenced, in 1930, the lubricants then used for nonferrous metals were found to be completely unsuitable. Lubrication with molten glass (Ugine-Séjournet process) was introduced in 1950 and is the most important method used today for the extrusion of steel sections because it fulfills most of the above requirements. The most suitable glasses soften between 200 and 300 ° C below the billet temperature. Table 3.23 gives some glasses that have been used successfully (Ref 45).

Solid glass is applied as a powder or in the form of fiber glass and forms a viscous liquid as it contacts the billet and surrounds the steel with a thin film. The thin glass film acts as a thermal barrier and prevents excessive heating of the dies and rapid billet cooling. It also protects the billet from oxidation between the furnace and the press. The method of lubrication is briefly described in the following paragraph.

The external surface of the billet is lubricated by sprinkling with glass powder or by rolling the hot billet over a carpet of glass powder before loading into the press. The inside surfaces of hollow billets are lubricated by sprinkling with a narrow shovel on the loading table and the powder is uniformly distributed as the billet rolls down the table. The ends of the steel billet are lubricated by either round glass discs or compacted powder between the hot billet and the cold die. The glass adjacent to the billet is heated by the metal and deforms with it to surround the extrusion with a thin uniform glass film. The choice of the most suitable type of glass depends on the extrusion temperature of the steel used. Accordingly, different glasses with appropriate viscosity ranges are used for different types of steels. Glass lubrication gives considerable problems in many cases (for example, steel tube production) because the glass has to be removed internally by sand blasting or hydrofluoric acid pickling. Lubrication by the suspension of a suitable material (for example, graphite) in easily evaporated liquids (petroleum) is, therefore, also used. The vapor provides protection and thermal insulation, and the graphite provides lubrication. A paste of graphite, oil and common salt has proved to be successful for steel tube extrusion (Ref 87). Use of this graphite-based lubricant eliminates the frequently overrated danger of carbonization and unpleasant side effects for the press area from severe vapor and graphite dust formation (Ref 91, 92).

Conical dies are used with both glass and oil-graphite-salt lubrication and the billets are always extruded without a shell. A die angle of $2\alpha = 126°$ is suitable for extruding tubes in most types of steel with oil-graphite-salt lubrication (Ref 87). The average die life for the well-proved hot working steel DIN No. 1.2343 is only 2 to 3 extrusions. The worn, washed-out die can be reused by welding and reworking, and up to 40 extrusions per die can be attained with intermediate dressing (Ref 90). Cast dies in this steel have a slightly inferior life but are much cheaper to produce (Chap. 5).

3.5.2.4. Billet Production

Round billets with diameters between 100 and 300 mm and billet lengths of 250 to 1000 mm are used for steel extrusion presses between 10 and 30 MN capacity (Table 3.22). The usual feed material is hot rolled round bar because it offers the best extrudability and guarantee of maintaining the properties required in the finished product. The following are possible methods for producing the round billets (Ref 94).

Chill Mold Casting

This method is unsuitable for extrusion. High extrusion ratios and excessive extrusion loads are needed to eliminate the cast structure. The deformation resistance of the cast material is higher than that of rolled or forged billets. Removal of the cast surface is very expensive because of the short billet lengths and the conical shape produced. There is also the difficulty of cutting the short ingots into billet lengths without generating excessive scrap.

Continuous Casting

The difficulties mentioned above do not occur in continuous casting, although the billets must still be machined and the cast structure removed. However, experiments with continuously cast billets have demonstrated that the desired homogeneous structure is not developed during extrusion. Further development work is being done to perfect the extrusion of cheap continuously cast material (Ref 96).

Hot Rolled Round Billets

The initial deformation and repeated recrystallization of hot rolled material make it the most suitable starting material for attaining the desired structural and mechanical properties in extruded products. The scrap in machining the billets is less than with other methods because it is possible to roll to narrow tolerances. Frequently, scalping suffices for preparing unalloyed or low-alloy steel billets (Ref 89).

Forged Round Feed Stock

Some alloy steels cannot be rolled to round bar and are available only as forgings. Forged stock frequently has to be used to obtain the optimum structural properties. Irregularities on the forged surface are not suitable for extrusion and have to be removed by turning. The wide dimensional tolerances produce a high volume of scrap.

The bars, 8 to 12 m long, are cut with perpendicular ends by circular saws to the calculated billet lengths in the bar store or at the press. Predrilled billets are used for tubes or hollow sections if piercing in the press is not possible. The billets travel from the cold circular saw to a deep boring machine, in which they are axially turned. Machining radii on the front face of the billet helps to improve the surface finish (Ref 89). If very narrow billet tolerances are required, the billets are sized by rolling (duo rolling mill) after billet heating and descaling.

3.5.2.5. Billet Heating

Scale formation and, in the case of heat treatable steels, surface decarburization have to be prevented during billet heating. A uniform temperature distribution is also needed. The following methods of heating can be used:

(a) Gas with a reducing or inert atmosphere.
(b) Salt or molten glass bath.
(c) Induction heating.

Heating in a salt bath is the best method for scale-free heating but is very inefficient and unsatisfactory because of high maintenance costs, large thermal losses to the surroundings, excessive salt losses and severe contamination of the environment (Ref 94). Gas-fired furnaces, in addition to their economical advantages, provide slow and uniform heating of the billet and some degree of homogenization, depending on the steel used, during the long heating time. Scale formation is avoided by using a reducing fuel gas atmosphere in furnaces sealed against air infiltration. The rotating hearth furnace is well suited for this purpose (Ref 75, 89).

Induction heating is the most suitable method for press programing that involves frequent changes and a very wide range of steels, because the furnace

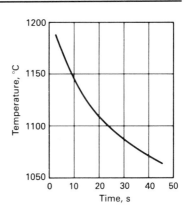

Fig. 3.54. Fall in temperature in a stainless steel billet of 130 mm diameter. *(From Ref 94)*

can be rapidly adjusted to temperatures suitable for the different billet sizes or steels. Many universal extrusion plants that produce everything from volume steel tubes to stainless steel tubes are equipped with induction billet heating furnaces for these reasons. The furnaces generally operate at mains frequency (Ref 91, 94). In tube production the billets often have to be pierced in a separate piercing press, and the billet heating system consists of induction heating before piercing followed by reheating in an induction furnace prior to extrusion. Induction furnaces with vertical coils have been developed to increase flexibility with very mixed programs. Horizontal coils are more suitable for programing that involves less frequent changes (Ref 96).

Very little scale is formed during the brief heating cycle of 5 to 15 minutes in induction heating. An inert gas is fed through the induction coil to give additional protection against scaling. This step is not, however, necessary for all steels. Scale formation during transfer from the heating furnace to the extrusion press container is minimized if glass lubrication is used. The billet is rolled over glass powder on a powder table as soon as it is withdrawn from the furnace and then transported as quickly as possible to the press. This latter step is also necessary to minimize temperature losses from the billet. The rapid cooling of a stainless steel billet of 130 mm diameter is shown as an example in Fig. 3.54. Additional steps to prevent rapid cooling of the billet might be necessary for the extrusion of thin-wall sections or tubes in high-alloy steels or special alloys when high extrusion temperatures have to be used to reduce the flow stress of the alloy. This problem is solved in the USA by placing the billet in radiation-protective sleeves before transporting it to the press. The sleeve is removed from the container in the press immediately before extrusion (Ref 93). If the billets are not coated with glass powder, some scaling is inevitable during transfer to the press, but it can be removed by brushing the billet or spraying it with water under high pressure (Ref 87).

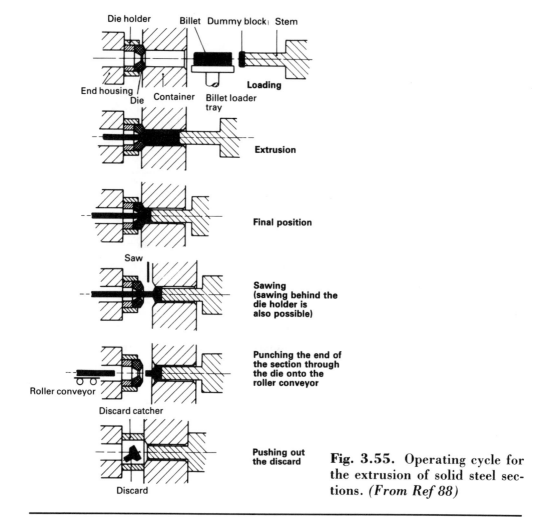

Fig. 3.55. Operating cycle for the extrusion of solid steel sections. *(From Ref 88)*

3.5.2.6. Extrusion of Steel Sections

The sequence for extruding steel sections after billet heating is as follows: the billet surface is coated with molten glass by rolling it down the powder table to the tray of the billet loader containing the dummy block. The loader then transports the billet to the container bore; the compacted glass lubricating disc is simultaneously placed in front of the die.

The type of glass and thickness of the lubricating disc are selected to give a uniform film of lubricant approximately 0.02 mm thick over the total length of the extruded product — maximum 25 m — at the high extrusion speeds used. The billet is extruded to give a discard length of 10 to 20 mm. The container is then opened and the extrusion cut from the discard by a hot saw (Fig. 3.55). After pushing or pulling the end of the extrusion onto the conveyor, the container is reopened and the die is removed from the press using the die slide or rotating die holder. The discard and dummy block are then pushed out and separated by the impact with the discard tray or given a light blow. A discard separating mechanism similar to that used in copper extrusion is not necessary (Ref 97). The die is exchanged for another one and dressed. The difficult problem of die life is discussed in Chap. 5.

The extruded product is transported transversely from the roller conveyor runout table to a cooling bed. The finishing of the section is relatively complicated because speed variations through the die give a bent and twisted extrusion. The degree of distortion depends on the shape of the section. Nonuniform metal flow is much more difficult to control at high temperatures than in copper or aluminum extrusion. One reason is the very short die life in steel extrusion. Correction of the section by cold stretching and twisting is feasible. Hydraulic stretchers similar to those used in aluminum extrusion are used to give a permanent deformation of 2 to 3% after or during detwisting with the rotating stretcher head. Glass and any oxide formed during cooling are largely removed during this operation (Ref 88, 95).

Sections straightened by stretching meet commercial requirements in most cases. Higher demands for straightness, degree of twisting, angularity and accuracy of shape are met by correction on roll-straightening machines or straightening presses. Narrow tolerances, bright smooth surfaces and higher mechanical properties are produced by cold drawing (bright drawing) the pickled extruded sections (Ref 95).

3.5.2.7. Extrusion of Steel Tubes and Hollow Sections

There are several methods for producing steel tubes and hollow sections, depending on the dimensions and the type of steel (Ref 87-89, 91, 98):

(*a*) Tube extrusion on vertical presses.
(*b*) Tube and hollow section extrusion on horizontal presses.
(*c*) Use of solid billets and piercing in the press.
(*d*) Piercing the billet in a separate piercing press.
(*e*) Drilling the billets.
(*f*) Lubricating with glass.
(*g*) Lubricating with a graphite-oil-salt mixture.
(*h*) Extrusion with a moving mandrel (tubes, hollow sections).
(*i*) Extrusion over the mandrel tip (hollow sections with complicated internal contours).
(*j*) Extrusion of thick-wall tubes on forging presses designed for vertical upward extrusion.

Table 3.24. Methods for Extruding Steel Tubes and Hollow Sections

Type of steel	Semifinished product	Range of diam sizes(a), mm	Method of piercing	Lubricant	Type of press
Unalloyed steels	Tube	40 to 120(b)	Tube press	Oil-graphite-salt	Vertical crank press
Unalloyed steels	Tube	50 to 160	Tube press	Oil-graphite-salt	Vertical or horizontal hydraulic press
Alloy steels	Tube	<60 >60	Deep boring machine, separate piercing press	Glass	Horizontal hydraulic press
Unalloyed and alloy steels	Sections	. .	Deep boring machine	Glass	Horizontal hydraulic press

(a) See also Table 3.22. (b) Wall thickness, 2.5 to 10 mm.

The different methods used in practice are summarized in Table 3.24 and are described in detail elsewhere in this book. In general, small-bore unalloyed steel tubes (volume production) (Table 3.24 and Fig. 3.52, a and b) are best extruded on vertical mechanical presses (Chap. 2) using graphite-oil-salt lubricants (Fig. 3.56). Alloy steel tubes or those with larger dimensions require higher extrusion loads than the upper limit of 16 MN of crank presses and are produced on hydraulic presses. Two methods are used to reduce the extrusion load: (a) glass lubrication and (b) piercing in a separate press. This separate piercing is needed to give the optimum glass lubrication for the tube extrusion process and to avoid unnecessary delays in the press cycle, during which the billet temperature would fall and the flow stress increase. Billets are pierced in the press only for large bores (Ref 88).

Drilled billets are generally used for the extrusion of hollow sections with the bore of the billet slightly greater than the mandrel diameter. Figure 3.57 depicts the operating sequence. The smallest inside diameter produced by normal tube extrusion is about 35 mm and the minimum wall thickness is about 2.5 mm (Table 3.22). The presses, however, operate most economically with dimensions much larger than these — that is, the extrusion process is very suitable for producing steel tube blooms (similar to those made by the Mannesmann rolling process) for stretch reducing by hot rolling to small-bore tubes. Integrated plants (Ref 91, 98) have, accordingly, been built to incorporate an extrusion press and a stretch reducing mill (Chap. 4).

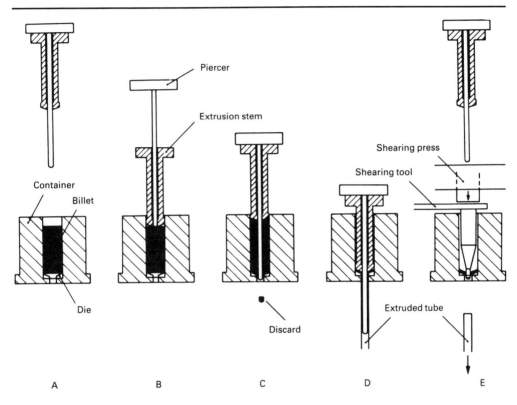

A = Initial position with the billet in the container
B = Start of piercing operation
C = End of piercing, start of tube extrusion
D = End of extrusion
E = Shearing the discard, which is lifted out

Fig. 3.56. Operating cycle for the extrusion of steel tubes with a vertical press. *(From Ref 87)*

The material flow and subsequent treatment can vary considerably according to production programing. Whereas unalloyed steels are produced from extruded blooms with stretch reducing mills and cooled in air on a cooling table, stainless steel tubes are quenched directly in water to retain a completely austenitic structure. Ball bearing steel tubes cool in air on a cooling table and then undergo a special heat treatment (Ref 91). Steel tubes are occasionally needed in sizes far in excess of those that can be manufactured even in large extrusion presses. The limit for extruded steel tubes is about 500 mm (Ref 99). Thick-wall tubes up to 1400 mm outside diameter and approximately 9 m long are produced by vertical upward extrusion on large forging presses (Chap. 2 and 4).

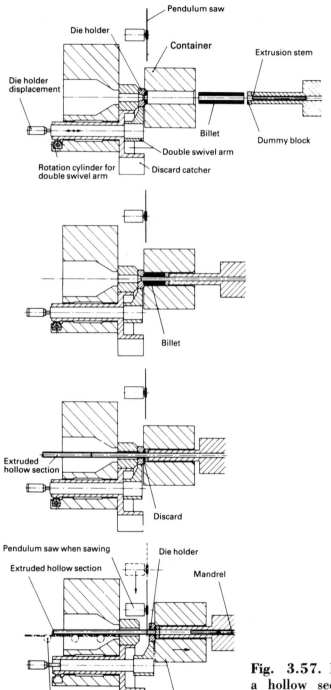

Fig. 3.57. Extrusion of a hollow section. *(From Schloemann-SIEMAG)*

**Table 3.25. Melting and Hot Working Temperatures of
High Melting Point Metals (From Ref 100)**

Metal	Melting temp, °C	Hot working temp, °C	Metal	Melting temp, °C	Hot working temp, °C
Vanadium	1890	1050 to 1200	Molybdenum ..	2620	1700 to 1800
Niobium.......	2468	1050 to 1200	Tungsten	3410	1700 to 1800
Tantalum......	3000	1200 to 1400	Chromium....	1857	≈ 1200

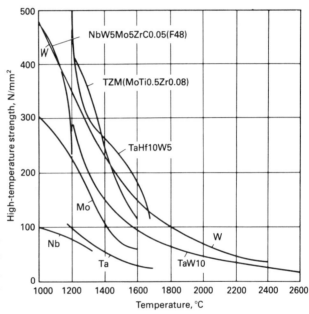

Fig. 3.58. High-temperature mechanical properties of some high-temperature metals and alloys as a function of temperature. *(From Ref 100)*

3.5.3. Extrusion of High Melting Point Metals

High melting point special metals are important in space technology, armaments, nuclear engineering and the chemical industry. The extrusion of these metals is described briefly below (Ref 100). Table 3.25 summarizes the melting points and hot working temperature ranges of the metals, all of which have a body-centered cubic lattice. The workability is, therefore, low, and high temperatures are needed to reduce the flow stress to a level that the tooling can withstand. The dependence of the high-temperature flow stress of these special metals on the temperature is depicted in Fig. 3.58. The strong influence of alloying additions on the flow stress and the workability is also clearly visible.

Alloying additions and impurities, particularly metalloids, also have a great effect on the hot ductility, and the temperature range for extrusion can be very narrow. The absorption of oxygen and nitrogen from the air at high temperatures also produces a brittle structure, at least at the surface. The deformation temperature should, thus, be as low as possible with due allowance made for the extrusion load. Molybdenum and tungsten oxidize at high temperatures but, instead of forming a scale, volatile trioxides (MoO_3 more than WO_3) are produced as a dense smoke. These reactions with the atmosphere can be avoided, if desired or necessary, by using an inert gas. Extrusion in a "skirt" (that is, in evacuated shells of CrNi 18/8 steel or a soft unalloyed steel) or surrounding the billet with a molten glass that acts as a lubricant in extrusion (Séjournet process) are two other suitable methods for protection from the air. Melting becomes more difficult as the melting point increases, and the high melting point metals must sometimes be produced by sintering powder to form a solid body. This method has to be used for tungsten, sometimes for molybdenum and, to a lesser extent, for chromium. High-purity chromium powder can be extruded in a stainless steel shell. The same process can be used to a limited extent with molybdenum but not for tungsten, because the sintering temperature is too high to produce compact bonding during extrusion. Tungsten must, therefore, be produced as a compact metal before it can be extruded.

3.6. Extrusion of Powdered Metals

There are numerous metals and alloys that cannot be cast to a compact shape; semifinished products in these materials must be produced by a powder metallurgical process. The powder is compacted in suitable molds to form billets (green billets) that must be strong enough to withstand manipulation and mechanical transfer to the extrusion press container without breaking up. There are two classes of material that are processed in this way:

(a) High melting point metals — e.g., chromium, molybdenum.
(b) Alloys or metal mixtures, the components of which are immiscible in the liquid phase — e.g., Al-Fe, Al-Pb, or metal-nonmetal mixtures like $Al-Al_2O_3$ (SAP).

Powder metal extrusion depends on deforming the individual particles, by stretching and increasing the surface area, to such an extent that the oxide skin tears and the newly formed surfaces of adjacent particles weld together. The strain must exceed a minimum, which has to be established for each case, and the method of working selected to give sufficient pressure for particle welding.

The compacted metal billets can be extruded hot or cold. Air has to be excluded during heating for hot extrusion to preclude oxidation of the grains.

The simplest method is to surround the billet with an airtight steel shell. A liquid lubricant can also be used with extrusion in a "skirt." No skirt is used in cold extrusion, and either a dry lubricant (graphite) or no lubricant has to be used. A liquid lubricant will penetrate the billet and hinder the welding of the particles. The usually slight elongation of the material after extrusion can be improved by heat treatment.

Bibliographic References

1. Pearson, C. E., and Smythe, J. A.: Brit. Non-Ferr. Met. Res. Ass. Rep. No. 18 (1931).
2. Pearson, C. E., and Parkins, R. N.: The Extrusion of Metals, London (1960).
3. Radley, J.: J. Inst. Electr. Eng. 80 (1937) p. 371.
4. Piercey, C. A.: The Nozzle Swirl Process, General Electric Rev. 43 (1943) p. 489/491.
5. Willis, J., and Bryant, A. J.: Das Kalt-Strangpressen von Aluminium und Aluminium-legierungen, Z. f. Metallkunde 61 (1970) p. 683/692.
6. Dangerfield, C. J., and Gwyther, L.: Production of Aluminium and Aluminium Alloy Tubes by Cold Extrusion, J. Inst. Metals 100 (1972) p. 233/238.
7. Vater, M. and Rathjen, C.: Untersuchungen über die Größe der Stempelkraft und des Innendrucks im Aufnehmer beim Strangpressen von Metallen, Fortschritt-Berichte VDI, Reihe 2, No. 9 (1966) p. 122.
8. Ames, A., Bielen, J., and Sauer, G.: Vorschlag zur Normung von Werkzeugen für Leichtmetallstrangpressen in Abhängigkeit der Preßkräfte, Z. f. Metallkunde 62 (1971) p. 716/720.
9. Akeret, R.: Die Produktivität beim Strangpressen von Aluminium-Werkstoffen. Einfluß von Werkstoff und Verfahren, Z. f. Metallkunde 62 (1971) p. 451/456.
10. Akeret, R.: Untersuchungen über das Strangpressen unter besonderer Berücksichtigung der thermischen Vorgänge, Aluminium 44 (1968) p. 412/415.
11. Akeret, R.: Sonderverfahren zum schnelleren Strangpressen von Aluminium-Hartlegierungen, Z. f. Metallkunde 64 (1973) p. 311/319.
12. Kaiser Aluminum & Chemicals, Inc.: Aluminum Extrusion Alloys, Oakland, California (1964).
13. Anonymous: Phosphate coating for aluminium extrusion, Metallurgia and Metal Forming 39 (1972) p. 115.
14. Kaiser-Aluminium-Werke Koblenz: Anwendungsmöglichkeiten für Strangpreßerzeugnisse aus Aluminium (1963).
15. Laue, K.: Umformung beim Strangpressen, Z. f. Metallkunde 58 (1967) p. 507/511.
16. Laue, K.: Möglichkeiten werkstoffgerechter Gestaltung von Leichtmetallprofilen, Z. f. Metallkunde 54 (1963) p. 667/671.
17. Stenger, H.: Besonderheiten bei der Herstellung von Strangpreßprofilen aus Aluminium-Eloxal- und Glänzwerkstoffen, Bänder-Bleche-Rohre 13 (1972) p. 454/461.
18. Rohrbacher, D.: Werkstattblatt 567: Richtlinien für das Gestalten von Aluminium-Strangpreßprofilen, C. Hanser Verlag, Munich (1972).
19. Göner, H., and Marx, S. (editors): Aluminium-Handbuch, VEB-Verlag Technik, Berlin (1971).
20. Zoller, H., and Ried, A.: Metallkundliche Gesichtspunkte bei der Entwicklung wenig abschreckempfindlicher AlMgSi-Legierungen, Z. f. Metallkunde 62 (1971) p. 354/358.
21. Lynch, C. V.: Metallurgical Aspects of Press Heat Treatment, Int. Extr. Technol. Sem., New Orleans (1969), Paper No. 25.
22. Lowe, J. B., and Barry, W. G.: Strangpressen der Legierung Alcan D65S, Second seminar on extrusion of AlMgSi alloys, Bad Homburg (1968) p. 32/36.

23. Aluminium information paper 04: Anodisch oxidiertes Aluminium für dekorative Zwecke, Aluminium-Zentrale Düsseldorf.
24. Scharf, G., and Gruhl, W.: Der Einfluß von Ausscheidungen auf das Rekristallisationsverhalten von AlMgSi-Legierungen, Z. f. Metallkunde 60 (1969) p. 413/421.
25. German Patent Office, Patent No. 1247030: Verfahren zur Wärmebehandlung von stranggegossenen Preß- oder Walzbarren aus Magnesium und Silizium enthaltenden Aluminiumlegierungen (1967).
26. Bergmaier, W.: Gedanken zur Gestaltung von neuen Aluminium-Strangpreßprofilen. Schweizer Aluminium Rundschau 18 (1968) p. 147/160.
27. Scharf, G., and Eulitz, J.: Einfluß von Barrenglühung und Preßbedingungen auf Umformbarkeit, mechanische Eigenschaften und Spannungsrißkorrosionsverhalten von AlZnMgl, Aluminium 49 (1973) p. 549/552.
28. Gruhl, W., Achenbach, D., and Faller, E.: Preßverhalten und Eigenschaften niedrig legierter AlZnMg-Werkstoffe, Metall 22 (1968) p. 206/211.
29. Kursetz, E.: Die Problematik der Fertigung von Hohlprofilen und Rohren beim Warmstrangpressen von Aluminium, Blech 16 (1969) p. 1/16.
30. Kursetz, E.: Die Wärmebehandlung von stranggepreßten Aluminiumrohren, Bänder-Bleche-Rohre 10 (1969) p. 601/607.
31. Steinmetz, A.: Doppeltwirkende Presse zum Ummanteln elektrischer Leiter mit Aluminium, Aluminium 46 (1970) p. 230/234.
32. Riemann, H.: Kabelmäntel ohne Haltestellen, Draht 19 (1968) p. 223/232.
33. Müller, E.: Neues kontinuierliches Preßverfahren zur Herstellung von Aluminium-Kabelmänteln ohne Haltestellen, Z. f. Metallkunde 52 (1961) p. 146/151.
34. Kursetz, E.: Das Warmstrangpressen hochfester Aluminiumlegierungen und Al-Automatenlegierungen, Draht 19 (1968) p. 770/775.
35. Zeiger, H.: Das Strangpressen von Zerspanungslegierungen des Aluminiums, Z. f. Metallkunde 62 (1971) p. 585/588.
36. Scharf, G. and Gruhl, W.: Paper No. 24, 5. Int. Leichtmetalltagung, Leoben (1968) p. 173/178.
37. Scharf, G., Achenbach, D., and Gruhl, W.: Beeinflussung der Grobkornbildung bei Preßprofilen aus Aluminiumlegierungen, Z. f. Metallkunde 60 (1969) p. 515/520.
38. Rosenkranz, W.: Untersuchungen über Grobkornbildung bei Strangpreßprofilen und Preßteilen aus Legierungen des AlCuMgSi-Typs, Aluminium 41 (1965) p. 555/566.
39. Kursetz, E.: Technische und wirtschaftliche Einflußgrößen beim Warmstrangpressen von Aluminiumdrähten, Draht-Welt 55 (1969) p. 343/351.
40. Malburg, P. G.: Aluminiumdraht, Herstellungsverfahren, Anwendungstechnik und Entwicklungsprobleme, Aluminium 45 (1969) p. 101/103.
41. Lynker, F. W., Markworth, M., Rosenkranz, W., and Winther, H.: Der Einfluß technischer Vorbehandlungen von Gußblöcken auf das Grobkornverhalten bei stranggepreßten Stangen und Profilen aus Legierungen vom Typ AlCuSiMn, Z. f. Metallkunde 64 (1973) p. 320/324.
42. Beatty, E. C.: How the properties and microstructure of 6063 alloy extrusions depend upon fabricating practice, Int. Extr. Technol. Sem., New Orleans (1969), Paper No. 10.
43. Beerens, H., and Feldmann, H.: Wärmebehandlung von Aluminium-Strangpreßprofilen aus der Preßhitze, Aluminium 47 (1971) p. 545/549.
44. Designing with thin walled extrusions, Precision Metal 27 (1969) p. 70/72.
45. Zolobov, V. V., and Zverev, G.: Extrusion of Metals, Moscow (1960).
46. Harris, C. S.: Extrusion of Magnesium, Machinery 53 (1947) p. 143/152.
47. Nuttal, K.: The Damping Characteristics of a Superplastic Zn-Al Eutectic Alloy, J. Inst. Metals 99 (1971) p. 266/270.
48. Schweinsberg, C.: Schaubild für das Pressen von Zinklegierungen, Metall und Erz.

49. Vereinigte Deutsche Metallwerke AG.: VDM-Handbuch, 2nd ed. (1964).

50. Blazey, C. L., Broad, L., Gummer, W. S., and Thompson, D. B.: The Flow of Metal in Tube Extrusion, J. Inst. Metals 75 (1948) p. 163/184.

51. Koltzenburg, K.: Stoffflußuntersuchung sowie Kraft- und Arbeitsbedarf beim Strang-pressen von Rohren aus Kupfer und Kupferlegierungen, Thesis TH Aachen (1970).

52. Cairns, J. H., and Such, D. B.: Recent Casting and Extrusion Developments in a Modern Copper Tube Mill, Int. Conf. Copper and its Alloys, Amsterdam (1970).

53. Schürmann, P.: Die Gießerei-Anlagen der Boillat AG., pro metal 24 (1971) p. 42/46.

54. Dies, K.: Kupfer und Kupferlegierungen in der Technik, Springer-Verlag (1967).

55. Mann, H., Kirch, A., and Tuschy, E.: Großhohlstrangguß von Nichteisenmetallen, Gießerei 49 (1962) p. 385/390.

56. Deutsches Kupfer-Institut: Niedriglegierte Kupferlegierungen (1966).

57. Deutsches Kupfer-Institut: Kupfer-Zink-Legierungen (1966).

58. Gubkin, C. L., and Sacharov, P. A.: Izv. A. N. SSR, Otd. mat. i est. nauk. (1937).

59. Lotz, W., Steiner, U., Stiehler, H., and Schelzke, E.: Preßfehler beim Strangpressen von Kupfer-Zink-Legierungen, Symp. "Strangpressen" DGM, Frankfurt (1970).

60. Broichhausen, J., and Feldmann, H.: Wärmebehandlung einiger Kupfer-Zink-Legierungen aus der Umformwärme, Metall 27 (1973) p. 1069/1080.

61. Landichow, A. D.: Herstellung von Rohren, Stangen und Profilen aus NE-Metallen, Fachbuchverlag Leipzig (1955).

62. Kafowi, J. and Sachs, B.: Verfahren zum Warmpreßbarmachen von Kupfer u. Zinn enthaltenden Legierungen, Deutsches Reichspatent 581 (1933).

63. Deutsches Kupfer-Institut: Legierungen des Kupfers mit Zinn, Nickel, Blei und anderen Metallen (1965).

64. Lepp, H.: Techn. Publ. Int. Tin Res. Dev. Council, Series D (1937).

65. Heubner, U., and Stenger, H.: Vergüten von Kupfer-Aluminium-Mehrstoff-legierungen durch Abschrecken und Anlassen, Metall 23 (1969) p. 431/443.

66. Landolt-Börnstein: Zahlenwerte und Funktionen, vol. IV, part b, p. 434, Springer-Verlag (1964), 6th ed.

67. Kramer, K. H., Arndt, R., and Budde, J.: Metallkundliche Untersuchungen und mechanische Eigenschaften der Titanlegierungen TiCu2, Metall 27 (1973) p. 983/988.

68. ASM, Metals Handbook, 8th ed., vol. 5 (1970).

69. Schey, J. A.: Metal Deformation Processes. Friction and Lubrication, Marcel Dekker, Inc., New York (1970).

70. Sabroff, A. M., and Frost, P. D.: Titanium Metallurgical Lab. Rep. No. 53; We're ready for volume business, say extruders of titanium, Steel 139 (1956) p. 142/145; Titanium Extrusion Knowhow gets big Boost, Steel 155 (1964) p. 46/48.

71. Lustmann, B., and Kerze, F.: The Metallurgy of Zirconium, New York, Toronto, London, McGraw-Hill (1955).

72. Miller, G. L.: Zirconium, Butterworth (England), 2nd ed. (1957).

73. Pardoe, J. P.: Extrusion of Metals for Nuclear Reactor Application, Metal Ind. (London) 100 (1962) p. 426/429 and 446/448.

74. Kieffer, R., Jangg, G., and Ettmayer, P.: Sondermetalle, Springer-Verlag (1971).

75. Armantrout, C. E., and Sims, C. O.: Improved beryllium alloys on the way, Materials Eng. (1971) p. 18/19.

76. Kaufman, A. K.: Int. Conf. Peaceful Uses of Atomic Energy, New York (1956).

77. Kaufman, A. K., and Kjellgren, B. R. F.: Status of Beryllium Technology in the USA, Proc. 1st Int. Conf. Peaceful Uses of Atomic Energy, Geneva (1956) p. 590/599 (Paper No. 820).

78. Stohe, J. A., and Chevigny, R.: Gamma Phase Uranium Extrusion, Proc. 1st Int. Conf. Peaceful Uses of Atomic Energy, Geneva (1956) p. 159/168, (Paper No. 351).

79. Stohw, S.A., and Cherinsky, K.: Int. Conf. Peaceful Uses of Atomic Energy, New York (1956).

80. Courtney, R.J.: Some Aspects of the Extrusion of Nickel-Based Alloys, J. Inst. Metals 99 (1971) p. 261/266.

81. Nickel-Informationsbüro: Die Nimonic-Legierungen.

82. Séjournet, J.: Brit. Patent No. 607 258 (1948).

83. Slater, I.G. *et al.*: Brit. Patent No. 1 064 951 and 1 002 612 (1960).

84. Toaz, M.W., Davies, G.F., and Johnson, R.D.: Production of Extrusion Billets of High Temperature Aircraft Alloys by Powder Metallurgy, Techn. Rep. AMC-TR-60-7-764 (1960).

85. Eckardt, H.: Verwendung stranggepreßter Stahlprofile, Int. Zeitschrift für Stahlverwendung: Acier-Stahl-Steel (1959).

86. Goodwin, J.-G., and Tombaugh, R.W.: Back Extrusion of Heavy-Walled Zircaloy – 2 Cups, ASME Paper 57-S-15 (1957).

87. Kolsch, A.: Strangpressen von Stahlrohren auf Kurbelrohrpressen, Z. f. Metallkunde 62 (1971) p. 649/652.

88. Schulte, W.: Strangpreßprofile aus Stahl: Herstellung und Einsatz im Containerbau, Klepzig-Fachbericht 77 (1969) p. 712/716.

89. Schulte, W.: Die Herstellung von Flossenrohren im Stahlstrangpreßverfahren, Klepzig-Fachbericht 78 (1970) p. 609/611.

90. Schulte, W.: Strangpreßprofile aus Stahl, Technische Rundschau 5 (1967).

91. Elkan, R.M.L., and Schieren, K.H.:Strangpressen von Stahlrohren, Bänder-Bleche-Rohre 5 (1964) p. 150/155.

92. Bensmann: Probleme beim Strangpressen schwer umformbarer Werkstoffe bei hohen Temperaturen, Paper presented at the conference "Strangpressen", Berlin (1973).

93. Kursetz, E.: Die Entwicklung der Strangpreßtechnik von Stahl und Sondermetallen in der amerikanischen Industrie, Z. f. Maschinenbau-Fertigung 95 (1962) p. 673/678.

94. Cox, R., McHugh and Kirk, F.A.: Some aspects of steel extrusion, J. Iron & Steel Inst. 194 (1960) p. 423/434.

95. Eckardt, H.: Aufbau und Betriebsergebnisse einer Strangpreßanlage für Stahlprofile, Stahl und Eisen 82 (1962) p. 883/896.

96. Elkan, R.M.L., and Cox, R.: Developments in steel extrusion, J. Iron & Steel Inst. 202 (1964) p. 236/260.

97. Veltjens, D.: Strangpreßanlagen mit Hilfs- und Folgeeinrichtungen für Kupferwerkstoffe, Z. f. Metallkunde 62 (1971) p. 87/99.

98. Klein, A., Schindler, K., and Hartenstein, R.: Extrusion and Stretch Reducing of Tubular Products, Iron and Steel Engineer 41 (1964) p. 97/105.

99. Kursetz, E.: Sonderverfahren für die Herstellung von nahtlosen Stahlrohren großen Durchmessers, Bänder-Bleche-Rohre 10 (1969) p. 492/495.

100. Schmidt, F.F., Klopp, W.D., Albrecht, W.M., Holden, F.C., Ogden, H.R., Jaffee, R.I.: W.A.D.D. Techn. Rep. 59-13 (1959).

101. Raitberg, L.K.: Experience in the Cold Extrusion of Aluminium-Alloy Blanks, Tsvetnye Metally 7 (1966) p. 76/77.

102. Quadt, R.A.: The cold extrusion of strong alloys, Modern Metals 15 (1959) p. 26/32.

103. Rogers, J.A. and Rowe, G.W.: An investigation of factors influencing lubricant behavior in hot extrusion, J. Inst. Metals 95 (1967) p. 257/263.

104. Grosch, J. and Jäniche, H.: Kaltpreßschweißen von Aluminiumpulver durch Strangpressen, Aluminium 50 (1974) p. 343/349.

105. Markworth, M., and Ribbecke, G.: Versuche zur Herstellung von stranggepreßten Profilen aus Titanlegierungen auf Leicht- und Schwermetallstrangpressen, Metall 28 (1974) p. 777/786.

106. Strassmann, I.: Beryllium-Halbzeuge und -Rohlinge, Metall 28 (1974) p. 245/250.
107. Sauve, C.: Lubrication Problems in the Extrusion Process, J. Inst. Metals 93 (1964) p. 553/559.
108. Hansen, M.: Constitution of binary alloys, McGraw-Hill, 2nd ed. (1958).
109. Guillet, L.: Revue de Métallurgie 21 (1924) p. 293/302.
110. Sabroff, A. M., Boulger, F. W., and Henning, H. J.: Forging Materials and Practices, Reinholf Book Corp., New York, Amsterdam, London (1968).
111. Evans, D. W.: Das Verhalten der Aluminium-Magnesium-Silizium-Legierungen nach dem Zustandsschaubild, Aluminium 38 (1962) p. 219/221.
112. Harris, I. R., and Varley, P. C.: J. Inst. Metals, 82 (1953) p. 379.
113. Pavlov, V. A., and Pereturina, J. A.: Phys. Met. Metallogr. 8 (1959) p. 88.
114. The Int. Nickel Company, Inc., Techn. Bulletin T-9.
115. van Horn, K., editor, Aluminum, vol. 3, p. 95, ASM (1967).
116. Groos, H.: Strangpreßanlagen zur Herstellung nahtloser Stahlrohre, Bänder-Bleche-Rohre 7 (1966) p. 833/838.
117. Wieland-Werke Ulm: Catalogue of Extrusion Defects No. Mi 17821, 11.04.
118. Pistulka, W., and Lang, G.: Spannungsrißkorrosions-Schnellprüfverfahren für Legierungen des Typs AlZnMg, Aluminium 53 (1977) p. 366/371.

4. Design and Construction of Extrusion Presses

4.1. Historical Background

The development of the extrusion press from the first simple lead press to the modern automatic extrusion plant represents an interesting chapter in the history of metal working. Several important dates mark the path to the versatile process used today for both nonferrous metals and steel. A brief summary is given below.

1797 The first lead press was designed by S. Bramah (England).

1820 Thomas Burn (England) built the first hydraulic press for lead pipes. This press contained in essence the basic components of a modern tube press: container, changeable die, stem with attached dummy block, and a moving mandrel screwed to the stem.

1837 Introduction of a bridge die with a replaceable bridge and mandrel (J. and C. Hanson).

1840 W. Armstrong built the first hydraulic accumulator.

1867 First gas-heated two-part container (Hammon).

1870 Construction of an indirect lead press (Haines and Werms).

1879 First cable sheathing press for lead in which the lead was extruded directly onto the cable (Borell).

1881 Twin ram cable sheathing press built by Krupp-Gruson.

1894 A decisive step forward: Alexander Dick built a horizontal extrusion press for the Deutsche Delta Metallgesellschaft in Düsseldorf. This

Fig. 4.1. Oldest extrusion press, built by Alexander Dick in 1901, with a capacity of 10 MN; in use until the end of World War I. *(From Wieland, Ulm)*

allowed high melting point alloys to be extruded for the first time (Fig. 4.1). Special features of the press included a tilting container that was moved to the horizontal extrusion position after the liquid metal had solidified, and a separate dished dummy block. The production rate of this press, the oldest one designed by Dick, was initially very low (25 to 30 extrusions in 10 hours). The one-piece container was another source of problems.

1896 Container constructed of several steel cylinders with a mixture of powdered graphite and borax between them (Nursey).

1904 First well-engineered four-column press by Krupp-Gruson.

1917 Steel extruded for the first time in a 20 MN press for the manufacture of steel clips.

1918 Twenty-four years after Dick's patent over 200 extrusion presses had been built.

1921 First experimental results on indirect extrusion published by R. Genders.

after Intensive research into flow patterns by Schweißguth, Plankensteiner,
1925   Doernickel, Trockels, Hanser, Sachs and Siebel; this initiated new developments in press design, especially in tooling technology.

1927/ First attempts to produce steel tubes in a Singer mechanical press.
1928

1933 Mechanical tube press built by Mannesmann in Witten according to a patent by Singer; 12 MN capacity.

1927/ Moving container and electric container heating.
1943

1943/ DEMAG-Hydraulik and Schloemann-SIEMAG built the first large-scale
1944   press installation with a capacity of 125 MN (Fig. 4.2 and 4.3).

after Improvements in horizontal and vertical extrusion presses and auxil-
1945   iary equipment, short-stroke presses, revolving presses, compact presses; extensive improvement of all moving parts — for example, horizontal die slide and rotating die holders to simplify die changing, internal piercer and mandrel movement; automation of control systems; oil hydraulic drive, especially for aluminum extrusion.

after Development of techniques for extruding steel and unusual metals
1955   including titanium, beryllium, zirconium, uranium. Hydrostatic extrusion opened new possibilities for working difficult metals and alloys. Advances in tooling technology allowed complex hollow sections to be produced in aluminum. Automation of production with presses controlled by punch cards.

4.2. Classification and Design of Extrusion Installations

The historical survey above indicates how extrusion press design has only in the past 20 years reached a technical level capable of providing optimum production conditions for the range of alloys extruded. Production schedules have become more versatile and the output has, at the same time, increased many times over. Consequently, there have been significant changes in the techniques used in extrusion, especially with aluminum and magnesium alloys, and new methods have been developed for steel and many other metals, opening new markets for extruded materials.

An extrusion installation consists of the following basic equipment: the extrusion press (Fig. 4.4a), the drive system (high-pressure pumps), the

Fig. 4.2. Extrusion press, 125 MN capacity, built by Hydraulik during World War II and delivered to the Madison works of the Dow Chemical Co. *(From DEMAG-Hydraulik)*

hydraulic fluid container, heaters and coolers for the hydraulic fluid, a high-pressure accumulator system, if necessary, for fast ram speeds of short duration in the range 50 to 400 mm/s, high- and low-pressure piping, the control system with interlocks, automatic controls and all the auxiliary equipment. The general layout of a typical installation is shown in Fig. 4.4b and includes the billet heater with the billet feed and transport system, discard separator, die changing mechanism and the handling equipment for the extruded product, including the runout table with quenching apparatus, the cross-transfer conveyor, roller conveyor, and stretcher.

Fig. 4.3. Rod and tube press, 120 MN capacity, designed by Schloemann. Two such presses were built during World War II: the first was taken in 1945 from the Waaren plant in Germany to the USSR; the second, shown in the photograph, now operates in the Lafayette, Indiana, plant of Alcoa. *(From Schloemann-SIEMAG)*

4.2.1. Types of Drive

Hydraulic extrusion presses can be classified into two basic types: those with accumulator drive, and those with direct pumping. The hydraulic medium can be water, oil or a non-inflammable fluid. In both systems, the operating pressure — that is, the maximum hydraulic pressure — is in the range of 205 to 310 bars. Higher pressures are used in large presses to keep the dimensions of the ram and pipes and the volume of fluid required to a moderate level. Sometimes pressure attenuators of 500 to 1000 bars are used. The choice of water or oil drive is dictated by the operating conditions. Water

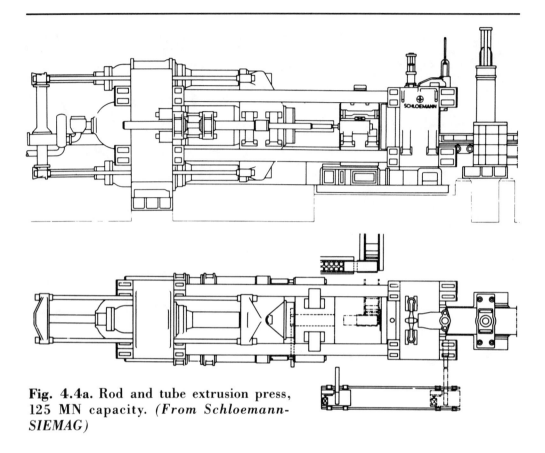

Fig. 4.4a. Rod and tube extrusion press, 125 MN capacity. *(From Schloemann-SIEMAG)*

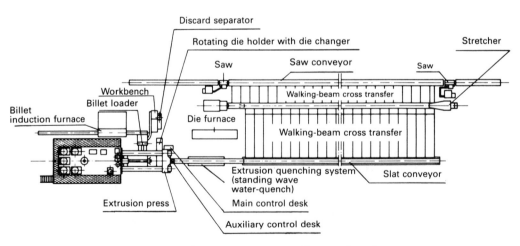

Fig. 4.4b. General view of an extrusion installation for aluminum sections. *(From Schloemann-SIEMAG)*

is usually selected for heavy metal extrusion presses exceeding 25 MN and with ram speeds above 50 mm/s. Direct pumping would require too many pumps. The total capacity of the accumulator installation is available for extrusion in accumulator drive systems and the system is recharged during the dead cycle time.

Direct oil pumping is used for ram speeds below 50 mm/s. The output from the pumps is controlled to enable the maximum extrusion speed to be developed throughout the extrusion cycle. Oil hydraulic drive units have been used on presses as large as 100 MN. There are significant differences between accumulator drive and direct pumping, apart from the design of the system. The efficiency of the plant depends on the choice of drive in relation to the press capacity, cycle time, and space available. In an accumulator system, water containing 1 to 3% of a corrosion inhibitor is pumped under pressure into high-pressure containers filled with compressed nitrogen.

The pumping operation is carried out by one or more pumps, usually with at least three pistons to eliminate the need for flywheels in the system. The pumps operate in the range of 120 to 300 rpm. The pressurized water is transferred by a valve system from the accumulators to the presses when needed. The compressed nitrogen accumulator system consists of one or more water bottles connected to a battery of nitrogen bottles, the compressed nitrogen contents of which provide the stored driving energy. Figure 4.5 shows the water accumulator system of a 50 MN rod and tube press.

Fig. 4.5. Water accumulator drive system of a 50 MN rod and tube press. *(From Schloemann-SIEMAG)*

Fig. 4.6. Direct oil hydraulic pumping system, cellar-type, for a 20 MN rod and tube press. *(From Loewy, Bournemouth)*

Multiplunger oil pumps are used for direct drive systems and they operate at speeds of up to 1500 rpm — much higher than those used for accumulator systems. The pumps should be as close to the press as possible to eliminate the need for long pipes. In direct pumping systems the various operating speeds of the press are usually provided for by having a continuously variable output (a servo valve system). The different speeds can also be obtained with pumps having a fixed output by diverting the appropriate quantity of fluid. This method is very inefficient, particularly at higher operating speeds. Therefore it is preferable to connect several pumps or pumps with variable outputs in series. This method allows large installations to be fitted with direct pumping. The required speed for each operation can be selected either continuously or by switching different pump combinations in and out of the circuit.

Fig. 4.7. Oil tank with high-pressure oil pumps and controls; drive system on a 17 MN extrusion press for aluminum. *(From Schloemann-SIEMAG)*

The oil hydraulic pumping station of a 20 MN rod and tube press shown in Fig. 4.6 consists of seven pumps in a cellar. Figure 4.7 gives a view of the pumping unit of a 17 MN package (type) extrusion press for aluminum. The characteristics of the two types of drive are compared in Tables 4.1 and 4.2. Occasionally, oil hydraulic systems are supplied with a combination drive — that is, direct oil pumping together with an oil accumulator of the piston type with positive separation of the oil and gas into two cylinders. This combined system has the advantage of providing ram speeds above 50 mm/s for short periods. This type of system is recommended if a very mixed range of products is extruded with most ram speeds below 50 mm/s.

4.2.2. Extrusion Presses for Nonferrous Metals

Hydraulic extrusion presses can be classified into two basic types: horizontal and vertical. Billets of heavy metals, light metals, steels and special alloys are extruded to rod, section, strip and wire in horizontal presses. Tubes and hollow products can also be produced by using a mandrel or, in certain cases, a welding chamber die. Rod, section, wire, and the like, are also extruded from heavy and light metal billets as well as steel on presses that, in contrast to the standard horizontal type, are fitted with an independent mandrel mover or piercer, but the main use of these presses is the production of tubes and hollow sections. A 50 MN rod and tube press is shown in Fig. 4.8.

Table 4.1. Comparison of Types of Drive for Extrusion Presses (From Ref 3)

Feature	Direct pumping with oil	Water accumulator
Type of drive	Direct pumping	Pumping via a high-pressure accumulator
Type of pump	Multiplunger pumps	Piston pumps
Operating fluid	Hydraulic with 89 to 185 Saybolt seconds at 55 °C or synthetic oil	Water with 1 to 2% corrosion-inhibiting oil
Cost of the operating fluid	Higher	Lower
Drive mechanism	Not necessary(a)	Drive belt or geared drive
Wear	Lower(a)	Greater
Current loss	Lower(a)	Greater
Feed line from pumps	Larger	Smaller(a)
Extension of the system for further presses	Not possible	Possible
Cost of the drive	Lower for slow extrusion speeds(a), higher for fast speeds	Higher for slow extrusion speeds, lower for fast speeds

(a) Preferable

Fig. 4.8. Modern horizontal 50 MN metal rod and tube extrusion press. *(From Schloemann-SIEMAG)*

Table 4.2 Advantages, Disadvantages and Main Areas of Application of the Two Types of Drive (From Ref 3)

Drive type	Advantages	Disadvantages	Main areas of application
Water accumulator drive	High ram speeds, low no-load losses from the drive system, unlimited for further presses, inexpensive operating fluid.	High capital cost; the earlier disadvantages of the complex throttling of the high-pressure water for speed control have been overcome.	Extrusion presses for steel, copper alloys, heavy metals and materials that can be extruded at fast speeds.
Direct pumping with oil	Low wear of rams, seals and controls; good control of extrusion speeds; low capital costs.	Not possible to extend the system to several presses; lower maximum speed than with water drive.	Extrusion presses for aluminum alloys and other light metals, and materials that can be extruded only at low speeds.
Combination drive with oil	Low ram wear despite higher ram speeds from the accumulator drive; simple control of ram speeds and, hence, automatic control of the extrusion speed (e.g., isothermal extrusion); good economics of the combination drive.	High capital cost that can, however, be justified in certain cases.	Extrusion presses for alloys that can be extruded at high or low speeds.

The use of vertical rod and tube presses is decreasing for nonferrous metals because of the limited press height and capacity, which necessitate the use of small billets. However, it must be remembered that fully automatic operation was first developed in vertical presses. A typical vertical piercing press of 10 MN capacity is shown in Fig. 4.9.

The wide range of flow stresses encountered in metals and alloys naturally necessitates different specific pressures and, consequently, press capacities. The variety of extruded products also requires different press sizes with corresponding container diameters. Table 4.3 summarizes the main areas of application of the different sizes of horizontal and vertical presses.

Fig. 4.9. Modern vertical 10 MN metal rod and tube extrusion press. *(From Schloemann-SIEMAG)*

A standardized range of press capacities has already been proposed. Modern horizontal extrusion presses are built in capacities from 6.3 to 200 MN, according to the requirements of the process, whereas vertical presses for nonferrous metals are usually limited to capacities between 6.3 and 16 MN.

Hydraulic presses can be further classified into direct and indirect types (see Chap. 2; Extrusion Processes). Direct horizontal presses were originally built with the container fixed to the end housing. The moving component was the main ram in the main cylinder; the ram moved the extrusion stem backwards and forwards. Significant developments in press design and in the auxiliary equipment have, however, been carried out in the past 20 years with

Table 4.3. Classification of Extrusion Presses for Nonferrous Metals and Steel

Type	Drive	Position of press axis	With or without piercing mechanism	No. of main cylinders	Operating pressure in bars	Max press capacity, MN		Type of construction	Range of press products
Horizontal extrusion presses	Hydraulic	Horizontal	Without	1	.. ..	5 6.3 8 10 12.5 16	.. 40 50 63 .. 80	2, 3 and 4 columns	From light and heavy metal alloys to bar, wire, section and strip products (tube over fixed mandrel) (a)
Horizontal rod and tube extrusion presses	Hydraulic	Horizontal	With	1	.. .. 200 250	20 25 31.5 ..	100 125 160 200	Frame construction up to 20 MN	From nonferrous metals and steel to bars, sections, etc., and tubes with independent mandrel movement
Vertical rod and tube presses	Hydraulic	Vertical	With or without	1	.. .. 315 (350)	5 6.3 8 10	12.5 16	Frame construction	Previously used for extrusion of heavy metal alloys to tubes and hollow sections
Crank-driven extrusion presses	Mechanical	Vertical	With or without	1	.. .. ..	6.3 8 10	.. .. ..	Frame construction up to 16 MN	Still used for mass production of steel tubes (also forging and piercing presses)
Cable sheathing presses	Hydraulic	Vertical or horizontal	..	1 or 2	.. ..	.. 16 .. 20	31.5 .. 40 50	Single and twin ram presses	Production of lead and aluminum cable sheaths; vertical twin ram press(b); opposed twin ram press(c)
Special design	Development of hydro-static extrusion	..	..	Horizontal tube presses with as many as three containers	..	..	..	..	.. ..

(a) Including use of welding chamber dies. (b) DEMAG-Hydraulik design. (c) Schloemann-SIEMAG design.

Fig. 4.10. Extrusion press for direct and indirect extrusion. *(From DEMAG-Hydraulik)*

the aim of reducing the dead cycle time (see section 4.4). These included the moving container, an idea known to extruders for 40 years, and the location of the piercing mandrel or mandrel mover in the main cylinder.

Indirect extrusion can be carried out by moving the container over a fixed hollow stem in the direction of the extrusion. The advantages and disadvantages of the indirect process are discussed in Chap. 2 (Extrusion Processes) and all that need be mentioned here is the significant reduction in the load required at the start of extrusion because of the absence of friction between the billet and the container. It is also possible to upset the billet at the start of extrusion using the indirect process and then, without interrupting the cycle, change to direct extrusion after a short ram movement (Fig. 4.10). If use of the indirect process is to increase, because of the advantages of better press utilization associated with longer billets and no friction, some thought must be given to the possibility of converting existing presses to this method by increasing the container stroke and installing new auxiliary equipment.

4.2.3. Horizontal Extrusion Presses

4.2.3.1. Types of Construction

Hydraulic rod and tube presses have been classified into three types and are illustrated in Fig. 4.11, 4.12 and 4.13.

Type I is a horizontal extrusion press for the production of rod, section and wire, without any built-in capacity for tube extrusion (Fig. 4.11a).

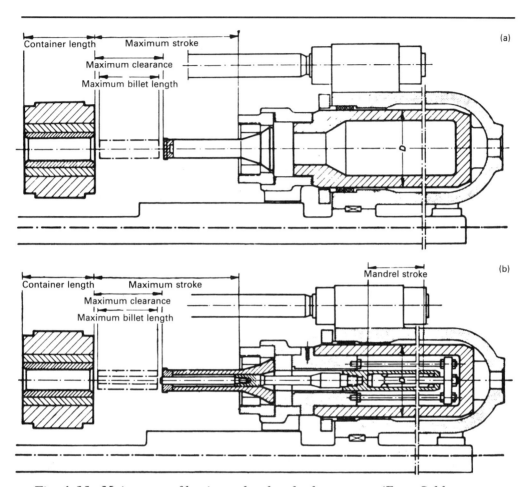

Fig. 4.11. Main types of horizontal rod and tube presses. *(From Schloemann-SIEMAG)*

Americans were the first to build an inexpensive, simple and easily transportable press that could be installed anywhere with the minimum of foundation work — in contrast to the oil hydraulic press installation erected on site. These very compact presses are constructed with the power pack and oil tank directly above the press and are known as package presses (Fig. 4.14). This method of construction was adopted by other press manufacturers in the 1950's and the presses were installed mainly by producers of aluminum window frames and fascias in order to be independent of metal extruders. A further development of this approach is the horizontal hydraulic press for rod, wire and section that can be converted at a later date into a rod and tube press of type II by adding a piercer.

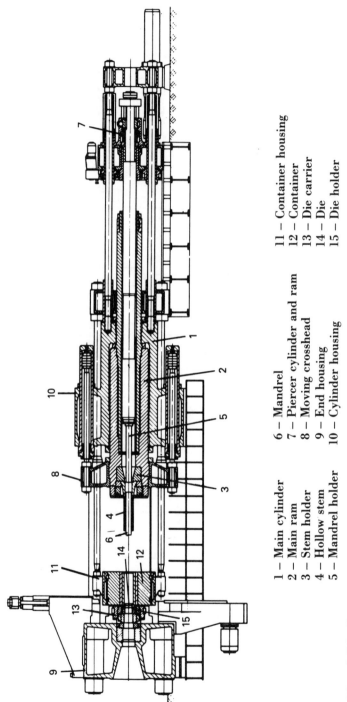

1 – Main cylinder   6 – Mandrel   11 – Container housing
2 – Main ram   7 – Piercer cylinder and ram   12 – Container
3 – Stem holder   8 – Moving crosshead   13 – Die carrier
4 – Hollow stem   9 – End housing   14 – Die
5 – Mandrel holder   10 – Cylinder housing   15 – Die holder

Fig. 4.12. Cross section through a horizontal rod and tube press with an external piercer. (*From Schloemann-SIEMAG*)

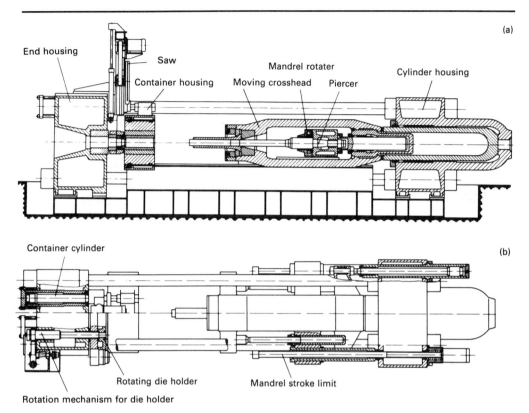

(a)

End housing

Saw

Mandrel rotater

Cylinder housing

Container housing   Moving crosshead   Piercer

(b)

Container cylinder

Rotating die holder   Mandrel stroke limit

Rotation mechanism for die holder

Fig. 4.13. Modern horizontal rod and tube press with an internal piercer. *(From Schloemann-SIEMAG)*

Type II is a horizontal hydraulic extrusion press with built-in mandrel movement for the extrusion of tubes from hollow cast billets. The load applied by the mandrel mover is about 2 to 3% of the press capacity (Fig. 4.11b).

Type III is a horizontal hydraulic extrusion press with a built-in piercer operated independently of the main ram movement. The capacity of the piercer is sufficient to pierce solid billets and is in the 10 to 20% range of the total press capacity. Extrusion presses of this type can have either an external (Fig. 4.12) or internal (Fig. 4.13) piercer. Presses with internal piercers are much shorter and are now the standard design for tube presses.

A practical example of a type III press is the large automatic extrusion press installed in a plant in Switzerland in August 1971. The installation consists of an oil hydraulic 72 MN piercing press with electronic and hydraulic controls, two low-frequency induction furnaces, a runout table and two

Fig. 4.14. Package-type extrusion press fully assembled in the manufacturer's plant. *(From Fielding, Bournemouth)*

stretchers, straighteners and saws. A view of the press is given in Fig. 4.15. It has two containers with internal diameters of 400 and 500 mm respectively, and a rectangular container 660 by 240 mm. Billets up to 700 kg and a length of 1400 mm can be used. Induction heating is used for the containers. The press is equipped with an internal piercer for billets to be pierced and extruded to large cylindrical tubes and hollow sections. Tubes can also be produced in the softer alloys by using either porthole or bridge dies.

4.2.3.2. Frame Construction

The main press frames built in the past 60 years consist of two platens connected by a number of cylindrical columns — usually four in modern presses. Three-column presses were once built and they had the advantage of more space between the columns for container changing, but only at the expense of stability. The occurrence of column failures initiated a detailed study of the elastic deformation and state of stress in the press frame. The

Fig. 4.15. Metal rod and tube press, 72 MN capacity; view from the rear with control desk and container. *(From Schloemann-SIEMAG)*

press frame should not be considered as a rigid body but as an elastically deforming structure. The magnitude of the deformation depends on the applied extrusion load and the dimensions and design of the platens and columns. An important part of press frame design is, therefore, to reduce the influence of one component of the press on another — for example, the effect of the deformation of the platen on the stress distribution in the column. Various methods have, accordingly, been tried for locating the columns in the platens and eliminating the column nuts. One successful solution is the use of a laminated frame with columns consisting of composite sets of flat steel bars. This practical solution was originally proposed by Loewy-Hydropress for drop forge presses and then used by Schloemann-SIEMAG as a prestressed tie bar construction on extrusion presses (Fig. 4.16a).

Hollow sleeves are used as compression members between the platens in the type of frame developed by Schloemann-SIEMAG. The tension members (in this case a set of plates) pass through the hollow sleeves and the platens,

Fig. 4.16a. Modern 31.5 MN aluminum extrusion press with laminated columns. *(From Schloemann-SIEMAG)*

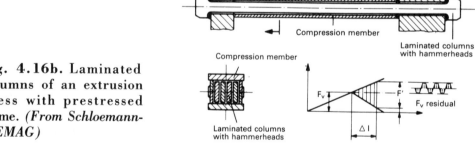

Fig. 4.16b. Laminated columns of an extrusion press with prestressed frame. *(From Schloemann-SIEMAG)*

and are externally held by hammerheads (Fig. 4.16b). This gives a prestressed press frame between the hammerheads. Prestressing can be achieved only between the column nuts in the platens on the standard design of column prestressing. This shrunk tie bar construction is extremely stiff and once the press has been aligned by the press manufacturer it need not be rechecked during erection or even after many years in service. Figure 4.17 shows the frame method of construction used by DEMAG-Hydraulik.

Fig. 4.17. Frame-type 50 MN extrusion press. *(From DEMAG-Hydraulik)*

4.2.3.3. Other Design Features

Besides the type of frame used, other important aspects of modern press design include the method of container movement and the arrangement of the piercer or mandrel mover mechanism. A cross section through a horizontal piercing press with an external piercer is given in Fig. 4.12 and one with an internal piercer in Fig. 4.13. The important features of modern presses can be recognized from these drawings:

(a) The container housing with the container-moving cylinders located in either the end housing or the main cylinder housing.

(b) The mandrel-moving mechanism (external and internal) with mandrel rotation and stroke limiting devices.

(c) The die slide or rotating die holder.

The container is supported on keys in a one-piece holder and is free to expand in all directions during heating. The load applied by the main ram is resolved into axial and radial components. The axial component has to be

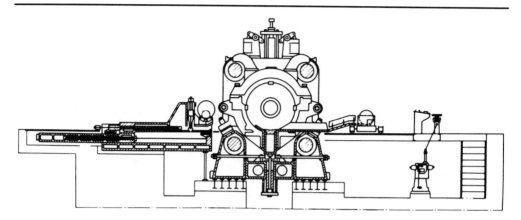

Fig. 4.18. Container holder with induction container heating. *(From Schloemann-SIEMAG)*

resisted by the die and its backers, and the radial component by the container. The container holder moves along the axis of the press and is designed to simplify container changes and the dummy block, shell and cleaning pad removal. The stripping load to clear the discard is usually greater than the sealing load between the container and the die. Rapid container changes can be carried out by using quick-release latches (Fig. 4.18 shows a container holder with induction heating). The moving container not only simplifies the exact alignment of the tooling but also makes it possible to separate the discard in front of or behind the die and, in particular, allows the discard to be stripped when using bridge dies.

The mandrel mover or piercer used to produce tubes or hollow sections can be either internal or external and the mandrel movement is independent of the main ram. The stroke of the mandrel is adjusted to the lengths of the billet and the mandrel. The movement of the mandrel can be controlled by a geared motor drive when extruding with a stationary mandrel. It is usual to differentiate between a mandrel mover and a piercer insofar as the load applied by the latter is sufficient to pierce solid billets. Hollow billets are used with a mandrel mover. The selection of the piercing capacity for tube extrusion depends on the alloy used and the dimensions of the billet and product. Usually 10% of the total press capacity is used for aluminum tube extrusion, 16 to 18% for copper, and up to 20% for steel.

No definite answer can be given to the question of whether an internal or an external piercer is better. The internal piercer is centrally supported in the moving crosshead and the total length of the press is much shorter. Improved accessibility is generally pointed out as the advantage of an external piercer.

High-quality tubes can be extruded to close tolerances in both light and heavy metals in both types of installation. Zilges (Ref 10) has listed several advantages of the internal piercer:

(a) The alignment of the moving crosshead is independent of the main ram and cylinder housing.
(b) The guide shoes are far enough apart to ensure positive stable guiding of the moving crosshead.
(c) The piercer can be aligned independently of the piercer ram and moving crosshead.
(d) The alignment possibilities mentioned above guarantee close tube tolerances even after many years in service.
(e) The stroke of the internal piercer need be only as long as the working stroke of the mandrel (an external piercer has to be capable of movement over the total piercer and ram stroke).
(f) The overall length of an extrusion press with an internal piercer is shorter and, consequently, the site and foundation costs are lower.

The important functions of the mandrel movement are described below. It makes it possible to extrude with relative movement between the mandrel and the stem when extruding with a moving mandrel. Thus, when difficult alloys or very hot billets are used, the mandrel moves relative to the die in the direction of extrusion and the stresses in the mandrel are, accordingly, reduced (relative stroke). The risk of mandrel necking as a result of excessive loading at temperature is reduced and the working life of the mandrel increased. Mandrel rotation is a necessary feature for the production of hollow sections with shaped mandrels. It can also be useful in tool alignment in normal tube extrusion.

Fast die changes have always been important and press manufacturers have developed several good solutions. The die slide has proved to be very suitable for aluminum extrusion. If it is fitted with two die stations, die changes can be performed on either side of the press, reducing the time required. A rotating die holder is more useful for very frequent die changes or in the extrusion of copper alloys or special alloys where the die has to be dressed or cooled after every extrusion. It is also suitable for large presses. Die changing then takes place on one side of the press only. Examples of the two methods are shown in Fig. 4.19 (end housing with die slide) and Fig. 4.20 (end housing with rotating die holder).

A sticking-billet tool for billets that cannot be extruded or a container-sealing plate for piercing solid billets can be inserted in place of the second die. A very practical solution is the division of the rotating head into two sections, one behind the other. The first rotating holder carries the die; the second carries the die holder, die backers and bolsters. The advantages of this arrangement are: easier die changing, lighter moving components, and

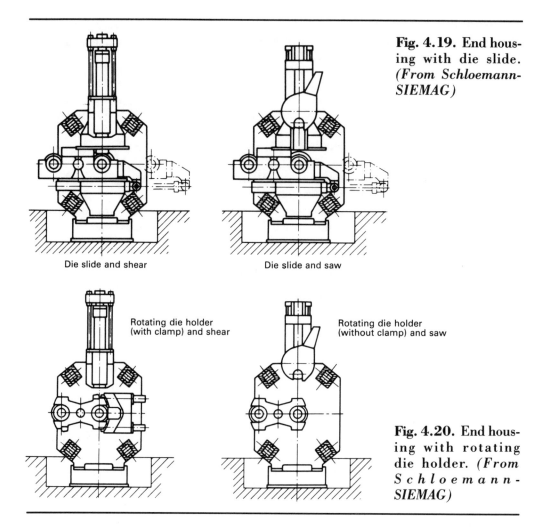

Fig. 4.19. End housing with die slide. *(From Schloemann-SIEMAG)*

Die slide and shear

Die slide and saw

Rotating die holder (with clamp) and shear

Rotating die holder (without clamp) and saw

Fig. 4.20. End housing with rotating die holder. *(From Schloemann-SIEMAG)*

shearing directly behind the die to free the extrusion. A shear or saw — or both — is built onto the end housing for the purpose of separating the extruded product from the discard. Shearing behind the die has particular advantages if welding chamber dies are used. Usually the shearing of the discard and dummy block takes place in front of the die by a vertical shear passing across the die face. The dummy block and discard fall and are lifted for either manual or automatic discard separation or fed into a separator operating as part of the press cycle.

Sections produced with multihole dies are guided through the end housing onto the runout table by graphite canisters behind the die. This reduces any damage to the sections, which are very delicate when they leave the die. A section saw or shear is used to cut the extruded product immediately behind the die. Aluminum sections can now be welded in the die so soundly that the weld can be stretched. In this case the extrusions are cut at a distance equal to the finished length from the die (about 6 m) and the weld is removed in the final cutting to length.

Often too little attention is paid to cooling the extrusion tooling. Die, mandrel and liner cooling are necessary, especially when extruding with high billet temperatures and long extrusion times. Only internal mandrel cooling will be discussed here. Internal mandrel cooling is very important because it operates throughout the entire press cycle. The system is designed to pass a constant stream of cooling water through the hollow mandrel. Experience has shown that this method increases the working life of the mandrels used for tubes and hollow sections, and a smooth internal surface is formed on the extruded product. All the moving components of the press installation must be adequately lubricated. Modern presses have a central lubrication system that feeds all the lubrication points with a sufficient supply of oil and grease. Water lubrication of the guides is also used in steel extrusion to remove glass and scale.

4.2.4. Vertical Extrusion Presses

Vertical hydraulic presses are now less popular in nonferrous metal production because their advantages for close-tolerance tubes and hollow sections have been surpassed by the improved design of horizontal tube presses. The past ten years have also demonstrated that the billets for vertical presses are too small and that the modern horizontal tube press is superior, with its better technological capabilities and more efficient handling equipment. Vertical presses are now used mainly in specialist plants (for example, steel tube production) and for small tubes and special sections in aluminum. Very small sections are extruded vertically through multihole dies (e.g., 24 holes). The structure of a vertical piercing press is shown in Fig. 4.21 (see also Fig. 4.9). The main cylinder and the two drawback cylinders for the moving crosshead and piercer are in the upper section of the press frame. The die holder and moving container are in the lower section. The container-moving cylinders are on each side of the press frame and the rams move the container via a mechanical linkage. The piercing cylinders are also attached to the sides of the frame and the rams connected by rods to the piercer crosshead. The use of vertical presses for large steel tube production is discussed in section 4.6.4.

4.2.5. Controls

Extrusion press control consists in operating the valves or appropriate mechanisms in the correct sequence to initiate the press movements. It is possible to classify control systems into three types: manual, remote and programed.

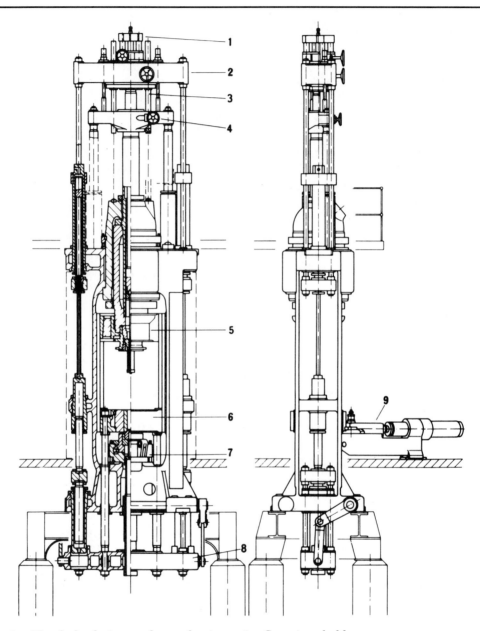

1 – Mandrel relative-stroke mechanism   6 – Container holder
2 – Piercer   7 – Tool holder with rotating die holder
3 – Mandrel stroke limit   and die ejector
4 – Mandrel stroke adjustment   8 – Container-mover mechanism
5 – Moving crosshead   9 – Shear

Fig. 4.21. Design of a vertical rod and tube press. *(From Schloemann-SIEMAG)*

4.2.5.1. Manual Control

This method is now out of date; the control valves of the hydraulic system are directly operated by the press operator using levers and hand wheels.

4.2.5.2. Remote Control

The control valves are operated by a mechanical force produced by a hydraulic or pneumatic actuator or by an electric motor. The signals to these auxiliary controls come from manually operated electric switches acting either directly or via solenoid valves. The switches are usually incorporated into a control panel. Unless an automatic switching sequence is incorporated, every press movement has to be individually initiated by operating the appropriate switch or push button (Fig. 4.22) even with remote control.

4.2.5.3. Programed Control

In this system the individual switching sequences for the consecutive movements of the press are effected by additional switching controls following a preselected program. Extrusion presses generally have a sequential control system in which every press movement initiates the following one via a limit switch. The relevant electrical controls can be either a contact system with normal relays, high-speed relays under a protective atmosphere (Reed relays) or contactless. The programed control system not only operates the press with its numerous movements during the cycle but also controls the auxiliary and runout equipment. The complicated sequences cannot be operated accurately

Fig. 4.22. Control panel with switch and push-button operation. *(From Fielding, Bournemouth)*

and quickly enough by manual controls and, therefore, the programed system is an obvious requirement for maximum efficiency in a modern extrusion plant. The extrusion cycle begins with the billet call and — using aluminum extrusion as an example — continues as follows:

Billet call: the billet temperature is measured by a thermocouple, either continuously in an induction furnace or intermittently in a gas-fired furnace. As soon as the required temperature is reached, the billet for the first cycle can be called by pressing the appropriate push button. The signal can be coordinated with the press cycle by a time relay and the next billet is then already in position at the start of the next cycle, reducing the dead cycle time.

Billet transport: the center line of the press is parallel to that of the furnace and, therefore, the billet has to be transported in a transverse direction. The billet travels from the furnace parallel to the press and activates a limit switch at the end of the roller conveyor. The end section of the conveyor is then tipped towards the press.

Billet and dummy block pusher: the billet rolls from the transporter into the billet loader and a dummy block is moved into position by the dummy block pusher. The billet and dummy block are then both pushed to the correct position on the billet loader.

Billet loader: the billet loader on most large presses is divided into two parts that can be operated either individually or together. The container is sealed against the die and a signal from a pressure switch in the hydraulic line initiates the loading of the billet into the center of the press.

Ram advance: when the billet loader has reached its final position it activates a limit switch that allows the main ram to advance. The ram moves forward at a low load but at a relatively fast speed and pushes the billet and dummy block into the container.

Billet loader 1 return: as the ram moves forward it activates a limit switch and this signals the return of the rear section of the billet loader as soon as the billet is far enough into the container.

Billet loader 2 return: the same sequence is repeated for the second half of the loader.

Billet upsetting: the ram advance continues until the billet contacts the die and there is a slight increase in the pressure in the hydraulic system. The prefill valve closes automatically and the system momentarily decompresses.

Extrusion: the valve that releases the extrusion pressure then opens and extrusion commences. The delivery control of the hydraulic pumps provides precise ram speed control.

Decompression of the main cylinder: when the desired discard length is reached, a signal from a limit switch opens a decompression valve.

Container decompression and stripping: the pressure drop in the system operates the low-pressure contact of a pressure switch and this provides a signal for the container decompression. The fall in the pressure in the hydraulic sealing line also initiates the stripping cycle, which continues until a limit switch is reached, via a pressure switch.

Container and ram return: when the container stripping limit switch has been operated, the ram and container travel back simultaneously — the ram to its initial position and the container to its shearing position.

Shear advance: a limit switch operated by the container as it reaches its shearing position starts the shearing sequence.

Shearing: the shear separates the discard and dummy block from the die.

Shear return: at the end of the shearing operation the position of the operating valve is reversed and the shear returned. A constant-pressure pump holds it in its idle position.

Container advance: the container advances when the shear operates a limit switch as it reaches its idle position.

Container sealing: a constant-pressure pump is switched into the circuit when the container has made contact with the die. This pump compensates for losses from the enclosed pressurized volume during container sealing and provides a good seal between the container and the die. The increase in pressure in the container sealing line operates a pressure switch that initiates the movement of the billet loader already holding a billet and dummy block, and the complete cycle recommences.

4.2.5.4. Programed Control with Choice of Speed Profiles During Extrusion

In Chap. 1 it was pointed out that the exit temperature varies during extrusion at a constant speed. There are metallurgical and economical advantages in extrusion with a constant exit temperature and knowledge of the relationship between the exit temperature and the ram speed has led to the development of several methods of "isothermal" extrusion in which the speed is varied to maintain a constant exit temperature. However, no reliable, practical method of continuously measuring the temperature of the extrusion has yet been found despite extensive research into contactless pyrometer (optical) or contact thermocouple methods of measurement. Consequently, direct isothermal extrusion controlled by the measured deviation of the exit temperature has found only limited application (see Chap. 2).

Another very attractive method of overcoming this problem has been used in industry. The extrusion speed can be kept under exact control by using suitable restrictive and regulatory systems, and can also follow a preselected speed profile over the extrusion stroke. The profile depends on the alloy and extrusion conditions, and is designed to give approximate isothermal extrusion. One well-known method is the speed measurement and control system developed by Schloemann. It was originally designed for aluminum extrusion but the principle can also be used on high-speed presses and even for steel extrusion. The ram stroke is divided into fractions of the billet length and the speed varied in a controlled manner during extrusion by giving each fraction a fixed speed. The billet length (ram displacement) fractions and the corresponding speeds can be adjusted on the control panel. The speed is measured by an incremental rotary encoder with a low moment of inertia; it gives 10 000 impulses per revolution, which can be scanned by a photoelectric cell. The press stroke can then be divided into 100 impulses/mm.

Control of a Water Hydraulic Press

A block diagram of the control system of a water hydraulic press is given in Fig. 4.23. A quartz crystal emits a frequency of 10 kHz, and a frequency divider and decade switch allow any frequency between 1 Hz and 10 kHz to be selected as a nominal value for the speed. The actual value is obtained from a rotary transducer on the press, designed to give one impulse for each movement of 0.01 mm. The comparison with the nominal value is performed in two ways: one uses the speed deviation in a specific time, and the other the displacement deviation. The control system is, accordingly, divided into two circuits.

An analog speed control circuit operates in parallel with a digital ram displacement control circuit. The former has the task of immediately eliminating large deviations and, therefore, the speed controller must be capable of adjusting the throttle valve very quickly. The digital displacement controller, on the other hand, works within the error region of the analog controller. The stabilization of these deviations takes place slowly, so that inaccuracies in the true measured value resulting from elastic deformation are minimal. Therefore, the displacement control must adjust the throttle valve and the delivery only gradually. The advantage of such a displacement control circuit is the constant ram speed during slow press movements even under unsteady loading.

The maximum deviation of the displacement control is limited to ± 5 mm. This prevents the true value from deviating too far from the nominal value, which would result in a speed above the maximum allowed. Both deviations (speed and displacement) are registered on a speed regulator that governs the setting of the throttle valve via an auxiliary circuit. Results obtained in practice indicate that it is advisable to divide the billet length into several sections and to allocate a nominal speed to each section. The procedure is as follows: The ram displacement is determined by a preset counter that receives its impulses from the displacement transducer fitted to the press (incremental rotary encoder). After each billet section has been extruded, the controls switch to the next nominal speed value for the following section. The displacement intervals and the desired

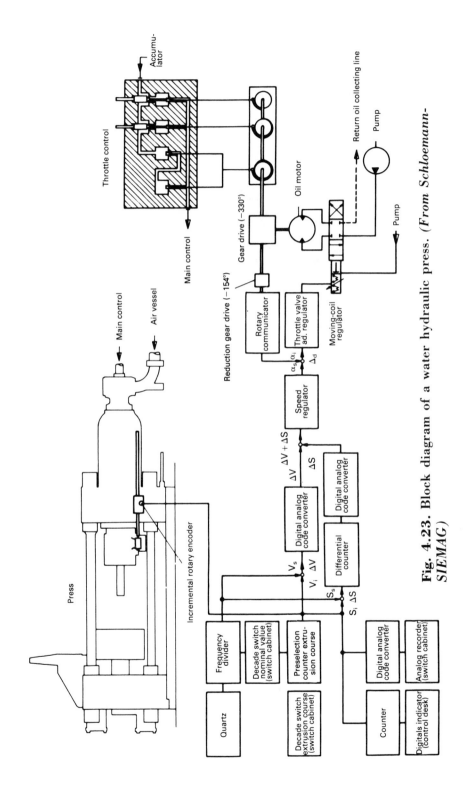

Fig. 4.23. Block diagram of a water hydraulic press. (*From Schloemann-SIEMAG*)

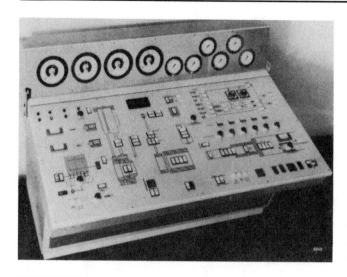

Fig. 4.24. Main control desk of a 20 MN rod and tube press. (*From Schloemann-SIEMAG*)

speeds can be preselected by switches on the main control panel (Fig. 4.24). Punched cards can also be used for the inputs of displacement intervals and nominal speeds with only slight modifications to the control circuitry.

Control of an Oil Hydraulic Press

Thorough investigations and measurements in oil hydraulic presses have demonstrated that speed control with direct pumping is simpler than in water hydraulic presses and can be based to a large degree on an analog system. A block diagram of one system is shown in Fig. 4.25. The actual value is again given by an incremental rotary encoder but its impulses are also fed into a path counter that divides the ram displacement into adjustable sections and coordinates the nominal speed values to these sections. The nominal value is compared as a voltage on the slide wire of a potentiometer with the set value. The difference is fed into an amplifier, the output of which is a measure of the pump adjustment. This adjustment process is again carried out by an auxiliary circuit.

The Schloemann system of speed measurement and control has already been used successfully on a large number of oil and water hydraulic presses for aluminum, heavy metals and steel. Fielding & Platt fitted a 35 MN piercing press for steel and nickel alloys with a punched card system from I.C.T. (International Computer and Tabulators, Ltd.) as far back as 1964. This system controls the extrusion speed throughout the complete press stroke. The punched card for the billet supply and extrusion temperature is fed into the I.C.T. reader (Fig. 4.26).

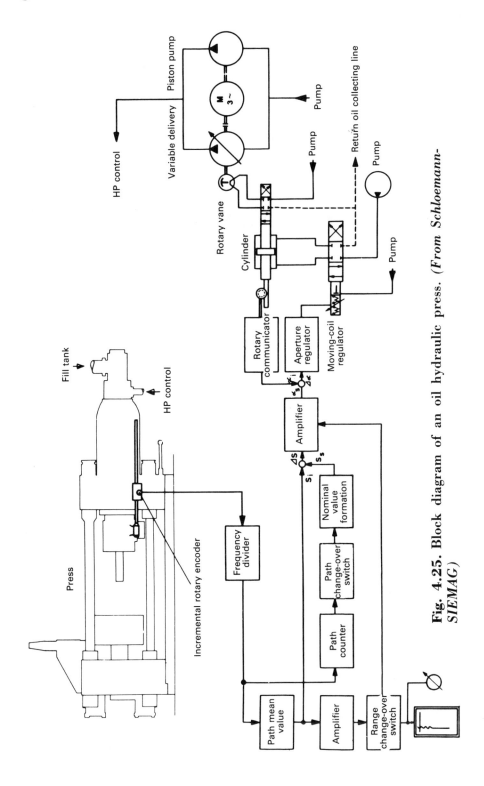

Fig. 4.25. Block diagram of an oil hydraulic press. *(From Schloemann-SIEMAG)*

Fig. 4.26. Rod and tube press, 35 MN capacity, for steel and nickel alloys with an ICT punched card control system. *(From Fielding, Bournemouth)*

4.2.5.5. Development Trends

The speed measurement and control system is an important step towards the full automation of extrusion plants operating under optimal conditions. It is axiomatic that the preselected values correspond to the alloy being extruded. Therefore, the data fed in must be based on a significant number of measured values taken from practice. The runout facilities after the press also have to be synchronized with the extrusion speed. Production planning can be greatly simplified by storing these data in a computer that also produces the punched cards for the extrusion operation. Press output is then independent of operating personnel.

However, expectations should not be too high. Punched card control only comes into consideration for large-scale production. An inflexible punched card control system creates problems with the frequent changes of program that take place in practice and the associated starting-up difficulties. A punched card or tape system would be advantageous for systems involving frequent changes in the production program only if the controls and speed regulator are backed up by a process computer that immediately reacts to deviations of the true values from the desired values and adjusts the controls accordingly.

A further step forward is the development of a computer controlled extrusion plant. For example: billet furnace, press, runout table, stretcher and saw form a unit in an aluminum extrusion plant controlled with punched cards. A general view of the operation of such a computer controlled installation is given in Fig. 4.27. In this case the computer is also used for the control of orders and stock control. When an order has been completed the punched

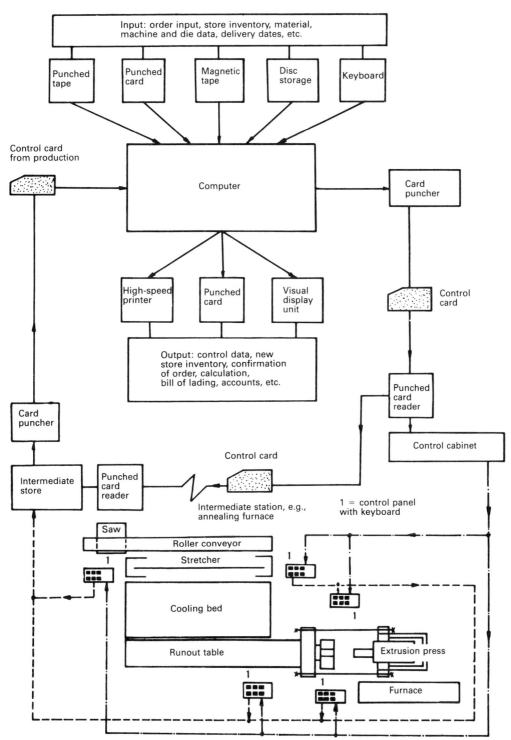

Fig. 4.27. Schematic diagram for a computer-controlled extrusion plant. *(From Ref 12)*

card follows the production flowline and finally arrives at the production planning department for verification and accounting.

4.3. Billet Heating Systems

4.3.1. Induction Heating

Low-frequency induction furnaces or high-speed gas furnaces are now used in most plants for heating billets to the correct working temperature. In contrast to the old gas-fired roller type furnaces, in which the round billets roll through the individual heating zones with long uncontrolled transit times, the low-frequency induction furnace and the continuous gas furnace give accurate temperature control with rapid heating. The basic structure of a low-frequency furnace consists of a horizontal coil in which three or four billets are heated to the desired temperature in a continuous cycle. A typical induction billet furnace installation is shown in Fig. 4.28.

The induction furnace is the most technically efficient unit for billet heating available, but a temperature difference is developed between the surface and the interior of the billet. In contrast to the radial temperature difference in billets heated by fuel combustion or resistance heating, the limited penetration of the induced heat — the skin effect — can present problems with some alloys when the time between extrusions is insufficient for the billet to attain thermal equilibrium. However, the total heat input in other methods of heating must pass through the billet surface and this can result in overheating if the rate of energy transfer is too rapid. With induction heating, the billets can be subjected to a higher energy input with very short heating times. Production requirements are the minimum radial temperature differ-

Fig. 4.28. Induction billet furnace viewed from the exit side. *(From Junker, Lammersdorf)*

ence at the maximum rate of heating although, even with induction heating, there is a definite temperature profile. A peripheral zone hotter than the core of the billet is particularly unfavorable in aluminum processing because the surface regions undergo the largest deformations during extrusion and are heated still further by friction. Therefore, billets are often surface quenched with a water spray as they leave the furnace. This accelerates the approach to thermal equilibrium between the core and the peripheral zone.

There are two methods of compensating for the radial temperature difference:

(a) Changing the coil length and hence the heating time.
(b) Increasing the power.

Temperature variation along the length of the billet is caused by the large temperature difference developed in induction furnaces between adjacent billets, which results in heat flowing to the front end of the colder billets. The specific surface energy transfer to each billet decreases as the number of billets of a specified length in the coil at any one time increases and this gives much more uniform heating across the billet section. If the electrical power is increased in the coil, the billet is heated to the desired temperature before it has passed through the coil and there is some time available for the temperature to approach equilibrium. The real temperature difference resulting from the increase in power will, naturally, be greater than that under normal production conditions but, after the time needed to reach thermal equilibrium, the difference is less than that obtained for the total time at a constant power input. Therefore, a power increase is more efficient than an increase in the coil length.

The ideal for any given production run is to combine coil length and excess power input to match as far as possible the demands of the extrusion process with the technical capabilities of the furnace. Axial temperature variations, which are usually neglected, can also have a negative influence in continuous billet processing. Furnace builders have developed several solutions including that of varying the distance between the billets in the furnace and of using field concentrators. The time required to heat the billet is mainly a function of the thermal conductivity of the alloy and the billet dimensions and, consequently, there are major differences in the heating times of different alloys. The time between loading the billet and its removal can vary from 3 to 20 minutes. In some cases, depending on the press capacity, several furnaces are installed to feed one press. Figure 4.29 shows six 370 kW induction furnaces with horizontal coils for steel billets, together with the control and instrument panel.

Induction heating has proved to be fast, flexible and economical. The accurate temperature control results in a high-quality extruded product. Rapid attainment of the required temperature with almost scale-free heating

Fig. 4.29. Six 370 kW induction furnaces, with control and instrument panels, for steel billets. *(From Ajax-Magnethermic)*

Fig. 4.30. Side view of a high-speed gas furnace for aluminum billets. *(From Junker, Lammersdorf)*

is a distinct advantage that induction furnaces have for the extrusion of steel and special alloys.

4.3.2. Gas Heating

The cheaper gas energy available in most metal fabrication plants has also been utilized for billet heating. The Granco Heater (made by Granco) was introduced several years ago in the USA and was soon put into use in many aluminum plants as a high-speed gas furnace (Fig. 4.30). The gas is fed through a large number of burners, and the flame or burning gas directly touches the billet surface. This system can attain high temperatures and a rapid heating rate but, despite the large number of burners, cannot equal the heating speed of the induction furnace. The heating period is three to five times longer, and longer furnaces must be used.

Billet transport is different in the two types of furnace. In the shorter induction furnace the billets are simply pushed along a guide plate through the coil. The length of the gas furnaces necessitates a chain or roller conveyor system. The chain conveyor runs under the furnace tunnel and the billets are carried through the furnace on supports, welded to the chain, which pass through a slot in the tunnel floor. Direct transport on a roller conveyor through the furnace is more efficient but is subject to increased wear and requires clean, straight-cut billets.

Cross sections through a high-speed gas furnace with a chain conveyor (a) and a roller conveyor (b) are depicted in Fig. 4.31.

4.3.3. Combined Gas and Induction Heating

A combination of both types of furnace has recently been introduced to take advantage of gas energy and has proved to be useful for certain purposes. The high-speed gas furnace is used for preheating and provides 50 to 55% of the total power; the induction furnace uses about the same amount to provide the final heating to the required temperature. This system has proved to be very suitable for heavy metal and steel extrusion if the preheating temperature in the gas section is in the 500 to 600 °C range. This prevents scaling, permits easy temperature measurement, and reduces damage to the billet conveyor. The induction furnace is used only to provide the final high temperature, with all the advantages of this type of furnace described above. The combination furnace is very economical and can realize an energy saving of 20 to 30%. A combination of different types of furnace can also be suitable for other purposes. For example, the two low-frequency induction furnaces of the 72 MN aluminum press shown in Fig. 4.15, with a maximum output of 12 t/h, are connected to a holding furnace that is used to attain thermal equilibrium, according to the requirements of the particular alloy. The charging side of the furnace can be seen in Fig. 4.32; the billet conveyors and charging mechanism are clearly visible.

Recently billet furnaces have been fitted with hot shears to overcome the disadvantages of short billet lengths. The as-cast lengths are charged directly into the furnace, eliminating the operation of cutting to special billet lengths (Fig. 4.33).

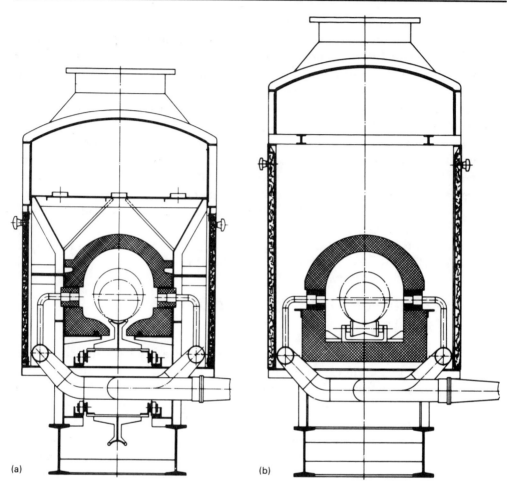

Fig. 4.31. Cross section of a high-speed gas furnace with: **(a)** chain conveyor system; **(b)** roller conveyor system. *(From Junker, Lammersdorf)*

4.3.4. Temperature Control

The temperature of each billet is measured and controlled in both induction furnaces and high-speed gas furnaces. The energy input is also regulated by the billet temperature. Thermocouples are used for temperature control with aluminum but optical methods are also used for the heavy metals. Care must be taken with optical measurement because billet surfaces vary considerably in practice. The heat radiated is largely dependent on the emission factor and, therefore, errors can occur.

In induction furnaces the energy requirements relative to the quantity of metal is practically independent of the output, if the appropriate coil for the

Fig. 4.32. Two induction furnaces with loading mechanism; the oil hydraulic drive system on the press platform can be seen in the upper left-hand corner. *(From Ajax-Magnethermic)*

Fig. 4.33. Hot billet shear and billet furnace for a 27 MN extrusion installation. *(From Sutton, Pittsburgh)*

billet diameter is available. The fuel consumption of the high-speed gas furnace increases considerably if the output falls, and the operating costs are then higher than for an induction furnace. A typical example is the use of small-diameter billets in large furnace tunnels.

4.4. Auxiliary Equipment and Handling Gear for Nonferrous Metal Extrusion

Along with the advances in press control, significant improvements have been made in auxiliary equipment, including the billet feed to the furnace, transport of heated billets to the press, subsequent treatment of the extruded product (quenching, stretching and cutting to length) and, finally, transport of the finished product. Press manufacturers now not only install the press but provide complete installations for everything from heating billets to cutting the cooled, stretched product. This development has been particularly sucessful in aluminum extrusion plants. The duration of the working cycle can be optimized by the press manufacturer who provides all the auxiliary equipment: the efficiency of a plant depends heavily on the operation of the auxiliary gear. The economics of the process are of primary importance and the automatic operation of the complete working cycle for different press programs includes the operation of both the press and the auxiliary equipment in order to minimize the dead cycle time in an extrusion cycle.

4.4.1. Billet Feed to the Furnace

Billets sawn to the optimum or a standard length are fed to the furnace via a billet magazine, the capacity of which should be sufficient not to require the continuous presence of an operator. In its simplest form, the billets are loaded on an inclined plane and roll one by one, as part of the press cycle, onto the charging conveyor. Only a few billets can be stored with this method and, therefore, a different system is generally used. The billets are individually lifted onto the charging conveyor by a hoist controlled from the press. The billet hoist, depending on the space available, can be situated immediately in front of the furnace or in the billet magazine. If the billet feed is so designed, several presses can be supplied by roller conveyors operating from a central station. The billets might have to pass through a brushing machine in their passage to the furnace or immediately after it, to remove any protective coating or sand.

Fig. 4.34. Hot billet shear and billet transfer gripping mechanism on a 20 MN extrusion press. *(From Schloemann-SIEMAG)*

4.4.2. Billet Transport to the Press

The transport system is usually part of the extrusion press. As the billets leave the furnace they either are cut to length by a hot billet shear (Fig. 4.34), which is possible with aluminum billets, or descend on a parallel or lateral conveyor. They are then moved from the conveyor to the billet loading station by a hydraulic ram or a roller mechanism if the billet loader cannot receive the billets directly from the furnace without any additional transport system. The billet loader tray generally has two sections and, after a separate dummy block — if used — has been loaded, both sections are lifted with the billet by hydraulic or pneumatic cylinders to the center line of the press. The first section of the loader tray is lowered as the main ram advances against the billet. The second section is removed when the billet has been pushed far enough into the container.

4.4.3. Auxiliary Equipment at the Press

The importance of auxiliary equipment for rational production is indisputable. For example, when extruding with a shell and no lubrication, the shell remains in the container and has to be removed with a cleaning pad.

After cutting behind the die, the discard, dummy block, shell and cleaning pad are removed as a unit in a special operation. The discard, dummy block and shell are then transferred to a horizontal separator where the cleaning pad is sheared off. The discard and dummy block then fall into a hopper or onto a conveyor belt and the dummy block is brought back to the billet loader via a cooling system. Figure 4.35 is a schematic diagram of an extrusion press for heavy metals with its auxiliary equipment. On the die side are the changer, roller conveyor and overhead crane, for transporting the dies, die backers and bolsters to the changer. The automation of this equipment has contributed a great deal to reducing the heavy manual work on presses in both aluminum and steel extrusion, which is considered in more detail in section 6.

4.4.4. Handling Equipment for Aluminum Extrusion Presses

4.4.4.1. Runout Table

The operations carried out on the exit side of the press in aluminum extrusion have been studied in great detail because of the enormous increase in the production of sections. The extruded length or lengths – when using multihole dies — used to be withdrawn manually and guided over a stationary table. This method is still used occasionally today. The stationary table was then replaced by a moving conveyor fitted with graphite slats. The sections are lifted from this conveyor and transported over a cross-transfer walking-beam cooling table. A second shorter cross-transfer walking-beam conveyor with a transfer mechanism is usually placed behind the stretcher as a holding station for the roller conveyor to the saw. This last conveyor feeds the stretched sections to the saw where they are cut into the required lengths.

A complete layout of an aluminum extrusion plant is shown in Fig. 4.36. The runout table is about 40 m long. A general view of a complete installation can be seen in Fig. 4.37, where the cut-to-length saw, in contrast to Fig. 4.36, is at the press end of the handling equipment. The cross-transfer conveyor is also of the walking-beam type. An important point in the design of an extrusion plant is the transport of the delicate sections without damage. Especially with large and heavy sections, this requirement can be achieved only by extensive mechanization of the material flow.

The following equipment is linked with the press control system:

(a) The slat conveyor runout table.
(b) The puller system on the runout table.
(c) The walking-beam conveyor to the stretcher.
(d) The second walking-beam conveyor from the stretcher to the saw.
(e) A mechanism for transporting the sections to and from the stretcher coupled with and controlled from the stretcher.

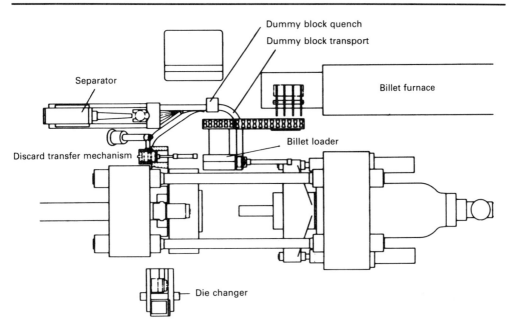

Fig. 4.35. Extrusion press with auxiliary equipment for heavy metals. *(From Schloemann-SIEMAG)*

The runout equipment of a 72 MN piercer press (Fig. 4.15) can transport, stretch and cut sections 40 m in length and up to 9.5 kg/m (Fig. 4.38).

4.4.4.2. Extrusion Pullers

The speed of the slat conveyor runout table is generally adjusted to be slightly faster than that of the extruded section. This applies a tensile load to the section, which then remains straight. However, this is frequently not sufficient, especially when small sections are extruded and they have to be pulled by hand. Some plants have mechanical or automatic pullers to eliminate this drawback. Pullers have proved to be very successful for the multihole extrusion of thin sections. The simplest form of a puller is mounted on or above the runout table and the jaws grip all the extruded sections together. The application of a low tensile load largely makes up for the differences in the strand speeds. Obviously, the material flow through the die is improved.

Pullers are also available with separate, individually operated jaws for each strand. The different strand speeds can then be ignored and each strand controlled with the optimum constant pull. A typical installation is shown in Fig. 4.39 and the exit from the graphite canister in Fig. 4.40. The sections are gripped by the hanging jaws. As soon as the extruded section contacts the back plate of the jaws they close, travel with the section over the runout table, and

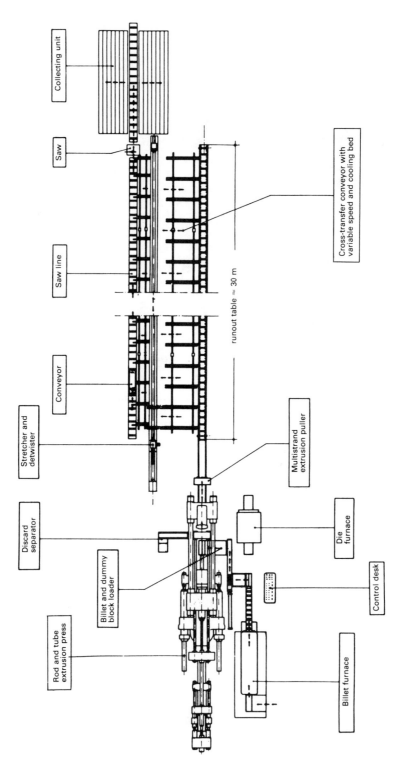

Fig. 4.36. Layout of a light-metal extrusion installation. *(From Ref 34)*

Fig. 4.37. Aluminum extrusion press, 20 MN capacity, with a 45 m runout table and a 0.25 MN stretcher. *(From Lindemann, Düsseldorf)*

Fig. 4.38. Runout table, walking-beam conveyor, and stretcher of a 72 MN aluminum extrusion press. *(From Schloemann-SIEMAG)*

release the section when the preselected length is reached. The sections can also be passed through a quench tank immediately after leaving the canister (Fig. 4.41) with the advantage of a relatively straight section after it has passed through the standing-wave quench.

4.4.4.3. Cooling the Extruded Product

The heat treatable alloys that form the bulk of aluminum production must be cooled rapidly from the extrusion temperature (Chap. 3). Usually, forced fan cooling is sufficient but water quenching is often needed. In the plant in Fig. 4.37, the product is air-cooled by overhead fans as soon as it

Fig. 4.39. Extrusion plant for aluminum sections, 20 MN capacity, with handling equipment and puller. *(From Loewy, Bournemouth)*

Fig. 4.40. Exit from the canister guide on the press in Fig. 4.39 with the automatic jaws ready to grip the section. *(From VDM-Frankfurt)*

Fig. 4.41. The 20 MN extrusion installation in Fig. 4.39, with two puller jaws in operation, pulling sections through the quench tank. *(From VDM-Frankfurt)*

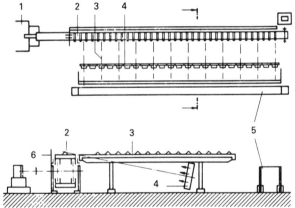

1 – Extrusion press
2 – Moving-slat conveyor
3 – Cross-transfer conveyor
4 – Fans
5 – Stretcher
6 – Protective screen

Fig. 4.42. Fan cooling system on the exit side of the press. *(From Ref 24)*

leaves the press. This very common system is inefficient, because the fans have to combat the hot air rising from the extrusion and this reduces the velocity of the cooling air. The heat transfer from the metal to the air depends, primarily, on the velocity of the air and its temperature at the metal surface and, thus, a sufficient number of fans with an adequate air velocity must be provided to reach the cooling intensity needed for the hardening of extruded thick-wall sections. Beerens and Feldmann (Ref 24) have studied this problem. Uniform mechanical properties are obtained over the full length of the extruded product if the air velocity along the axis of the press is equal to that at the first station of the cross-transfer conveyor.

Figure 4.42 is a schematic diagram of a fan cooling system that fulfills these requirements. The fans under the cross-transfer conveyor blow the air in the direction of the press axis. The deflector (6) diverts the air upwards

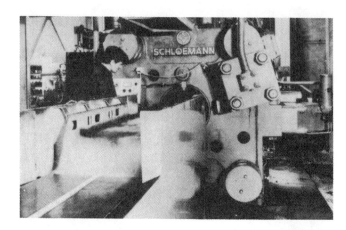

Fig. 4.43. Standing wave quench in a 17 MN press. *(From Schloemann-SIEMAG)*

between the sections. Some products (discussed in Chap. 3) have to be quenched in water at the press to achieve the desired mechanical properties. A water tank with rapidly agitated water is installed between the press and the runout conveyor. Water is fed in at the front and back to produce a standing wave and the extrusion passes through it (Fig. 4.43).

4.4.4.4. Stretchers

The stretcher for straightening extruded products is situated within the cross-transfer conveyor system and consists of gripping heads mounted on the bed. The position of the heads can be adjusted to match the length of the product. The head that applies the stretching load is fixed to the bed and the tailstock can be moved and locked on the bed at various positions. The ends of the extruded product are clamped between the hydraulically or pneumatically operated jaws. The stretching load is a function of the section shape and yield stress of the alloy, and is applied by a hydraulic cylinder that moves the headstock. The cylinder is mounted on a crosspiece that must be capable of withstanding the full stretching load. A trial run on a 1 MN stretcher is shown in Fig. 4.44.

4.4.4.5. Saws

The straight as-extruded lengths of sections are cut to the finished lengths or multiples of it on the cut-to-length saw. The sections are moved up against the gage stop set to the required length. Frequently, a continuous product is formed during aluminum extrusion by using the billet-to-billet process. The section must be cut as it reaches the end of the runout table before it can be lifted transversely. The cutting station should be as close to the press as possible. Cutting is best carried out by a flying saw. The extrusion need then only be slowed down and not stopped. Whether a high-speed circular saw,

Fig. 4.44. Trial run on a 1 MN stretcher. *(From VDM-Frankfurt)*

Fig. 4.45. Runout table and saw (right). *(From Lindemann, Düsseldorf)*

cutting torch or other method is used, a stopmark resulting from stopping the press should be avoided: the length of section from any stopmark to the cutting station has to be scrapped. High-speed circular saws are used to cut the stretched section to the finished lengths. The saw is situated at the end of a roller conveyor fed by the cross-transfer conveyor. The roller conveyor can move either in the extrusion direction (Fig. 4.39) with the saw at the far end, or in the opposite direction with the saw at the front end of the runout table (Fig. 4.45). The second arrangement makes better use of the available space.

4.4.5. Runout Equipment for Heavy Metal Extrusion Presses

Aluminum extrusion presses can generally be equipped with the optimum runout equipment for a standard product (for example, sections) because it represents 80 to 90% of production. However, production in heavy metal extrusion is more varied. Different materials are extruded into different shapes including rod, wire, section, tube and strip. Consequently, a wide speed range is needed with exit speeds up to 720 m/min. The various alloys sometimes need very different quenching conditions to obtain the desired properties.

The problem in heavy metal extrusion is that very few products are produced in sufficient quantity to allow for the optimum use of the press and the auxiliary equipment — as is the case with architectural sections of AlMgSi0.5. The only exception is copper tube extrusion where straight tubes in standard sizes and long lengths are produced without any change in the press program. These tubes are then drawn down through a series of draw benches to produce large coils with the final dimensions. A typical installation is shown in Fig. 4.46 and 4.47. In all other cases, a practical solution has to be worked out for each product in accordance with the available facilities. Veltjens (Ref 3) has described the equipment available.

4.4.5.1. Runout Equipment

4.4.5.1.1. Fixed Runout Table

In its simplest form the runout table consists of a flat bed of sufficient length covered with steel, cast iron or graphite plates. This type of runout is used only for heavy products with large cross sectional areas extruded in single lengths. A sweep-off arm is used for the transverse movement.

4.4.5.1.2. Moving Runout Table

V Trough

The V trough runout table has many uses. It can be moved in the direction of extrusion and tipped to one side, and is suitable for sections, rods and tubes. The V shape straightens the sections to a slight degree and prevents excessive buckling. At the start of extrusion the V trough — lined with steel, graphite or hardwood plates — is stationary; that is, the product slides into it. After separation the channel moves forward and tips the extruded product either onto a storage table, into a water quench, or onto a cross-transfer conveyor. Many products, however, are sensitive to this relative movement — for example, $(\alpha + \beta)$-brass. It is also possible to extrude (e.g., copper)

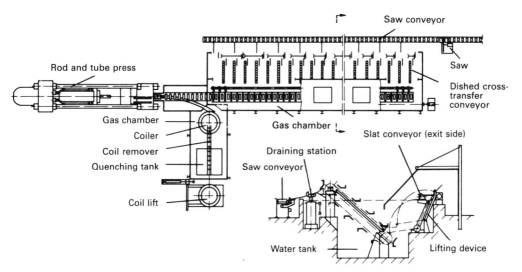

Fig. 4.46. Rod and tube extrusion installation for copper wire and tube. *(From Schloemann-SIEMAG)*

Fig. 4.47. Extrusion installation, 25 MN capacity, for heavy metals; wire and section lines *(From Loewy, Bournemouth)*

Fig. 4.48. Rod and tube extrusion installation, 31.5 MN capacity, with moveable runout trough and concave slat conveyor. *(From Schloemann-SIEMAG)*

directly into water flowing through the channel. Figure 4.48 shows a runout table with a V channel.

Roller Conveyor

A direct-drive roller conveyor can be used to eliminate the relative motion between the extruded product and the runout table mentioned above. The rollers are either cylindrical or V-shaped, depending on the shape of the section. The distance between the rollers depends on the rigidity of the extruded product, and plates are fitted between the rollers to prevent the front end of the product from hitting them. A lifting device between the rollers or a pusher mechanism provides the final transverse movement. The roller conveyor system can cope with fast exit speeds up to 720 m/min.

Slat Conveyor

The slat conveyor runout table fitted with steel or graphite slats is very similar to the type used in aluminum extrusion but the heavier product demands a more stable design. Slat conveyors are particularly suitable for sections and flat shapes. The product can be either lifted or pushed to the side. The system cannot match the high speeds of the roller conveyor; its maximum is of the order of 150 m/min.

Air Cushion System

An air cushion runout system is very useful for protecting the sensitive surfaces of hot extruded products. It works in combination with a guiding and cooling system.

4.4.5.2. Puller System

The high temperatures involved prevent the use of manual guiding in the majority of cases and mechanical — if possible, automatic — pullers offer significant advantages. Pullers can be fitted to all the runout systems mentioned above. The extruded product is automatically gripped by jaws at the start of extrusion and is then pulled with a light and, as far as possible, constant load. These conditions must also be met when sections with small cross sections are extruded and multihole dies have to be used. A more detailed description is given in the corresponding section for aluminum extrusion (4.4.4.2; see also Fig. 4.39).

4.4.5.3. Cooling Equipment and Cross-Transfer Conveyor Systems

Heavy metal extrusions are either quenched in water — for rapid cooling or the immediate exclusion of air — or cooled in forced or still air. The technological reasons for quenching copper sections are discussed in Chap. 3. Water containers incorporated in the runout system are used for quenching. The total length of the extruded product passes into the container and is completely surrounded by water (Fig. 4.49). The exit table between the platen and the water container should be as short as possible. It is usually fitted with spray rings with the nozzles pointing in the extrusion direction to keep water away from the die. The extruded product is guided through the water container and is then mechanically lifted and moved sideways. Various cross-transfer conveyor systems, including walking-beam and slat conveyors (Fig. 4.48 and 4.50), are used for cooling in still air. The width of the cross-transfer conveyor must be coordinated with the speed and temperature of extrusion.

4.4.5.4. Coilers for Wire, Tube and Strip

Extrusion presses for wire production are usually fitted with two or three coilers, either one behind the other or side by side. The wire, depending on the position of the axis of the coiler, is usually fed from above in the coiling direction through guides. Underwater coilers have been developed for production runs incorporating a rapid quench (for example, to prevent scaling in copper wire production).

A 15 MN press with two Garrett coilers arranged in series is shown in Fig. 4.51. These coilers allow the wire to be coiled without tension and can operate with a relatively large difference between the coiling speed and the extrusion speed. The coils have an inside diameter of about 500 mm and a maximum outside diameter of 900 mm. The coiling speed and the acceleration and retardation of the coilers can be matched to the properties of the alloy. The extrusion speed is then automatically controlled.

In addition to the coilers used for solid sections of 6 to 50 mm diameter with a drum diameter of 1200 mm, which give coils up to 1000 kg, coilers are

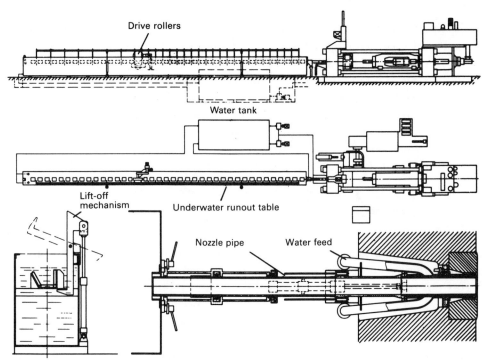

Fig. 4.49. Equipment for extruding into water. *(From Schloemann-SIEMAG)*

Fig. 4.50. Cooling table in the form of a plate conveyor. *(From Schloemann-SIEMAG)*

now available with a drum diameter of about 2000 mm for the direct coiling of thin-wall tube. The tube, up to 60 mm outside diameter and 4 mm wall thickness, can then be further processed on drum drawing benches or Schumag machines (Fig. 4.52). Extruded strip for rolling on small mills is extruded through single-hole dies and coiled on horizontal coilers, usually built in-house and situated on the runout table immediately after the end housing. The coiling equipment is designed to be easily dismounted and moved to the

Fig. 4.51. Extrusion installation, 15 MN capacity, with two Garrett coilers. *(From Loewy, Bournemouth)*

Fig. 4.52. Tube finishing line for copper tubes, with straightener, splitter, saw and coiler. *(From Schumag, Aachen)*

side or lowered below the floor to provide room for an insert that forms a flat runout table for products that cannot be coiled.

4.4.5.5. Combination Handling Gear for Mixed Extrusion Programs

The various types of handling equipment for heavy metal extrusion presses described above and their possible combinations enable runout systems to be built for any given extrusion process or press program, and production efficiency can be increased by automation. However, as mentioned previously, the preconditions for such systems are seldom encountered, and most heavy-metal extrusion plants are equipped with universal systems for extruding rod, section, tube, strip and sometimes wire in, often, very different alloys. Consequently, no general rules can be given apart from the need for easy and rapid program changes. The installations described below are given only as examples.

Figure 4.53 shows a complete layout for extruding section, strip and wire. Two Garrett coilers for wire are mounted at floor level and the coils pass from them along a short cross-transfer conveyor onto a slow-motion cooling bed moving in the extrusion direction and then to a coil collecting station. The coils are covered by a movable intermediate table (e.g., a slat conveyor) when sections and flat products are extruded onto the runout table. The products are transferred by a walking-beam conveyor, on which they are cooled, to the saw line and cut to length at the end of the line.

A different arrangement for a combination brass wire, tube and section press is given in Fig. 4.54. A fixed runout table with a puller and a pusher transfer system, a walking-beam cross-transfer conveyor, an immersion quench tank (for cooling thick-wall sections), a roller conveyor to the sawing station, and a saw are provided for tubes and sections. The two in-line coilers operate with protective covers because of the sensitivity of the brass being coiled. These covers are placed in the coiler after the previous coil has been moved to the side. The covers travel with the cooling wire coils on the coil conveyor to the final cooling station, where they are quenched. The protective covers are then removed from the coils and returned on another conveyor system. The coils are collected on a capstan.

The installation in Fig. 4.55 is similar, but it has a slat conveyor runout and a cross-transfer slat conveyor. A universal rod and tube press with a movable runout channel is shown as a further example in Fig. 4.56. The coils of wire are transported from the two coilers in front of the press to the back, and the material flow of the coiled and straight products is therefore separate. The universal heavy metal rod and tube press in Fig. 4.57 has a water tank filled with a protective gas atmosphere to prevent oxidation of copper products.

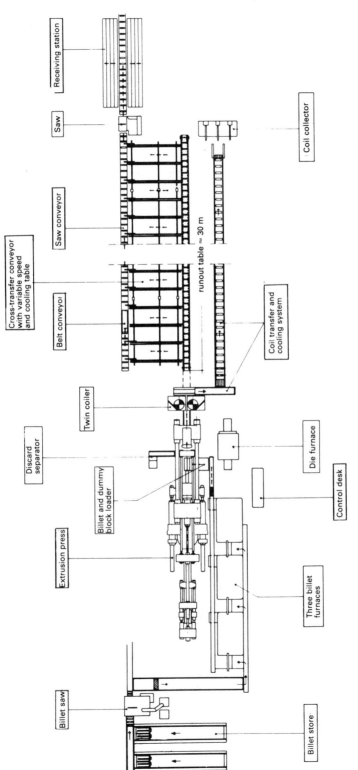

Fig. 4.53. Layout of a heavy-metal extrusion installation for section, strip and wire.

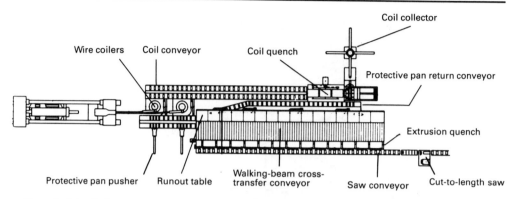

Fig. 4.54. Schematic diagram of an extrusion installation for producing heavy brass tubes and sections, as well as wire. *(From Schloemann-SIEMAG)*

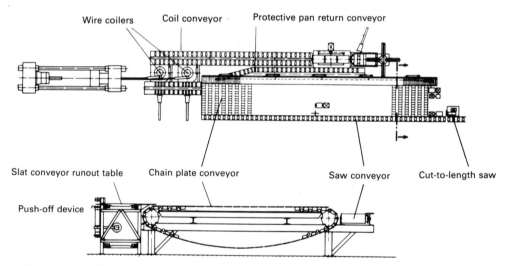

Fig. 4.55. Schematic diagram of a special extrusion installation for the production of brass sections and wire. *(From Schloemann-SIEMAG)*

4.5. Hydraulic Cable Sheathing Presses

An important application of the extrusion process is cable-sheathing—that is, coating electric cables with lead or aluminum. Continuous operating screw presses were developed about 60 years ago exclusively for sheathing cables with lead, but hydraulic cable-sheathing presses that completely fulfilled industrial requirements were not developed until much later. The most important demand of cable plants is for a continuous aluminum sheathing process without any interruption, and this has been possible only in the past 10 years.

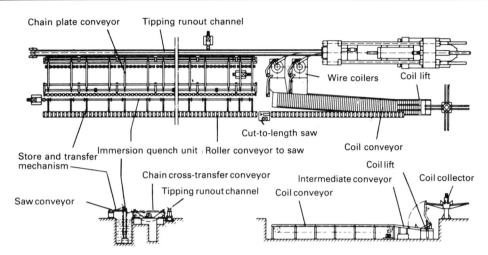

Fig. 4.56. Schematic diagram of a rod and tube press with movable runout channel and shell conveyor. *(From Schloemann-SIEMAG)*

Fig. 4.57. Rod and tube press, 60 MN capacity, for heavy metals. *(From Schloemann-SIEMAG)*

It is interesting to note that the principal German press manufacturers — Hydraulik-DEMAG and Schloemann-SIEMAG — have adopted two different methods to overcome the major initial difficulties in sheathing aluminum cable: by stopmarks and the evacuation of air from the container. Molten metal can be used for the lead sheathing process but the high temperatures and the danger of burning the cable insulation exclude this method for aluminum. Riemann (Ref 22) has investigated variations in the cable sheath at the stopmark formed when the press is recharged. The decrease in thickness is the result of the fall in pressure (the pressure applied by the ram on the aluminum) at the stopping point if the annular clearance is not increased by moving the die in accordance with the pressure drop.

In addition to the wall thickness deviations mentioned in Chap. 3, temperature variations also occur; they are the result of discontinuities in the transition zone between two charges. All these disadvantages can be eliminated only by using twin ram presses for continuous cable sheathing. A typical vertical press, designed by Hydraulik, is shown in Fig. 4.58; the method of operation is explained in Chap. 2.

Fig. 4.58. Cable sheathing press, 30 MN capacity, for producing endless cable sheaths of aluminum or lead without stopmarks. *(From DEMAG-Hydraulik)*

Fig. 4.59. Aluminum cable press, 16 MN capacity; input side. *(From Schloe–mann-SIEMAG)*

Schloemann has built a twin ram horizontal press with the crosshead situated between two containers. Two independently operating induction furnaces are used, together with two prefill tanks, pumps and accumulator systems (Fig. 4.59). The two induction furnaces operating in parallel heat the billets to the extrusion temperature and discharge them as part of the press operating cycle. There is a billet available in both furnaces 20 to 30 seconds after the billet call signal. The signal for the next pair of billets is automatically initiated as the press approaches the fully forward position. The hot billets are pushed out and two cold ones loaded into the furnaces. Billet loaders move the hot billets into the press and the extrusion stems charge them into the containers.

Figure 4.60 diagrams a cross section through the press. The core of the cable passes through a water-cooled protective tube in the crosshead and the aluminum sheath is uniformly cooled by water immediately on leaving the die. The position of the die can be altered by a hydraulically operated screw adjuster to prevent necking at the stopmark when the load on the press crosshead is removed. The annular clearance between the die and mandrel tip is slightly increased and this compensates for the necking.

Similarly, the wall thickness of the sheath can usually be maintained at a constant value by using the hydraulic die adjuster before and after the break

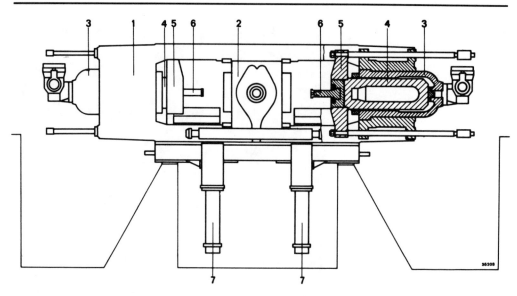

1 – Main frame
2 – Container with die adjuster and
    extrusion chamber
3 – Press cylinder with prefill valve

4 – Main ram
5 – Stem holder in moving crosshead
6 – Extrusion stem
7 – Billet loader

Fig. 4.60. Schematic diagram of an aluminum cable press with two press cylinders opposite each other. *(From Schloemann-SIEMAG)*

in the extrusion cycle. The double billet process requires identical operating conditions on both sides of the press. The volumes and temperatures of the billets and containers must be identical. In addition, the friction and flow behavior of the aluminum as it enters the die head must also be the same on both sides — that is, the stems must have the same speeds, controlled by a suitable synchronizing system.

To summarize, both types of cable presses have proved themselves in practice. Successful operation depends on the prevention or good control of stopmarks to guarantee a constant cable thickness and sheath dimensions.

4.6. Extrusion Presses for Steel

As mentioned in Chap. 3, problems associated with tooling have played a decisive role in the introduction of steel extrusion. In aluminum extrusion, no difficulties occur in the use of tooling made from the customary hot working steels. For copper and copper alloys, the operating limits of hot working steels are reached, in most cases, when the resultant temperature eventually causes overheating of the dies. The usual range of hot working steels can be used for steel extrusion only if the heat transfer from the product to the die is significantly reduced by a suitable insulating lubricant and the contact time is as short as possible (ram speds as high as 400 mm/s).

4.6.1. Mechanical Presses for Steel Tubes

Steel tubes were extruded in 1927/28 with the use of a conventional lubricant (grease) — that is, before a more suitable lubricating agent was found and before steel sections could be extruded in hydraulic presses. The first attempts were made in Germany by Kronprinz, using Singer's patents. A mechanical tube extrusion press was used, made possible by the design and development of a special mechanical crank-type tube press fitted with flywheels. The method of operation of this press allowed the rapid deformation process to be completed during one stroke and, accordingly, the contact time between the hot extrusion and the tooling was extremely short. Tubes of unalloyed or low-alloy steels are mass produced by this process but the production is limited to relatively short lengths. The mechanical press plant in Fig. 4.61 has a capacity of 16.5 MN and includes a billet loading mechanism, a rotary furnace and a descaler.

When the economics of the various methods for manufacturing steel tubes are compared, the decisive technical criteria are: the inexpensive production of marketable lengths and small quantities. These requirements are largely fulfilled by the vertical mechanical crank-operated press with its high output of about 180 extrusions per hour, and this type is preferred for the mass production of carbon steels and ball bearing tubes.

4.6.2. Hydraulic Extrusion Presses for Steel Tubes and Sections

The well-established advantages of hydraulic presses for extruding heavy metals have also been applied to steel with the emphasis on vertical presses. Figure 4.62 shows a plant with two vertical 16 MN presses for producing steel tubes. The various manufacturing requirements in terms of section, material and batch sizes in steel extrusion place considerable demands on the machinery and auxiliary equipment. Consequently, its feasibility is open to question in some cases when compared with section rolling, in spite of the high cost of rolling. This applies, in particular, to the production of high-alloy steel tubes where the variable programing requires careful billet preparation in billet processing machines and the use of both solid and hollow billets of the various alloys. The piercing and extrusion operations cannot always be carried out in one heat, because of the high extrusion temperatures, and

Fig. 4.61. Mechanical crank press, 16.5 MN capacity, for extruding steel tubes. *(From Schloemann-SIEMAG)*

therefore the billet heating furnaces, piercing and extrusion presses should be close together.

The layout of a horizontal steel tube extrusion plant is illustrated in Fig. 4.63 and consists of a 30 MN tube and rod press with a 12 MN piercing press and the appropriate billet furnaces. A view of a complete installation for producing high-alloy steel tubes is given in Fig. 4.64. The press has an output of about 80 extrusions per hour.

4.6.3. Auxiliary Equipment

4.6.3.1. Application of the Lubricant

Before the billet is loaded into the press it has to be coated on all sides with a lubricant: glass, an oil-salt-graphite mixture or a similar lubricant effective

Fig. 4.62. Two vertical hydraulic tube presses, 16 MN capacity. *(From Schloemann-SIEMAG)*

at the high extrusion temperatures. A lubricating disc or similar medium should also be used for every extrusion to protect the die from excessive heat. Special equipment for rapid die changing and dressing is shown schematically in Fig. 4.65.

4.6.3.2. Die Changing

The development of hydraulic steel extrusion plants has been further extended to meet the needs of high outputs in horizontal presses. The output of one installation was significantly improved by incorporating a multiple container holder and a rotating die holder (Fig. 4.66). There are, however, considerable operating problems. The auxiliary operations of billet loading, lubrication, discard separation, and the like, are performed during the extrusion time and this reduces the dead cycle time accordingly. Such a press, however, has disadvantages as far as tooling is concerned. The dwell time and the related billet cooling — and, consequently, the danger of scaling —

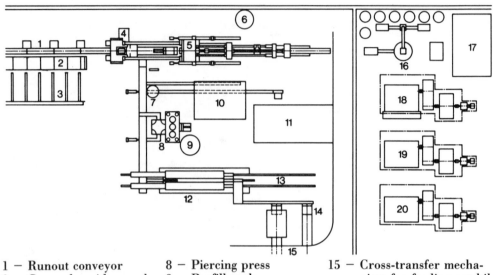

1 – Runout conveyor
2 – Covered rapid quench tank
3 – Cooling table
4 – Die changing station
5 – Rod and tube press
6 – Prefill tank
7 – Rotating transport table
8 – Piercing press
9 – Prefill tank
10 – Three mains-frequency reheating furnaces
11 – Billet loader
12 – Mains-frequency billet furnaces
13 – Billet feed mechanism
14 – Billet store
15 – Cross-transfer mechanism for feeding cut billets to the furnace
16 – High-pressure water accumulator station
17 – Water reservoir
18 – Pump 1
19 – Pump 2
20 – Pump 3

Fig. 4.63. Layout of a steel tube extrusion installation. *(From Fielding, Bournemouth)*

Fig. 4.64. Steel tube plant, 31 MN capacity, with a 12 MN piercing press. *(From Loewy, Bournemouth)*

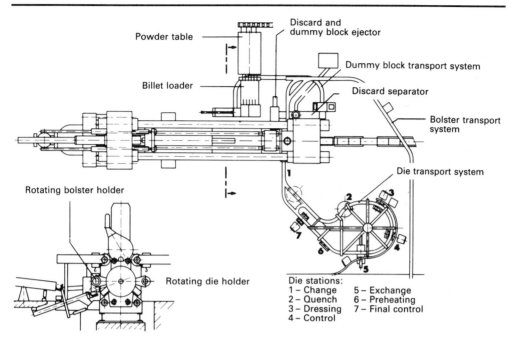

Fig. 4.65. Rod and tube press, with auxiliary equipment, for steel. (*From Schloemann-SIEMAG*)

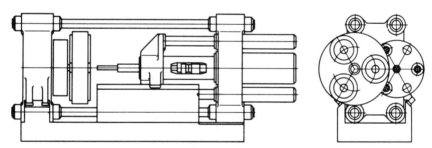

Fig. 4.66. Diagram illustrating the principle of a steel tube press with rotating die and container holders. *(From Fielding, Bournemouth)*

increase when the hot billet is loaded outside the press. A typical installation can be seen in Fig. 4.67 where a conical die is fitted into a rotating die holder.

4.6.3.3. Cooling From the Extrusion Temperature

High-alloy steel tubes are quenched in water immediately after extrusion in the production of finished blooms to retain an austenitic structure. On the other hand, ball bearing tubes are, after any necessary stretch reduction, slowly cooled in air on a cooling bed and then subjected to a special heat treatment.

Fig. 4.67. Die with conical entry installed in a rotating die arm. *(From Fielding, Bournemouth)*

4.6.3.4. Horizontal Tube Extrusion Press Combined With a Hot Stretch Reducing Mill

An automatic, hydraulic tube press and hot stretch reducing mill have been coupled to reduce the manufacturing costs of steel tubes and to extend the range of dimensions produced. This combination installation appears to point the way to the future and is, therefore, described here in detail. Its annual capacity is 100 000 t of steel tubes in diameters ranging from 1⅜ in. to 6½ in. It permits variations in the production sequence according to the specifications of the product. Low-carbon steels, tool steels and stainless steels are produced. The production sequence is given below (Fig. 4.68).

The billets are transported in railway cars from the foundry to the storage area (1) and moved from there to the transport stations (2) by cranes. A conveying mechanism takes the billets to a weigh station in front of the cold saws (3) where they are divided and transferred (4) to the six saws. Loading of the saw inlet tables is controlled by automatic equipment that determines the priorities in the work sequence of the cranes. The billets advance to the twin cold saws (5) installed in each line, and multiple cuts are made simultaneously. The billets are then automatically conveyed to pallets (6) which are moved to storage or taken by forklift for direct processing. The pallets are automatically unloaded at the receiving station for the horizontal induction furnaces (7) when a signal comes from one of the four parallel induction furnaces (8). Manipulators (9) on the exit side of the furnaces move the billets to a roller conveyor (10) which advances each billet to the hydraulic descaler (12). The billets are then loaded into the container of the piercing press (13). Alternatively, the program can take the billets from the induction furnaces to a sizing mill (11) and then feed them to the hydraulic extrusion press (15) for

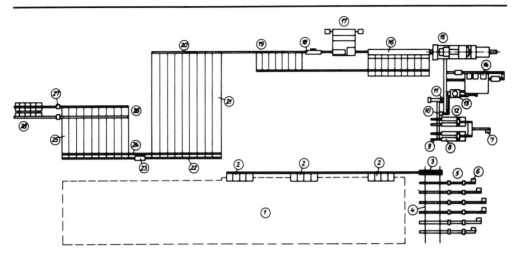

Fig. 4.68. Horizontal tube extrusion press combined with stretch reducing equipment for producing steel tubes with diameters from 1⅜ to 6½ in. *(From Ref 30)*

piercing and extrusion. Three vertical induction furnaces (14) are available and are used only if the billet temperature is too low for optimum extrusion after the separate piercing operation. The extruded product travels into a muffle at the exit side of the press (16) and then enters the stretch reducing mill (17). A flying hot saw (18) cuts the products to length and the tubes are moved along a roller conveyor (19), through a high-speed kickout mechanism (20) and onto the cooling bed (21). The cooled tubes then travel along another roller conveyor (22) into the straightener (23), and are discharged by a high-speed mechanism (24) to the cross-transfer conveyor (25, 26) feeding the cold saw. The tubes are cut to the required finished length by two cold saws (27).

This combination of stretch reducing mill and extrusion press has also been used for vertical tube presses. The installation in Fig. 4.62 with two vertical steel tube presses also has a stretch reducing mill connected in line to the exit sides (not visible in the photograph).

4.6.4. Vertical Tube Presses for Large Tubes

The structure of the largest vertical presses, with a capacity of 300 MN, deserves special attention. They are equipped for special forging processes and also for the indirect extrusion of large seamless steel tubes (Fig. 4.69). The 300 MN press in Fig. 4.70 and 4.71 was built by Cameron Iron Works, Ltd.,

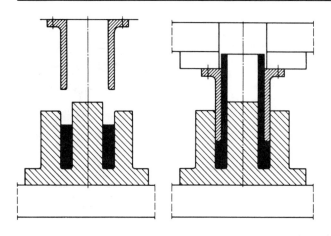

Fig. 4.69. Indirect extrusion of steel tubes in a vertical forging press. *(From Ref 12)*

Fig. 4.70. Vertical forging press, 300 MN capacity, for producing seamless steel tubes. *(From Cameron Iron Works, Inc., Houston)*

Fig. 4.71. Vertical forging press, 300 MN capacity, with a 90 MN preforging press. *(From Cameron IronWorks, Inc., Houston)*

and is located in Livingston, Scotland. Seamless steel tubes are manufactured in this press up to an outside diameter of 1200 mm and 12 m in length, and are removed from above. The maximum billet weight is approximately 15 tonnes. A 90 MN preforging press can be seen in the foreground of Fig. 4.71. Medium- and high-alloy steel tubes can be formed by this process with a maximum diameter of 600 mm. Production will certainly increase in importance.

4.7. Hydrostatic Extrusion

The principle of hydrostatic deformation has been known for a long time and its application to extrusion has been studied in laboratories since 1940. After approximately 30 years of development work, particularly by Fielding & Platt, Ltd., and ASEA, these two firms constructed the first industrial hydrostatic extrusion presses. The following major problems had to be solved to reach this stage of development:

(a) The pressurizing medium, usually oil, must be brought to a working pressure of 20 kbar or more.
(b) The high fluid-pressure requires reliable methods of sealing and high-quality sealing material.

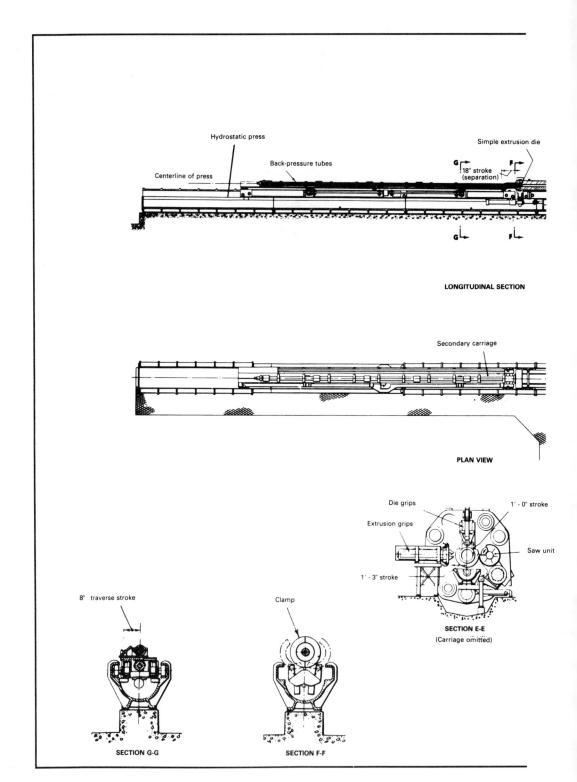

LONGITUDINAL SECTION

Hydrostatic press

Back-pressure tubes

Centerline of press

Simple extrusion die

G

F

18" stroke
(separation)

Secondary carriage

PLAN VIEW

Die grips

1' - 0" stroke

Extrusion grips

Saw unit

1' - 3" stroke

SECTION E-E
(Carriage omitted)

8" traverse stroke

Clamp

SECTION G-G

SECTION F-F

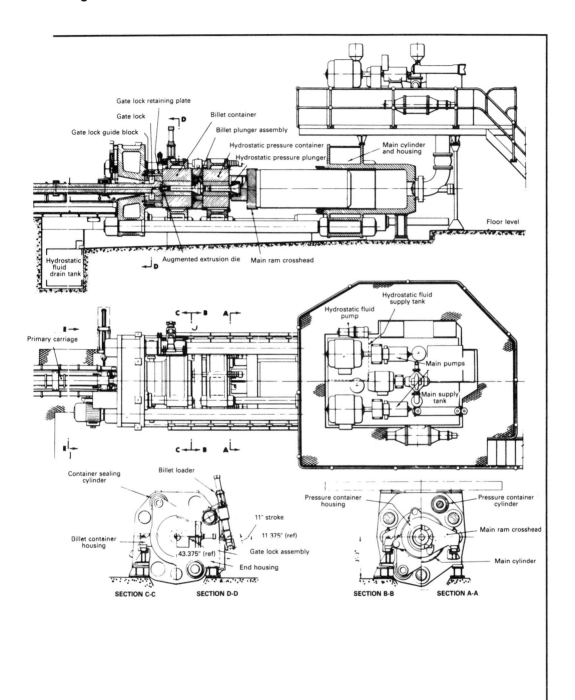

Fig. 4.72. Horizontal hydrostatic 16/0.8 MN extrusion press. *(From Ref 31)*

(c) The press frame and housings must be very stable to withstand the high longitudinal tensile stresses resulting from the high fluid-pressures, and to keep elastic deformation to a minimum.

(d) The container is subjected to high tangential stresses during extrusion and the inner liner may crack if the elastic strains are too high.

Diverse practical solutions for these presses were developed by the firms mentioned above.

4.7.1. Design of the Fielding Press

This press is of the horizontal three-column type (Fig. 4.72). The main cylinder moves the hydrostatic pressure plunger of the first of two hydrostatic containers arranged one behind the other. The press in Fig. 4.73 can apply a maximum load of 16 MN.

The first hydrostatic pressure plunger (12), with a diameter of 127 mm, compresses the hydrostatic fluid in the first container (11) at a load of $15.696 \cdot 10^3$ N over an area of 12 668 mm^2 = a pressure of 12.6 kbar. Pressures up to 30 kbar can be produced with smaller plungers and smaller container diameters. A second plunger (10) is attached to the front of the first container. This plunger is used to load the billets, seal the billet container and augment the hydrostatic extrusion (Chap. 2). The hydrostatic fluid is transferred to the billet container (9) through a hole in the billet plunger ram to give the same hydrostatic pressure during extrusion as that in the first hydrostatic pressure container. Both containers can be moved independently by auxiliary rams located in the main cylinder housing or end housing. The billet container is sealed with a load of 1.82 MN (on the 16 MN press) against the gate lock assembly before the extrusion cycle starts.

The rated output of this Fielding press is 45 billets per hour. As well as normal or augmented extrusion without any back pressure, it is also possible to extrude with hydrostatic back pressure using the back pressure tubes on the exit side of the press (Fig. 4.72).

4.7.2. Design of the ASEA Press

ASEA used a completely different press and container design from that described above in order to effectively resist the mechanical stresses developed in the press frame and container during hydrostatic extrusion. The press frame and container are designed to be prestressed by wrapping high-strength steel wire with a square cross section under tension around a rigid structure, using a special technique. The structure is then always in compression even at the maximum working pressure. One or two liners are pressed into the wire-wound containers as a final operation. The basic features of a

Fig. 4.73. Hydrostatic 16 MN extrusion press; main cylinder on the left, end housing on the right. *(From Fielding, Bournemouth)*

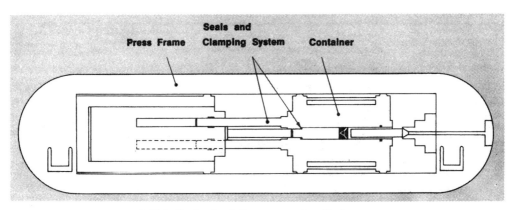

Fig. 4.74. Principal features of a Quintus press.

Quintus press are shown in Fig. 4.74. The load is applied from the main cylinder through the plunger to the hydrostatic fluid in the container with the billet. In contrast to the Fielding press, the high-pressure container and the billet container are combined into one unit. An auxiliary system comes into play when a billet is unexpectedly extruded completely; the excess energy accelerates the main plunger forwards. Simultaneously, the pressure increases in the auxiliary cylinders in the main plunger to a value high enough to stop the plunger movement.

Fig. 4.75. Hydrostatic Quintus extrusion press; main cylinder on the right, exit side on the left.

Figure 4.75 shows a Quintus press fitted with a billet feed and loader system. The billets are conically turned at the front end to give a good seal between the billet and conical die, to prevent fluid loss during container sealing.

Bibliographic References

1. Weitzel, F.: Die Entwicklung der Strangpresse. Handbuch: Werkzeuge und Werkzeugstahl für das Strangpressen. Edelstahlwerke Buderus (1966).
2. Dohrn, W.: Wirtschaftlichkeit verschiedener Antriebsarten bei hydraulischen Pressen. Z. f. Metallkunde 46 (1955) p. 405/414.
3. Veltjens, D.: Strangpreßanlagen mit Hilfs- und Folgeeinrichtungen für Kupferwerkstoffe. Z. f. Metallkunde 62 (1971) p. 87/99.
4. Köblitz, P.: Strangpressen in "Aluminium Handbuch". Herausgegeben von H. Göner und S. Marx, VEB-Verlag Technik, Berlin (1969).
5. Müller, E.: Hydraulische Pressen und Druckflüssigkeitsanlagen, Band 3. Herstellung von Rohren, voll- und hohlprofilierten Stangen und Drähten sowie Kabelmäntel aus NE-Metallen. Springer-Verlag, Berlin (1959).
6. Zolobov, W., and Zverev, G. I.: Pressovanie Metallov, Moscow (1959).
7. Dohrn, W., and Stapel, H.: Hydraulische horizontale Strang- und Rohrpresse. Z. f. Metallkunde 51 (1960) p. 65/72.
8. Dohrn, W., and Schmoll, H.: Hydraulische horizontale Strangpresse. Z. f. Metallkunde 51 (1960) p. 29/35.

9. Wyss, F., and Germann, R.: Die neue 7200 Mp Rohr- und Strangpreßanlage im Alusuisse-Halbzeugwerk. Chippis, Schweizer Aluminium-Rundschau 10 (1971) p. 347/351.

10. Zilges, F. J.: Strang- und Rohrpreßanlagen für Schwermetall. Z. f. Metallkunde 60 (1969) p. 85/93.

11. Zilges, F. J.: Strang- und Rohrpreßanlagen für Aluminium. Aluminium 47 (1971) p. 213/220.

12. Zeitlin, A.: Recent Advances in Extrusion Presses. International Extrusion Technology Seminar, New Orleans (1969).

13. Dohrn, W., and Demming, F.: Hydraulische vertikale Strang- und Rohrpressen. Z. f. Metallkunde 51 (1960) p. 135/142.

14. Haverkamp, B.: Geschwindigkeits-Meß- und Regeleinrichtung an Strang- und Rohr-pressen. International Extrusion Technology Seminar, Paper 19, New Orleans (1969).

15. Haverkamp, B.: Lochstreifengesteuerte Metallstrangpresse. Aluminium 43 (1969) p. 167/170.

16. Elkan, R. M. L., and Cox, R.: Development in Steel Extrusion. J. Iron & Steel Inst. 202 (1964) p. 236/260.

17. Haffner, E. K. L., and Elkan, R. M. L.: Extrusion Presses and Press Installations. Metallurgical Reviews 2 (1957) p. 263/303.

18. Putz, J.: Moderne Blockerwärmungsanlagen. Z. f. Metallkunde 62 (1971) p. 21/26.

19. Hardt, K.: Temperaturverhältnisse bei der induktiven Erwärmung von Aluminium-blöcken zum Strangpressen. Aluminium 43 (1967) p. 565/571.

20. Hertl, A., and Maier, H. O.: Der heutige Stand von Strangpreßanlagen für Al-Werkstoffe. Z. f. Metallkunde 62 (1971) p. 112/116.

21. Müller, E.: Neues kontinuierliches Preßverfahren zum Herstellen von Aluminium-Kabelmänteln ohne Haltestellen. Z. f. Metallkunde 53 (1961) p. 147/151.

22. Riemann, H.: Kabelmäntel ohne Haltestellen. Draht 19 (1968) p. 223/232.

23. Steinmetz, A.: Doppelt wirkende Presse zum Ummanteln elektrischer Leiter mit Aluminium. Aluminium 46 (1970) p. 230/234.

24. Beerens, H., and Feldmann, H.: Wärmebehandlung von Aluminium-Strang-preß-profilen aus der Preßhitze. Aluminium 47 (1971) p. 545/549.

25. Elkan, R. M. L., and Schieren, K. H.: Strangpressen von Stahlrohren. Bänder-Bleche-Rohre 5 (1964) p. 150/155.

26. Kolsch, A.: Strangpressen von Stahlrohren auf Kurbelrohrpressen. Z. f. Metallkunde 62 (1971) p. 649/652.

27. Groos, H. H.: Strangpreßanlagen zur Herstellung nahtloser Stahlrohre. Bänder-Bleche-Rohre 7 (1966) p. 833/838.

28. Kursetz, E.: Die Entwicklung des Warmstrangpressens von Stahl und Sondermetallen in der amerikanischen Halbzeugindustrie. Luftfahrttechnik, Raumfahrttechnik 15 (1969) p. 86/90.

29. Courtney, R. J.: Some Aspects of the Extrusion of Nickel-Based Alloys. J. Inst. Metals 99 (1971) p. 261/266.

30. Klein, A., Schindler, K., and Hartenstein, R.: Extrusion and Stretch Reducing of Tubular Products. Iron and Steel Engineer 41 (1964) p. 97/105.

31. Hydrostatic Extrusion at the U.K.A.E.A. Installation of a 1600/80-ton Press in the Springfield Works. Metal Forming (1968) p. 107/110.

32. ASEA: Quintus, Hydrostatic Extrusion Press, Type QE. ASEA Publication A Q 14.102E.

33. Zilges, F. J.: Eine neue Strangpresse für die Leichtmetallindustrie. Aluminium 50 (1974) p. 456/461.

34. Laue, K.: Wirtschaftlichkeit und Leistungssteigerung beim Strangpressen. Z. f. Metallkunde 60 (1969) p. 891/897.

5. Extrusion Tooling

This chapter is concerned with the practical problems in the design, manufacture and application of the tooling used in extrusion and discusses the steps that can be taken in design, material technology and organization to reduce the number of mistakes and defects in the production and treatment of the tooling. The correct choice of steel for the stresses developed is of particular importance. Although many of the items mentioned here may be obvious to the specialist, all the problems relevant to economical production are included. The tooling is, without doubt, the key to the economical extrusion of rod, tube and, in particular, sections. The standardization of tooling is considered, because this is also important for cost-conscious production.

5.1. Construction and Terminology of Extrusion Tooling

5.1.1. Construction of the Tool Sets and Terminology

5.1.1.1. Summary of Tooling and Terminology

Extrusion tooling consists of several individual items assembled together into a tool set and is briefly summarized below. A number of different names are frequently encountered for the various components and this, obviously, hinders understanding in technical circles, especially on international technical committees. The extrusion division of the German Metallurgical

Society (DGM) has, therefore, prepared a glossary of the most important names and expressions in four languages (German, English, French and Italian) and it is presented in Table 5.1.

Figures 5.1 to 5.14 depict the individual tools and their assembly. A more detailed view of the tooling involved in the actual deformation process is shown in Fig. 5.15a. The main parts of extrusion presses are identified in Fig. 5.15, b and c.

The tooling necessary for any particular process depends on the product — rod, tube or section — the type of press available, and the alloy to be worked. Tooling used to be classified into extrusion tooling and auxiliary tooling. The latter included the container, stem, and the like, which were considered to be components of the press. The extrusion tools, including the die, mandrel, dummy block, stem head, and welding chamber dies, are used for deformation and have to be continually replaced because they are subjected to high rates of wear. This division into auxiliary tools and extrusion tools no longer applies if the inner liner is classified under the auxiliary tooling; it is part of the container, even though it is subjected to a rate of wear equal to that of the die. The only tools that actually produce a change in shape are the die and sometimes the mandrel.

5.1.1.2. Securing the Die in Its Holder

Only heavy metals were fabricated when the extrusion process was first introduced and the high exit temperatures necessitated very rapid die changes for cooling after each extrusion. Rapid die changing is also advantageous, from an economical point of view, when operating a varied program with only a few runs through each die. These requirements resulted in a die arrangement that was particularly suitable for heavy metal extrusion. The die is inserted into the front of the die holder, using a tapered cone, and it can be removed easily and rapidly. Figure 5.16 shows three different applications of a double taper (from 10° to 30°) for the fit between the following:

(a) Container and die holder, and the die and die holder.
(b) Container and die, the die and its holder.
(c) Container and die backer, and the die and its holder.

This die system is still used today in its original form for the extrusion of heavy metals and occasionally for aluminum alloys. However, the advantage of a rapid die change is offset by the wear of the taper in the die holder after a long period in service and the die can then fall out. In addition to sealing, the die and mandrel must also be accurately centered if acceptable concentric tubes are to be extruded. The die holder, therefore, has to align the center lines of the die and the inner liner, but this requirement cannot be met with the closed systems shown in Fig. 5.16. Schloemann developed a new

(text continued on page 320)

Table 5.1. Extrusion Terminology (Numbers Refer to Components in Fig. 5.1 to 5.15c)

No.	English	German	French	Italian
1	die holder carrier	Werkzeugaufnehmer	tampon, porte-outillage	porta attrezzatura
1.1	die head	Werkzeugkopf, Mundstück	porte-outillage	carrello porta attrezzatura
1.2	die slide	Werkzeugschlitten	tiroir porte-filière	slitta porta attrezzatura
1.3	rotating die holder	Werkzeugdreharm	tiroir pivotant	dispositivo porta matrice girevole
1.4	rotating die holder	Werkzeugdrehkreuz	revolver	porta matrice a revolver
2	tooling set	Werkzeugsatz	éléments d'outillage	insieme dell'attrezzatura
2.1	die holder	Matrizenhalter	porte-filière	porta filiera
2.2	tooling for extrusion	Preßwerkzeug	outillage de la presse	attrezzatura di pressa
2.3	backing ring, backer	Stützwerkzeug	contre-filière	sottomatrice
2.4	bolster	Druckplatte	contre-appui, disque d'appui	controfiliera
2.5	subbolster	Hilfsdruckplatte	plaque de fond, contre-disque	anello di appoggio della controfiliera
2.6	pressure ring, die backing ring	Druckring	plaque d'appui, siège de filière	anello di pressione
2.7	horseshoe clamp	Spannbügel	plaque d'arrêt	anello di tenuta
2.8	spacing ring	Beilage	cale	anello (piatto)
3	extrusion dies	Strangpreßwerkzeuge	outils de filage	attrezzature pressa
3.1	die	Matrize	filière, matrice	matrice, filiera
3.2	die housing	Gehäuse, Kammer	filière, corps de filière	porta filiera
3.3	die insert	Matrizeneinsatz	filière insérée, coeur de filière	matrice (per profili cavi)
3.4	adjustable die insert	justierbarer Matrizeneinsatz	coeur de filière adjustable	matrice a inserto intercambiabile
3.5	die mandrel	Dorn	aiguille	ago
3.6	single-hole die	Einlochmatrize	filière à un écoulement en une pièce	matrice a una luce in pezzo unico
3.7	multihole die	Mehrlochmatrize	filière à plusieurs écoulements	matrice a più luci
3.8	prechamber die	Vorkammermatrize	filière avec préchambre	matrice a precamera
3.9	bridge die	Brückenwerkzeug	filière à pont	attrezzatura a ponte

(continued)

Table 5.1., contd. Extrusion Terminology (Numbers Refer to Components in Fig. 5.1 to 5.15c)

No.	English	German	French	Italian
3.10 ....bridge		Brücke	pont	ponte
3.11 ....spider		Tragkreuz (Spider)	spider	spider
3.12 ....solid single-hole bridge die		einteiliges Einloch-Brückenwerkzeug	filière à pont avec un écoulement en une pièce	matrice a ponte a una luce in pezzo unico
3.13 ....multipart single-hole bridge die		mehrteiliges Einloch-Brückenwerkzeug	filière à pont avec un écoulement en plusieurs pièces	matrice a ponte a una luce in più pezzi
3.14 ....solid multihole bridge die		einteiliges Mehrloch-Brückenwerkzeug	filière à pont avec plusieurs écoulements en une pièce	matrice a ponte a più luci in pezzo unico
3.15 ....multipart multihole bridge die		mehrteiliges Mehrloch-Brückenwerkzeug	filière à pont avec plusieurs écoulements en plusieurs pièces	matrice a ponte a più luci in più pezzi
3.16 ....solid single-hole spider die		einteiliges Einloch-Spiderwerkzeug	spider avec un écoulement en une pièce	attrezzatura spider a una luce in pezzo unico
3.17 ....multipart single-hole spider die		mehrteiliges Einloch-Spiderwerkzeug	spider avec un écoulement en plusieurs pièces	attrezzatura spider a una luce in più pezzi
3.18 ....multipart multihole spider die		mehrteiliges Mehrloch-Spiderwerkzeug	spider avec plusieurs écoulements en plusieurs pièces	attrezzatura spider a più luci in più pezzi
3.19 ....solid single-hole porthole die		einteiliges Einloch-Kammerwerkzeug	outillage porthole avec un écoulement en une pièce	attrezzatura porthole a una luce in pezzo unico
3.20 ....multipart single-hole porthole die		mehrteiliges Einloch-Kammerwerkzeug	outillage porthole avec un écoulement en plusieurs pièces	attrezzatura porthole a una luce in più pezzi
3.21 ....multipart multihole porthole die		mehrteiliges Mehrloch-Kammerwerkzeug	outillage porthole avec plusieurs écoulements en plusieurs pièces	attrezzatura porthole a più luci in più pezzi
3.22 ....welding chamber		Schweißkammer	chambre de soudure	camera di saldatura
3.23 ....feeder ports		Zuführöffnungen (Einläufe)	entrées de métal	luci di alimentazione

	German	French	Italian
3.24.....spreader plate	Expansions-Vorkammerscheibe	plaque de préformage	precamera di allargamento
3.25.....feeder plate	Vorfüllscheibe	plaque de préchambre	disco di precamera
3.26.....orifice, hole	Matrizendurchbruch	écoulement	luce matrice
3.27.....bearing face	Matrizenlauffläche	portée de travail	labbro di filiera
3.28.....bearing length, die land	Preßkanallänge, Länge der Matrizenlauffläche	hauteur de portée	altezza del labbro di filiera
3.29.....die face	Matrizen-Stirnfläche	face de la filière	faccia matrice
3.30.....conical die face	konische Matrizen-Stirnfläche (Einlaufkonus)	face conique de la filière	superficie conica di filiera
3.31.....die entry radius	Radius der Einlaufkante	angle d'entrée	imbocco
3.32.....die relief	Hinterfräsung, Hinterdrehung (Durchbruch)	dégagement arrière	scarico
3.33.....external taper	Matrizen-Außenkonus	cône extérieur	conicità della superficie esterna
4.......mandrels	Dorne (am Stempel)	perceurs, aiguilles	mandrini, aghi
4.1.....mandrel	Preßdorn	aiguille	mandrino, ago
4.2.....piercing mandrel, piercer	Lochdorn	perceur	mandrino foratore
4.3.....fixed mandrel	feststehender Dorn	mandrin fixe	mandrino fisso
4.4.....stepped mandrel (fixed)	abgesetzter Dorn	mandrin à épaulement	mandrino a punta rastremata
4.5.....mandrel release	mitlaufender Dorn	mandrin mobile	mandrino mobile
4.6.....mandrel tip	Dornspitze	nez d'aiguille, tête de mandrin	testa del mandrino
4.7.....replaceable mandrel tip	eingesetzte Dornspitze	tête de mandrin démontable	testa di mandrino intercambiabile
4.8.....piercing stem	Dornstange	tige de perceur, pilon de perceur	prolunga mandrino
4.9.....mandrel holder	Dornhalter	porte-mandrin	prolunga mandrino
4.10.....floating mandrel	schwimmender Dorn	mandrin flottant	mandrino flottante
5.......additional tooling	sonstige Werkzeuge	outils auxiliares	altre attrezzature
5.1.....container	Blockaufnehmer, Rezipient	conteneur	contenitore, recipiente
5.2.....liner	Innenbüchse	âme	bussola
5.3.....liner holder	Zwischenbüchse	frette intermédiaire	bussola intermedia
5.4.....outer mantle	Aufnehmermantel, Mantel	manteau, frette extérieure	mantello

(continued)

Table 5.1., contd. Extrusion Terminology (Numbers Refer to Components in Fig. 5.1 to 5.15c)

No.	English	German	French	Italian
5.5	pressure pad, dummy block	Preßscheibe	grain (de pousée).	disco pressatore
5.6	extrusion stem, ram, pressing stem, punch	Preßstempel	fouloir, pilon	asta pressante
5.7	solid stem	Vollstempel	bélier plein, fouloir	asta pressante piena
5.8	hollow stem	Hohlstempel, Lochstempel	bélier creux, fouloir creux	asta pressante forata
5.9	ejecting disc, cleaning disc, clean out block, clearing pad	Putzscheibe, Auspreß-scheibe	plaque de nettoyage, grain racleur	disco raschiante
6	container tool seal	Werkzeugabdichtung zum Aufnehmer	fermeture du conteneur	chiusura contenitore
6.1	flat seal	Flachdichtung	portée plate	appoggio piano
6.11	flat seal die	flach abgedichtete Matrize	filière plate	attrezzatura con appoggio piano
6.2	taper seal	Konusabdichtung	portée conique	appoggio conico
6.21	taper seal die	konisch abgedichtete Matrize	filière à cône	attrezzatura con appoggio conico
6.3	double taper seal	Doppelkonusabdichtung	portée à double cône	appoggio a doppia conicità
6.31	double taper seal die	doppelt konisch abge-dichtete Matrize	filière à double cône	attrezzatura con appoggio a doppia conicità
6.4	straight seal	Zylinderabdichtung	portée cylindrique	accoppiamento cilindrico
6.41	straight seal die	zylindrisch abgedichtete Matrize	filière cylindrique	attrezzatura ad accoppiamento cilindrico
7	extrusion press components	Elemente der Strangpresse	éléments de la presse à filer	elementi della pressa
7.1	extrusion press	Strangpresse	presse à filer	pressa estrusione
7.2	billet loader	Blocklader	chargeur de billettes	caricatore billette
7.3	loading ramp	Ladeschale	table de chargeuse	culla porta billette
7.4	platen, end housing	Gegenhalter, Querhaupt, Gegenholm	sommier	frontone della pressa
7.5	main cylinder	Hauptzylinder	cylindre principal	cilindro principale
7.6	main ram	Hauptpreßkolben	piston principal	pistone principale

	English	German	French	Italian
7.7	piercer cylinder	Lochzylinder	cylindre perceur	cilindro di foratura
7.8	piercer ram	Lochkolben	piston perceur	pistone di foratura
7.9	advance cylinder	Vorschubzylinder	cylindre d'avance	cilindro di avanzamento
7.10	return cylinder	Rückzugzylinder	cylindre de recul, cylindre de rappel	cilindro di ritorno
7.11	longitudinal movement for die head	Werkzeugkopf-Verschiebung (Mundringverschiebung)	coulisseau longitudinal d'outillage	cassetta porta matrice
7.12	run-out table	Auslaufbahn, Auslauftisch	table de sortie	banco di estrusione
7.13	discard separator, butt separator	Preßrest-Trennvorrichtung	cisaille pour résidu	separatore disco
7.14	dummy block return	Preßscheibenrückführung	recyclage du disque presseur	riciclo disco pressante
7.15	shear, saw	Schere, Säge	cisaille, scie	trancia, sega
7.16	wedge	Verschlußkeil	coin, verrou	otturatore
7.17	canister, can	Kanister	bouteille	canister
7.18	die heating furnaces	Werkzeug-Anwärmöfen	fours de filières	forni di riscaldo attrezzature
7.19	stem holder	Stempelhalter	porte fouloir	dispositivo porta-asta pressante
7.20	container shifting cylinder	Aufnehmer-(Rezipienten-)Verschiebezylinder	cylindre de déplacement du conteneur	cilindro di spostamento del contenitore
7.21	discard chute	Preßrest-Austragrinne	évacuation des restes	evacuazione fondello
7.22	column, laminations	Säule, Lamellen	colonne, lamelles	colonna, lamelle
7.23	moving crosshead	Laufholm, bewegliches Querhaupt	support mobile du piston principal	supporto mobile del pistone principale
7.24	cylinder crosshead	Zylinderholm, Zylinder-Querhaupt	support fixe du cylindre principal	supporto fisso del cilindro principale
7.25	column nut	Säulenmutter	écrou de colonne	dado della colonna
7.26	main ram	Hauptkolben	piston principal	pistone principale
7.27	piercer tie rod	Lochdorn-Zugstange	colonne du cylindre perceur	colonna del mandrino foratore
7.28	piercer moving crosshead	Lochdorn-Laufbahn	support mobile du piston du perceur	supporto mobile del mandrino foratore
7.29	piercer return cylinder	Lochdorn-Rückzugzylinder	cylindre de rappel du perceur	cilindro di ritorno del mandrino foratore
7.30	piercer ram	Lochdorn-Kolben	piston du perceur	pistone del mandrino foratore
7.31	piercer cylinder	Lochdorn-Zylinder	cylindre du perceur	cilindro del mandrino foratore

(continued)

Table 5.1., contd. Extrusion Terminology (Numbers Refer to Components in Fig. 5.1 to 5.15c)

No.	English	German	French	Italian
7.32	piercer cylinder prefill valve	Lochdorn-Zylinder-Vorfüllventil	vanne du cylindre du perceur	valvola del cilindro del mandrino foratore
7.33	piercer rotation device	Dorndrehvorrichtung	mécanisme de rotation du perceur	dispositivo di rotazione del mandrino foratore
8	semifinished products	Halbzeuge	semi-produits	semi lavorato
8.1	extrusion, extrude	Preßstrang	profilé filé	estruso
8.2	bar, rod	Preßstange	barre	barra (estrusa)
8.3	tube	Preßrohr	tube (filé)	tubo (estruso)
8.4	shape, section	Preßprofil	profilé	profilato
8.5	solid shape	Vollprofil, offenes Profil	profilé plein	profilato aperto
8.6	semihollow shape	Halbhohlprofil	profilé semi-creux	profilato semi-cavo
8.7	hollow shape	Hohlprofil	profilé creux	profilato cavo
8.8	coil	Ring, Bund	couronne	corona
9	raw material	Vormaterial	matières premières	matiere primiere
9.1	billet	Preßbarren, Preßbolzen	billette	billetta
9.2	hollow billet	Hohlbarren, Hohlbolzen	billette creuse	billetta cava
9.3	discard, butt	Preßrest	culot, résidu	fondello
9.4	shell	Preßschale, Schale	chemise	camicia
10	extrusion operation:	Preßvorgang:	opération:	operazione:
	loading	Laden	charger	caricare
	insertion	Einstoßen	pousser dans le récipient	introdurre
	upsetting	Stauchen	compression	comprimere
	decompression	Entlüften	décompression	decomprimere
	piercing	Lochen	perçage	forare
	extrusion	Auspressen	filage	estrudere
	upsetting of shell	Schale stauchen	refoulement de la chemise	comprimere la camicia
	return stroke	Rückzug	retour du fouloir	ritirare
	cutting, sawing	Trennen, Sägen	séparation, sciage	tagliare
	ejection	Ausstoßen	extraction	espellere

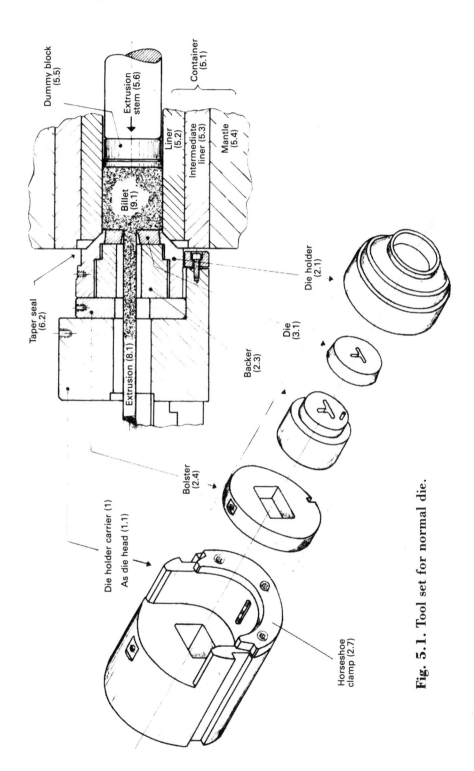

Fig. 5.1. Tool set for normal die.

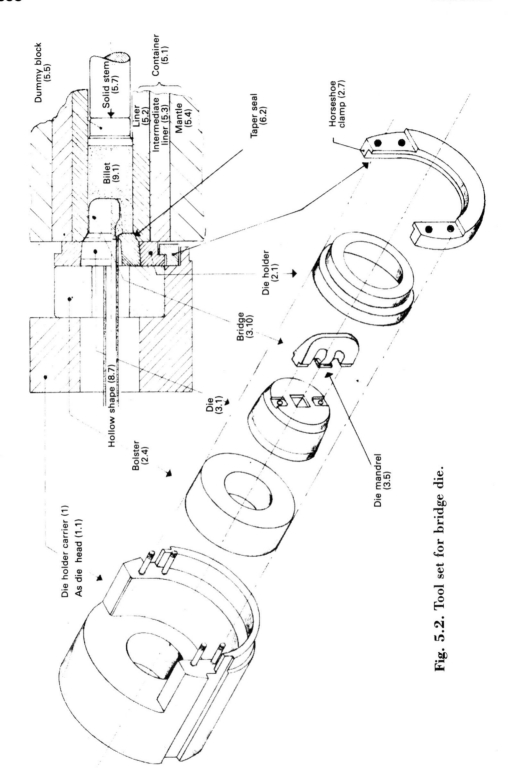

Dummy block (5.5)

Solid stem (5.7)

Container (5.1)

Liner (5.2)

Intermediate liner (5.3)

Mantle (5.4)

Billet (9.1)

Taper seal (6.2)

Horseshoe clamp (2.7)

Die holder (2.1)

Bridge (3.10)

Die (3.1)

Hollow shape (8.7)

Die mandrel (3.5)

Bolster (2.4)

Die holder carrier (1)
As die head (1.1)

Fig. 5.2. Tool set for bridge die.

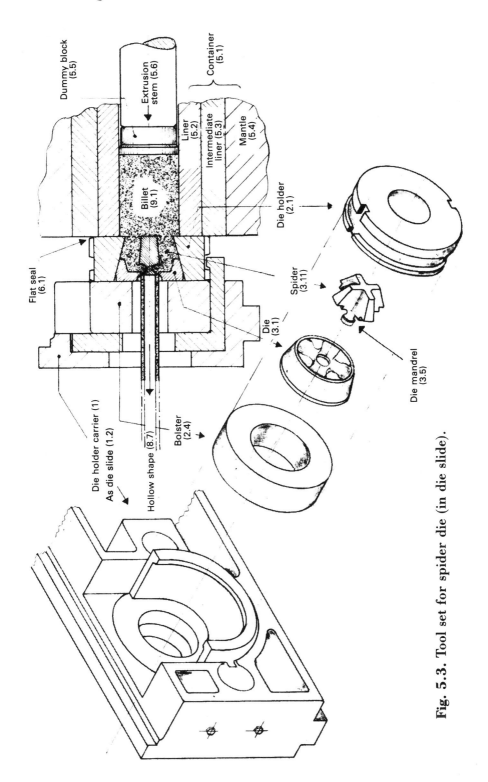

Fig. 5.3. Tool set for spider die (in die slide).

Dummy block (5.5)

Extrusion stem (5.6)

Container (5.1)

Liner (5.2)

Intermediate liner (5.3)

Mantle (5.4)

Billet (9.1)

Die holder (2.1)

Spider (3.11)

Flat seal (6.1)

Die (3.1)

Die mandrel (3.5)

Die holder carrier (1)

As die slide (1.2)

Hollow shape (8.7)

Bolster (2.4)

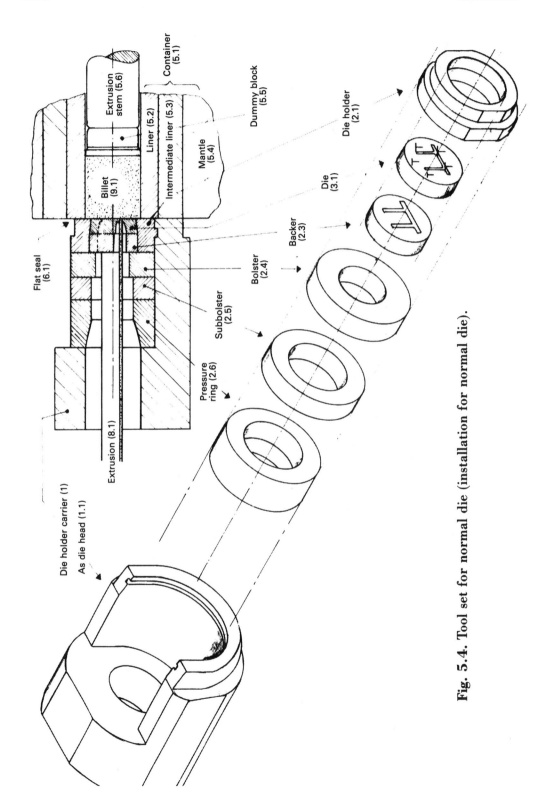

Flat seal (6.1)

Die holder carrier (1)
As die head (1.1)

Extrusion (8.1)

Pressure ring (2.6)

Subbolster (2.5)

Bolster (2.4)

Backer (2.3)

Die (3.1)

Die holder (2.1)

Extrusion stem (5.6)

Liner (5.2)

Billet (9.1)

Intermediate liner (5.3)

Mantle (5.4)

Dummy block (5.5)

Container (5.1)

Fig. 5.4. Tool set for normal die (installation for normal die).

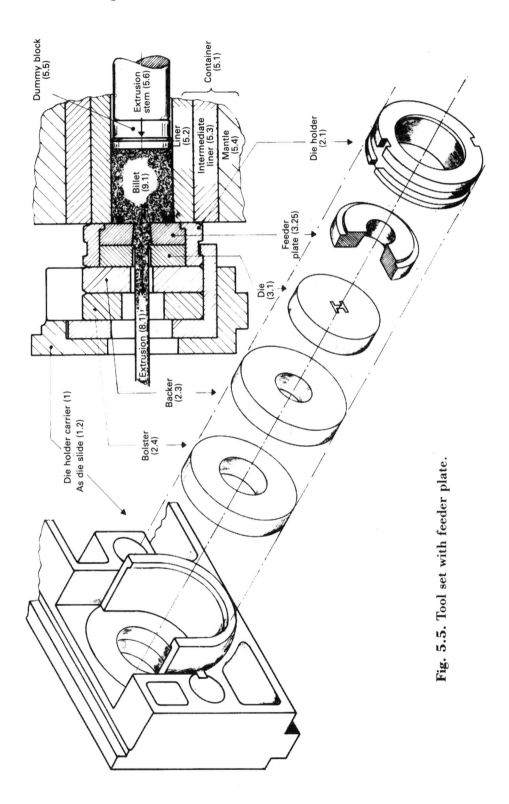

Dummy block (5.5)

Extrusion stem (5.6)

Liner (5.2)

Intermediate liner (5.3)

Mantle (5.4)

Container (5.1)

Billet (9.1)

Die holder (2.1)

Feeder plate (3.25)

Die (3.1)

Backer (2.3)

Extrusion (8.1)

Bolster (2.4)

Die holder carrier (1)

As die slide (1.2)

Fig. 5.5. Tool set with feeder plate.

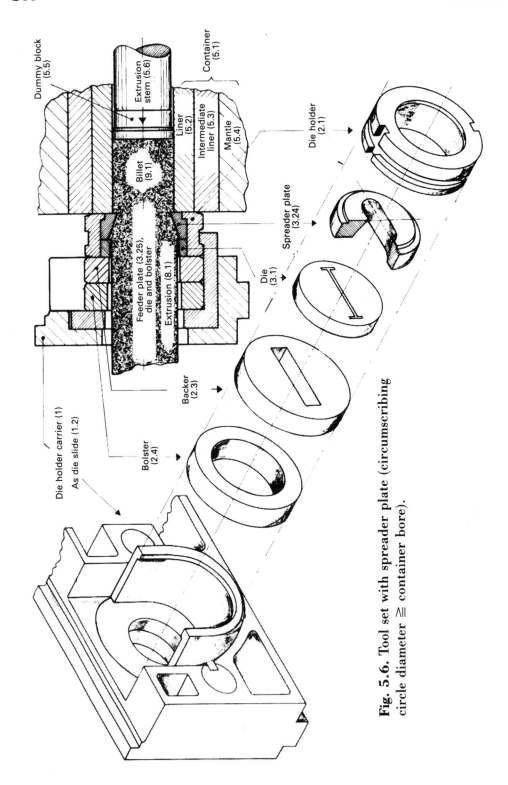

Fig. 5.6. Tool set with spreader plate (circumscribing circle diameter ≧ container bore).

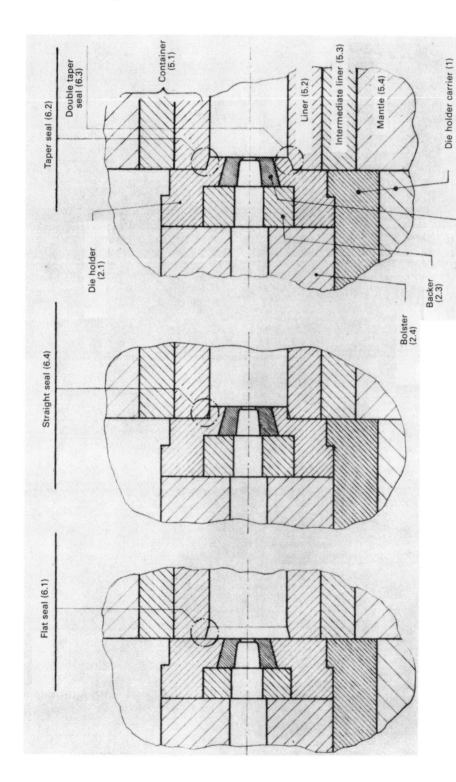

Fig. 5.7. Container tool seal (die diameter ≦ container bore).

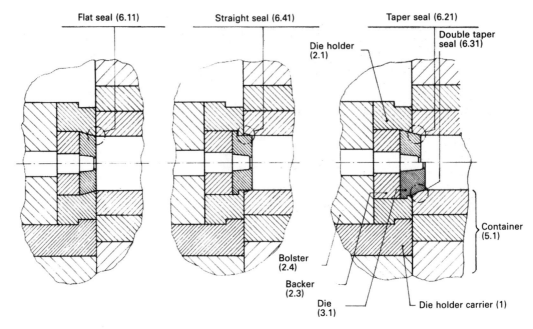

Fig. 5.8. Container tool seal (die diameter $\geqq$ container bore).

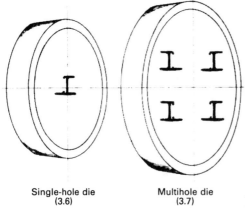

Single-hole die
(3.6)

Multihole die
(3.7)

Fig. 5.9. Single-hole and multihole dies.

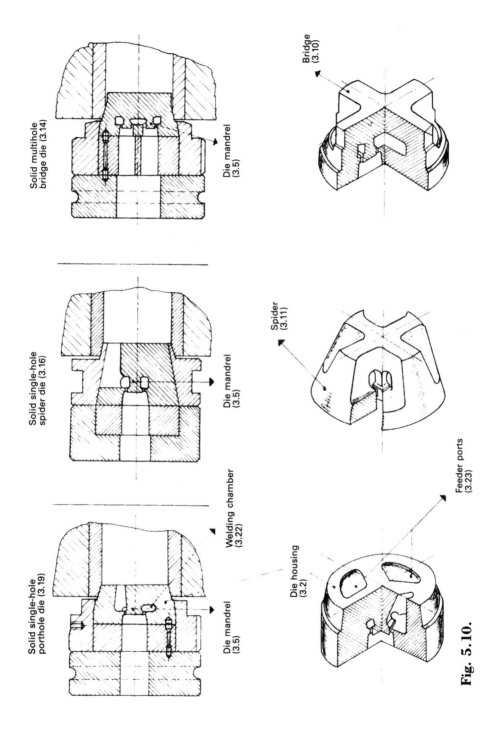

Solid multihole bridge die (3.14)

Die mandrel (3.5)

Bridge (3.10)

Solid single-hole spider die (3.16)

Die mandrel (3.5)

Spider (3.11)

Welding chamber (3.22)

Solid single-hole porthole die (3.19)

Die mandrel (3.5)

Die housing (3.2)

Feeder ports (3.23)

Fig. 5.10.

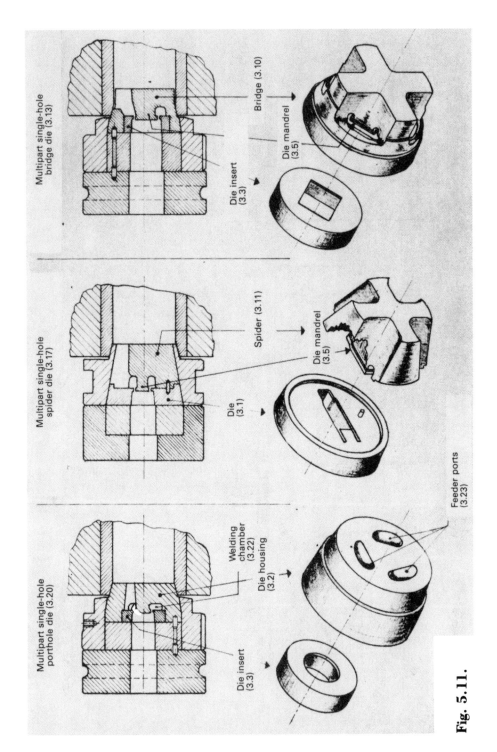

Multipart single-hole bridge die (3.13)

Bridge (3.10)

Die mandrel (3.5)

Die insert (3.3)

Multipart single-hole spider die (3.17)

Spider (3.11)

Die mandrel (3.5)

Die (3.1)

Multipart single-hole porthole die (3.20)

Welding chamber (3.22)

Die housing (3.2)

Feeder ports (3.23)

Die insert (3.3)

Fig. 5.11.

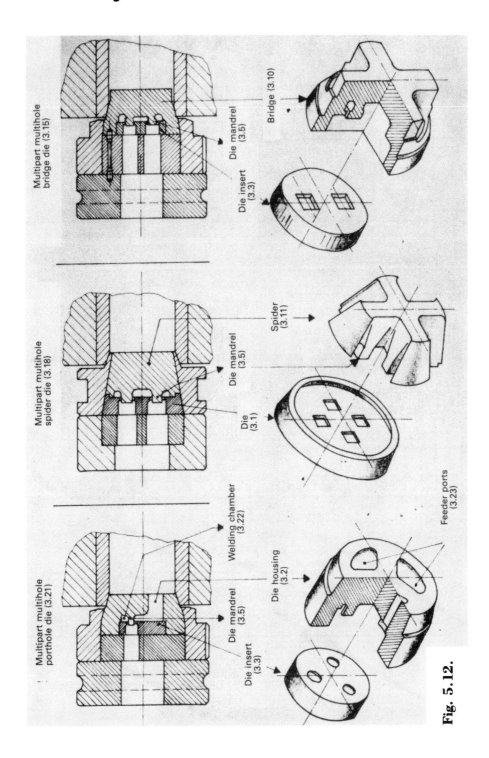

Multipart multihole bridge die (3.15)

Die mandrel (3.5)

Bridge (3.10)

Die insert (3.3)

Multipart multihole spider die (3.18)

Die mandrel (3.5)

Spider (3.11)

Die (3.1)

Multipart multihole porthole die (3.21)

Welding chamber (3.22)

Die mandrel (3.5)

Die housing (3.2)

Feeder ports (3.23)

Die insert (3.3)

Fig. 5.12.

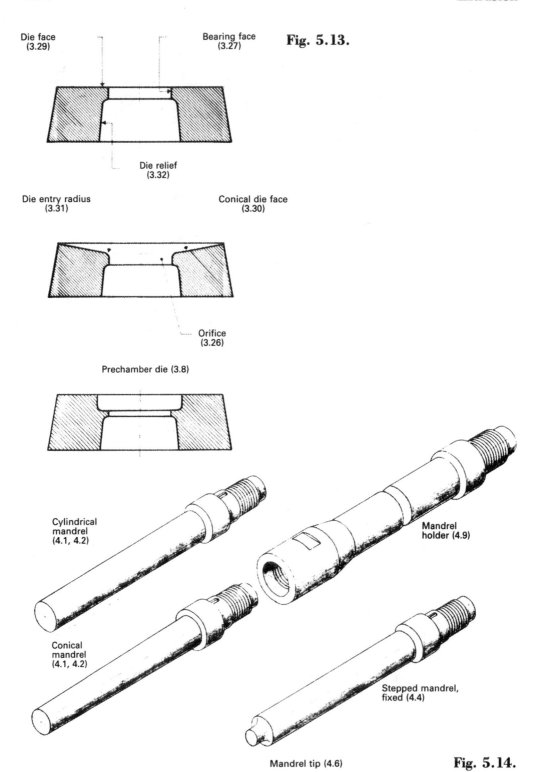

Die face
(3.29)

Bearing face
(3.27)

Fig. 5.13.

Die relief
(3.32)

Die entry radius
(3.31)

Conical die face
(3.30)

Orifice
(3.26)

Prechamber die (3.8)

Cylindrical
mandrel
(4.1, 4.2)

Mandrel
holder (4.9)

Conical
mandrel
(4.1, 4.2)

Stepped mandrel,
fixed (4.4)

Mandrel tip (4.6)

Fig. 5.14.

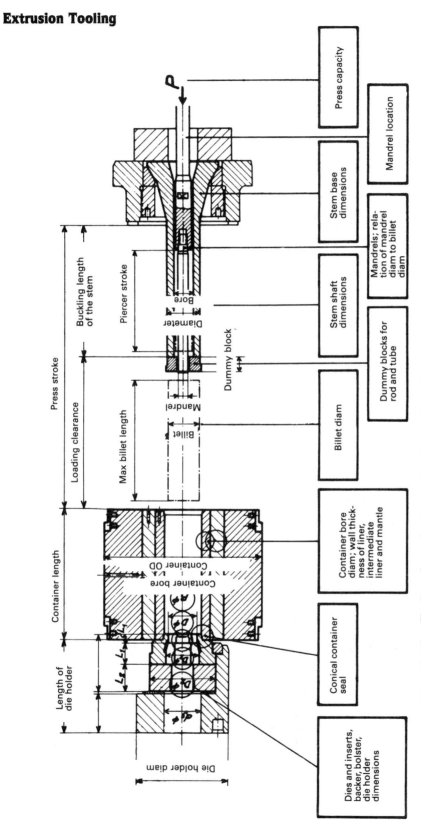

Fig. 5.15a. Tooling for a horizontal tube and metal extrusion press.

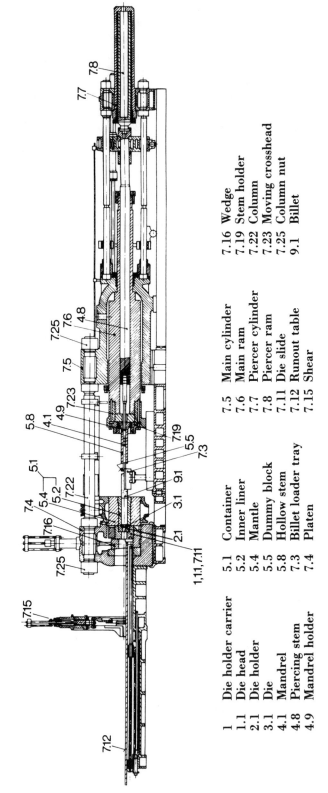

Fig. 5.15b. Horizontal tube and metal extrusion press with external piercer (old design).

1	Die holder carrier	5.1	Container	
1.1	Die head	5.2	Inner liner	
2.1	Die holder	5.4	Mantle	
3.1	Die	5.5	Dummy block	
4.1	Mandrel	5.8	Hollow stem	
4.8	Piercing stem	7.3	Billet loader tray	
4.9	Mandrel holder	7.4	Platen	

7.5	Main cylinder	7.16	Wedge
7.6	Main ram	7.19	Stem holder
7.7	Piercer cylinder	7.22	Column
7.8	Piercer ram	7.23	Moving crosshead
7.11	Die slide	7.25	Column nut
7.12	Runout table	9.1	Billet
7.15	Shear		

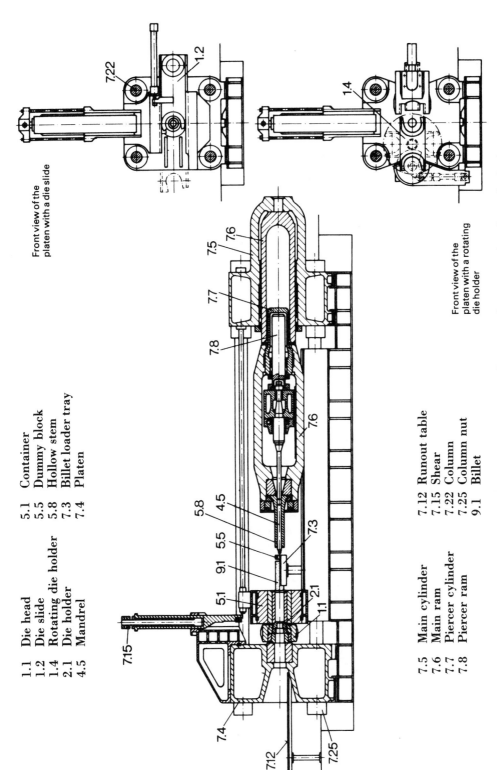

Front view of the
platen with a die slide

Front view of the
platen with a rotating
die holder

1.1	Die head	5.1	Container
1.2	Die slide	5.5	Dummy block
1.4	Rotating die holder	5.8	Hollow stem
2.1	Die holder	7.3	Billet loader tray
4.5	Mandrel	7.4	Platen

7.5	Main cylinder	7.12	Runout table
7.6	Main ram	7.15	Shear
7.7	Piercer cylinder	7.22	Column
7.8	Piercer ram	7.25	Column nut
		9.1	Billet

Fig. 5.15c. Horizontal tube and metal extrusion press with internal piercer (modern design).

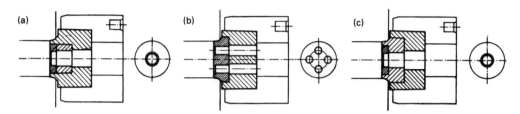

Fig. 5.16. Die design, old style: the slightly tapered die is loaded into the front end of the die holder.

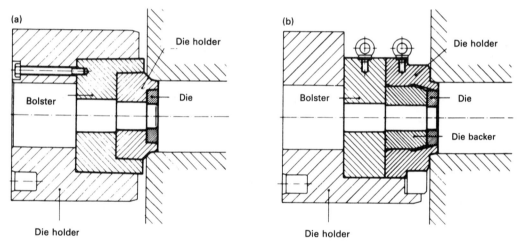

Fig. 5.17. Comparison of enclosed **(a)** and open **(b)** type of die holder.

method that is still preferred for extrusion temperatures up to 600 °C. The tapered dies of this open system are inserted into the back of the die holder and the danger that the die will fall out is thus eliminated. The die is changed by slackening the bolts of the clamp and lifting the die holder and die out with ring bolts. The die and the appropriate backers can then be easily changed. This system has many advantages over the earlier system: the die can be more easily centered because of the fewer critical tolerances that have to be maintained and the machining is simpler. However, the most important feature of this system is the satisfactory support of the die by the backer, which reduces the danger that dies will burst.

    The two methods of construction, closed and open, are compared in Fig. 5.17.

Inserting the die from the rear allows for further simplification when extruding sections. Alignment is essential when extruding tubes but it can be dispensed with for the extrusion of sections.

5.1.1.3. Sealing Between the Container and the Die Holder

A taper or double taper seal, a flat seal or even a straight seal can be used between the container and the die or die holder. If either a taper or straight seal is used, as in Fig. 5.7 and 5.8, the diameter of the die is a function of the inside diameter of the container. According to a statistical survey, the most common taper angle α is $10°$ and the most common taper length is 30 mm.

The die diameter required for sealing the container to the die is, depending on the requirements, obtained from:

$$D_1 = (1.0 \text{ to } 1.23) \cdot D_o \text{ and } D_1 = (1.16 \text{ to } 1.36) \cdot D_o$$

The die diameter given by this relationship can also be used for a flat seal as shown in Fig. 5.7 and 5.8.

The radial components of sealing pressure transmitted through the taper seal to the die and die holder can exert a considerable influence on the behavior of the die during extrusion, including a significant reduction in the size of the die apertures. This alters the wall thickness of the section and the change in material flow can be so severe that the dimensions of the product fall outside the tolerances required. This disadvantage is avoided if the flat or straight methods of sealing are used. Practical experience has shown that a significant increase in die life is obtained merely by removing the radial loads on the tooling.

Almost all modern presses use only flat or straight sealing, with very good results. The flat seal allows for the use of practically all the desired die diameters. However, if the die's outside diameter extends into the sealing area, the depth of the tool stack and die holder must be held within close tolerances. Large differences in the depth can result in protrusion of the die surface and damage to the sealing area of the container. The seal is made by pushing the rear face of the container against the die holder. The specific pressure on the surface increases as the sealing or contact area is reduced and this prevents metal from flowing between the container and the die holder during extrusion. However, the sealing area should not fall below a certain minimum; if it does, the applied specific pressure will be too high and the sealing area will be damaged. The die is fitted with a suitable collar or taper to hold it in the die holder when a straight seal is used. The taper or collar must be capable of withstanding the tensile loads developed in the die when the container is stripped at the end of extrusion. These tensile loads are particularly high when the discard is stripped from a bridge die. Collars have been sheared off by these loads and, therefore, they must be thick enough to resist such loads.

5.1.2. Functions of the Individual Tools

The functions of the individual tools of the tool set can be seen in Fig. 5.1 to 5.14:

Tool	Function
Die	Forms the section.
Die holder	Holds the die and, to some degree, the die backer.
Die backer	Supports the die to prevent die collapse or fracture.
Bolster	Transmits the extrusion load from the backer to the die carrier.
Pressure ring.......	Extends the length of the die set to the dimensions of the die carrier.
Die carrier........	Holds the complete die set in the press.
Bridge/spider.......	Divides the deforming metal and supports the mandrel.
Feeder plate, die recess	Balances the metal flow to the die.
Extrusion stem	Transmits the extrusion load through the dummy block to the billet.

5.1.3. Dimensioning of Extrusion Tooling

From 1971 to 1973 the extrusion division of the DGM (German Metallurgical Society) examined the design and calculation procedures that had been established in the 1950's and compared them with the practice of the German extrusion industry. The results have been condensed into a new set of guidelines. The new guidelines are discussed below and relate the dimensions of the tooling to the circumscribing circle diameter, the cross section of the product, and the alloy. The following symbols are used:

D_o = Inside diameter of the container
D_{1000} = Inside diameter of the container for a specific pressure of 100 kp/mm^2 $\approx$ 1000 N/mm^2 (D_{1000} is a very important reference value and the basis for many calculations.)
D_B = Billet diameter
D_1 = Die diameter
D_2 = Diameter of the die backer
D_C = Circumscribing circle diameter of the extruded product
D_T = Outside diameter of the die set
L_D = Die thickness
L_B = Die backer thickness
$L_D + L_B$ = depth of the die set (die + backer)

L_T = Total depth of the tool stack (die + support tools) to the support in the end housing

L_{DB} = Thickness of the dummy block

L_C = Container length

F = Extrusion load

p = Specific pressure

t_t = Length of the taper in the container liner when using taper sealing

α = Angle for taper sealing

5.1.3.1. Die Diameter

The maximum diameter of the circumscribing circle of a section is, for a given internal diameter D_o:

$$D_{C\ max} = 0.8 \cdot D_o \text{ to } 0.85 \cdot D_o \text{ (mm)}$$

The diameter of the die needed for a given circumscribing circle diameter depends on the type of section, its degree of difficulty and the alloy. For simple shapes, rod, tube and flat sections, the diameter of the die should be, according to practical experience:

$$D_1 = (1.25 \text{ to } 1.45) \cdot D_C \text{ (mm)}$$

In the borderline case for $D_{C\ max}$:

$$D_1 = (1.0 \text{ to } 1.23) \cdot D_o \text{ (mm)}.$$

With more complicated sections, including those with thin walls or sections in the alloys more difficult to extrude, experience has shown that the minimum diameter is:

$$D_1 = (1.45 \text{ to } 1.6) \cdot D_C \text{ (mm)}$$

in order to be able to use the maximum possible circumscribing circle diameter with a given container.

The borderline case of $D_{C\ max}$ then gives:

$$D_1 = (1.1 \text{ to } 1.36) \cdot D_o \text{ (mm)}$$

The diameter of the circumscribing circle is usually less than the maximum and, for economical reasons, the die diameter is naturally matched to that of the circumscribing circle, or multihole extrusion is used to utilize the maximum possible die diameter.

5.1.3.2. Die Thickness

Die thickness has been considerably reduced in the past few years because it was realized that the die does not have to withstand the extrusion load: this is the function of the correctly dimensioned backer. Extruders have, accordingly, increased the thickness of the support tooling, within the limits of the size of the die carrier, to improve stiffness and resistance to die collapse. The survey of extruders gave the following thicknesses:

20, 25, 30, 40, 50, 70 and 100 mm

The die thickness can also be expressed as a function of the reference parameter D_{1000}, and press manufacturers use:

$L_D = (0.12 \text{ to } 0.22) \cdot D_{1000}$ (mm)

5.1.3.3. External Diameter of the Die Set

As mentioned above, press designers use the reference dimension D_{1000}, which is defined in the list of symbols (section 5.1.3). It is the basic parameter for determining individual tool sizes. The outside diameter of the tool set is, according to practical experience:

$D_T = 2.65 \cdot D_{1000}$ (mm)

5.1.3.4. Thickness of the Die Backer and the Total Depth of the Tool Set

The thickness of the die and its backer is obtained from D_{1000} by using:

$L_D + L_B = (0.65 \text{ to } 1.0) \cdot D_{1000}$ (mm)

and the total depth of the tool set is:

$L_T = 2.8 \cdot D_{1000}$ (mm)

5.1.3.5. Thickness and Outside Diameter of the Dummy Block

The following formula has proved to be applicable for the thickness of the dummy block:

$L_{DB} = (0.5 \text{ to } 0.75) \cdot D_{1000}$ (mm)

This value of L_{DB} can be used for dummy blocks for both solid and tube extrusion. The outside diameter is a direct function of the inside diameter of the container.

5.1.3.6. Stems for Rod and Tube Extrusion

The design of extrusion stems varies according to the size, shape and operating stresses. Frequently, the rigidity of the stem is the factor that determines the specific pressure that can be applied during extrusion. The value of 1100 N/mm^2 generally should not be exceeded but much higher pressures are found in production. Pressures up to 1350 N/mm^2 are now used for zinc alloys, difficult aluminum alloys, and, above all, for nickel alloys and steels.

5.1.4. Dies for Sections and Hollow Shapes

Extrusion dies can be divided into simple ones used for solid and open shapes and those with welding chambers (porthole, spider and bridge dies) for semihollow and hollow shapes. The normal type of die for solid and open semihollow shapes can, in principle, be used for all metals that are extruded. Hollow sections in a variety of shapes and sizes are reserved for aluminum alloys apart from the simple hollow sections that can be produced in the heavy metals or steel with a mandrel (independent mandrel movement). The development of die design for simple and complicated aluminum sections is described first of all because the products extruded have a significant position in the world market (Fig. 3.9).

A die for an aluminum section has to fulfill the following requirements:

(a) Accurate dimensions and product shape, to avoid the need for any corrective work.
(b) Maximum possible working life.
(c) Maximum length of the extruded section.
(d) A good-quality surface finish maintained over many extrusions — i.e., infrequent die cleaning.
(e) High extrusion speeds.
(f) Low manufacturing costs.

These requirements are usually fulfilled with rod and simple shapes. However, as the complexity of the die increases, it becomes increasingly more difficult to comply with all six requirements. Many factors have to be considered in the design and construction of a die, including the flow pattern, maximum specific pressure, geometrical shape of the section, wall thickness and tongue sizes, shape of the bearing surfaces (die lands), and the tolerances of the section. Incorrect metal flow can give rise to areas of critical deformation, which form visible streaks on the surface of the finished product.

Much skill and experience are required to obtain uniform metal flow through all parts of the die, especially with unsymmetrical shapes and different wall thicknesses. The resistance to flow is greatest in the narrow parts of the die, and the bearing lengths in these regions have to be reduced. If insufficient attention is paid to these preventive measures, the extruded product will be twisted and warped.

5.1.4.1. Dies for Solid Sections

Some basic rules have to be followed during the initial laying out of a die for solid shapes and these determine the position of the die aperture. The center of gravity of the section — where most material flows — should be placed as close to the edge of the die as possible because the material tends to flow faster in the center than at the edge.

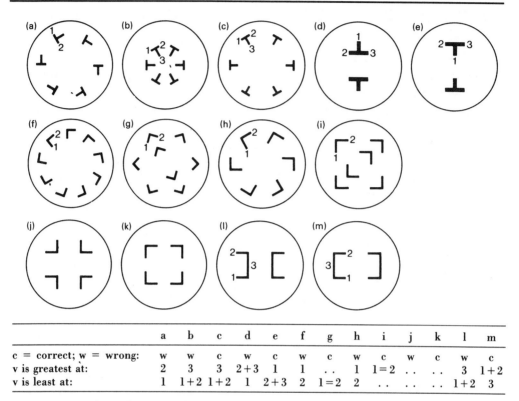

	a	b	c	d	e	f	g	h	i	j	k	l	m
c = correct; w = wrong:	w	w	c	w	c	w	c	w	c	w	c	w	c
v is greatest at:	2	3	3	2+3	1	1	..	1	1=2	..	..	3	1+2
v is least at:	1	1+2	1+2	1	2+3	2	1=2	2	..	..	..	1+2	3

Fig. 5.18. Location of die apertures according to v, the rate of flow.

Large cross sections also run relatively more quickly than smaller, thinner sections. These facts allow for some balancing to be achieved without different bearing lengths. A symmetrical section is always placed with the axis of symmetry coinciding with the center of the die. If multihole dies are used, the apertures should be arranged as symmetrically as possible. Figure 5.18 illustrates the correct arrangement for T, L and U shapes. Basically, the centers of gravity of each section must be placed on the center of gravity of the segments. This does, however, depend on the size of the container and the number of strands.

It is also important that the layout of a multihole die is arranged to prevent extrusions from rubbing together or running on top of each other as they leave the press. A flat surface and not the edge of a leg or rib should run along the runout table. Recessed dies (Fig. 5.19 to 5.21) and welding chamber dies (Fig. 5.22) are used for semihollow sections in addition to the normal flat dies in order to minimize the deflection of long, thin tongues in the die. These

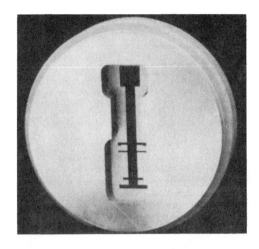

Fig. 5.19. Recessed die. *(From Aluminium Matrix N.V., Arcen, Netherlands)*

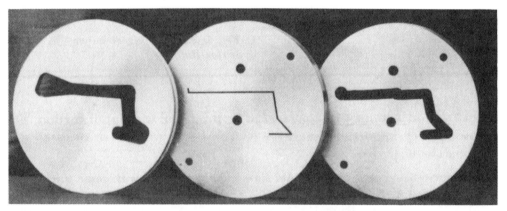

Fig. 5.20. Three-part feeder plate die: left, feeder plate; center, die; right, die backer. *(From Aluminium Matrix N.V., Arcen, Netherlands)*

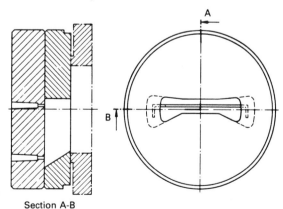

Section A-B

Fig. 5.21. Expansion feeder plate die. *(From Ref 57)*

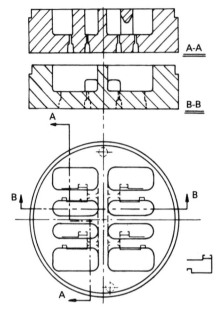

Fig. 5.22. Welding chamber die. *(From Ref 57)*

dies allow for sections with long legs to be produced without distortion. The following very important measures can be taken with these recessed and welding chamber dies:

(a) Improved control of the metal flow in thin sections with some thick areas (recessed die).
(b) Sections can be extruded that are too large for the available container and in extreme cases an expansion feeder plate can be used to produce extrusions wider than the container diameter (Fig. 5.21).
(c) Semihollow sections with long, narrow tongues can be extruded to higher tolerances and with less danger of die failure (e.g., the multihole welding chamber die in Fig. 5.22).

5.1.4.2. Dies for Hollow Sections and Special Dies

Dies for extruding complicated hollow sections are being produced today that would not have been thought possible a few years ago. This is, of course, closely related to the development of extrusion technology with improvements in the hot working steels and heat treatment, and advances in the engineering of extrusion plants.

However, it has almost been forgotten that the talented inventor Alexander Dick was far ahead of his time, but that his ideas could be realized only

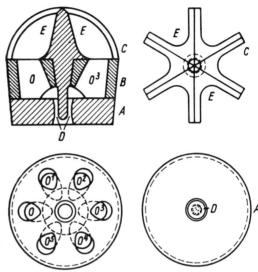

Fig. 5.23. First bridge die with six inlets, designed by Alexander Dick (Patent No. 99405, dated March 30, 1897).

when the necessary technological and mechanical requirements became available. Dick developed the welding die that now plays an important role in producing aluminum tubes and hollow sections (Fig. 5.23). This three-part die consists of a bridge with the supports forming six openings, but the design is not capable of withstanding the high mechanical and thermal stresses. A comparison of Dick's welding die to those used today for welded tubes and hollow sections clearly shows that he had recognized the principle of the welding chamber die 70 years ago. The bridge die most closely approaches Dick's idea. The dies used for hollow sections are: bridge dies, spider dies and porthole dies.

5.1.4.2.1 Bridge Dies

The modern bridge die developed from the earlier pattern (Fig. 5.24), which is still frequently used today, to its present form shown in Fig. 5.25. The bridge die is principally used when the surface finish is of paramount importance. The die operates at low temperatures, because the discard is removed at the end of each extrusion. The die therefore remains clean and can always be sprayed with an atomized lubricant. The large discard is a disadvantage, because of the high scrap rate. The discard is stripped from the die when the container is opened and the continual alternating stresses of tension and compression can result in accelerated wear or premature fracture. Bridge dies are the most expensive of the hollow section dies, because of the very high machining costs (Fig. 5.26).

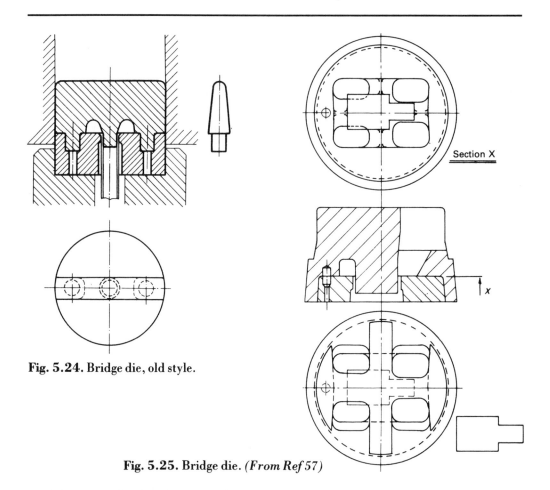

Fig. 5.24. Bridge die, old style.

Section X

X

Fig. 5.25. Bridge die. *(From Ref 57)*

Fig. 5.26. Bridge die. *(From Aluminium Matrix N.V., Arcen, Netherlands)*

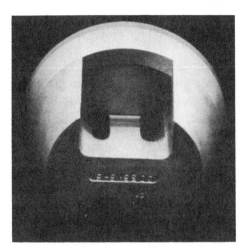

Fig. 5.27. Spider die. *(From Aluminium Matrix N.V., Arcen, Netherlands)*

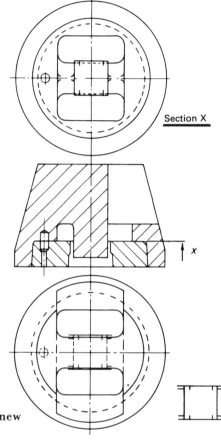

Section X

Fig. 5.28. Spider die, new style. *(From Ref 57)*

5.1.4.2.2. Spider Dies

The spider die originated in America and is mainly used for large hollow sections with low extrusion ratios (Fig. 5.27). The use of this type of die is decreasing, because it has to be cleaned by pickling for a long time before any checks or alterations can be made. The residue in the conical section can be only partly removed in the press. The new design developed by Keller (Ref 57) has eliminated many of the disadvantages of the old construction and has proved itself in practice (Fig. 5.28).

Construction of the mandrel in the form of an enclosed bell, with the die inserted into the back, has resulted in three marked advantages:

(a) Increased stability of the die, because an enclosed component reduces the danger of cracking or fracture.

(b) The uniform, large welding chamber around the section gives a favorable material flow.

(c) The quality of the internal surfaces of the section need not be so high as that of the external surfaces and, therefore, the die can be replaced frequently at a low cost and the working life of the tool is increased.

5.1.4.2.3. Porthole Dies

This type of die can almost always be used and represents the best and most suitable development for modern requirements. Porthole dies are also suitable for multihole dies and the enclosed type of construction gives a high degree of stability (Fig. 5.29 and 5.30). The porthole die can also be used with the maximum section circumscribing circle diameter relative to the container diameter (e.g., Fig. 5.31); the die also acts as the die holder. A favorable extrusion ratio can be selected by using the optimum material flow; heating to relatively low temperatures should then be sufficient. The discard can, depending on the shape of the section, also be partly removed. This type of die is used for sections with very critical tongues and cross sections. However, because the die is manufactured from a single piece of steel, correction by filing and clearing by polishing are difficult. Very difficult sections with large variations in wall thicknesses or many openings can be extruded only with porthole dies (Fig. 5.32). The section in Fig. 5.33 with very long ribs could only have been extruded with a one-piece porthole die. This design has the major disadvantage that die correction is very difficult because of the poor accessibility to the guiding region of the die.

5.1.4.3. Dies for Stepped Sections

Kursetz (Ref 9) has described the development trends in the American aircraft industry where aluminum sections with very large cross sections are extruded for aircraft and rocket construction on some of the largest presses now in existence, with capacities of 120 to 250 MN. Varying cross sections are often required for heavy girder sections and initially these were machined at great expense to give the final product. The more economical process of stepped extrusion was, therefore, developed.

Stepped sections have been extruded in Germany with split dies since the 1950's and the process found to be suitable for simple shapes (see Fig. 2.5). Experience has shown that changing the split dies is very difficult with more complex sections. The major disadvantage of the process is the time needed for die changing and the resulting billet cooling, which, naturally, makes it more difficult to extrude the next section of the stepped product.

American extrusion plants have developed a die system in which the die sets are arranged one behind the other. This approach has the advantage that the tool set is secured by a double wedge lock, although the press had to be altered to include this feature. The process is shown in Fig. 5.34. After

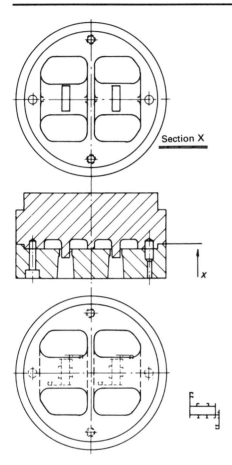

Section X

Fig. 5.29. Porthole die. (*From Ref 57*)

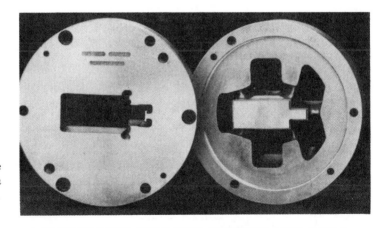

Fig. 5.30. Porthole
die. (*From Aluminium
Matrix N.V., Arcen,
Netherlands*)

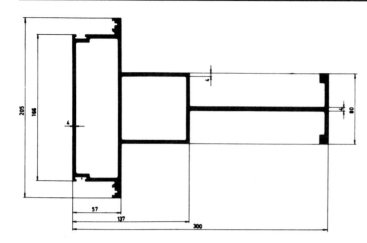

Fig. 5.31. Section with large variation in shape; can be produced only with a porthole die in the die holder.

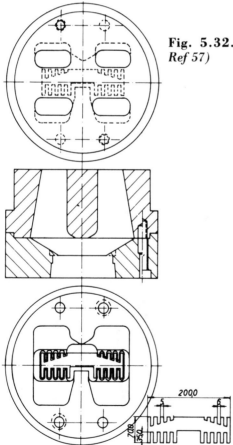

Fig. 5.32. Porthole die. *(From Ref 57)*

Fig. 5.33. One-piece porthole die. *(From Aluminium Matrix N.V., Arcen, Netherlands)*

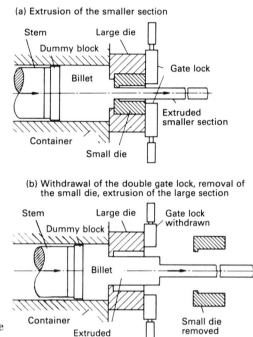

(a) Extrusion of the smaller section

Stem

Dummy block

Large die

Gate lock

Billet

Extruded
smaller section

Container

Small die

(b) Withdrawal of the double gate lock, removal of
the small die, extrusion of the large section

Stem

Large die

Gate lock
withdrawn

Dummy block

Billet

Container

Small die
removed

Extruded
larger section

Fig. 5.34. Arrangement with double gate lock for stepped sections. *(From Ref 9)*

the first section has been extruded, the wedges are removed to free the first die set and the first part of the extrusion is pushed out by the larger following section.

5.2. Manufacture of Extrusion Dies

An efficient extrusion works also needs a good die shop with a capacity matching the needs of the complete plant. If the plant has several manufacturing divisions — extrusion, drop forging, etc. — a central tool shop is more practical. On the other hand, if only a few extrusion presses have to be supplied, there is no sense in organizing a large shop capable of producing all the dies; in these cases the tooling, especially the dies for sections, should be made outside when required. However, this brings with it the danger that the plant will not have the experienced toolmakers needed for technical development in the future.

The design and construction of extrusion dies has already been described and the following sections will discuss their correct layout and dimensions.

5.2.1. Layout of the Die Apertures (Die Design)

The simplest extrusion process is the production of round bars and there are usually no difficulties in the single-hole extrusion of round bars. Metal flow during extrusion is very dependent on the alloy being worked; the shape of the die entry and the dimensions of the die aperture are determined by the characteristics of the individual alloy. For example, the conical bearing faces are critical in the extrusion of heterogeneous alloys, such as magnesium and zinc alloys. A slope on the front face also allows some materials to be extruded at economical speeds without the appearance of transverse cracks on the product. The die profiles commonly used are shown in Fig. 5.35 for different metals.

5.2.1.1. Dimensioning According to Stress Criteria

The following factors have to be considered in designing a die for any specific alloy:

(a) The size and shape of the orifice.
(b) The extrusion ratio, which determines the size of the press required and the number of strands.
(c) The location of the strands (see Fig. 5.18).
(d) The maximum specific pressure and, thus, the calculation of the stresses in the die and its deflection.

The maximum specific pressure of the press under consideration should normally be used for all static calculations. The opinion that an allowance can be made for the loss in pressure resulting from friction is false, because if sticking occurs the material stops flowing immediately after upsetting and the pressure increases to the maximum. The operating temperature of the die is used as a basis for die calculations (about 400 °C for aluminum) (see Fig. 5.46).

Dies with self-supporting tongues present particular difficulties in die design and dimensioning. Tongues in large sections can be supported by the die backer and bolster, but this is not possible for small sections with long narrow tongues; they must be designed to prevent any large deflections, which can result in loss of tolerance or in fracture. The ratio of the length of tongue L_t to its width b_t is critical for the deflection:

$$i = \frac{L_t}{b_t}$$

This classic and very simple method of calculation is still used today, but the simple expression can only give approximate results. The finite element

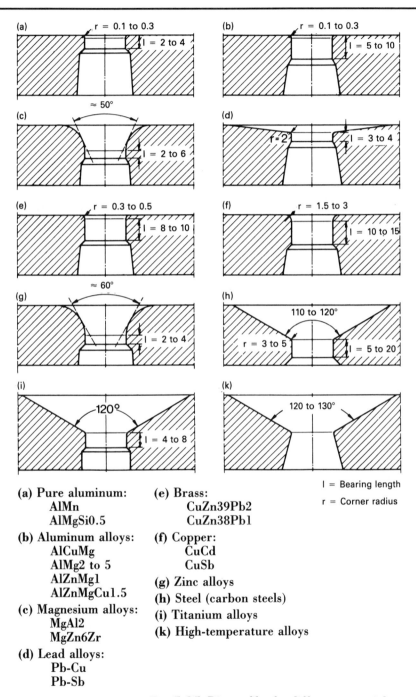

Fig. 5.35. Die profiles for different materials.

(a) Pure aluminum:
  AlMn
  AlMgSi0.5
(b) Aluminum alloys:
  AlCuMg
  AlMg2 to 5
  AlZnMg1
  AlZnMgCu1.5
(c) Magnesium alloys:
  MgAl2
  MgZn6Zr
(d) Lead alloys:
  Pb-Cu
  Pb-Sb
(e) Brass:
  CuZn39Pb2
  CuZn38Pb1
(f) Copper:
  CuCd
  CuSb
(g) Zinc alloys
(h) Steel (carbon steels)
(i) Titanium alloys
(k) High-temperature alloys

l = Bearing length
r = Corner radius

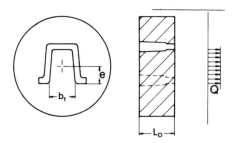

1. **Pressure on the die:**

   Specific pressure $p = \dfrac{F}{A_o}$ (F = press load; A_o = container cross section); Q = area load on tongue = $p \cdot A_T$ (A_T = area of tongue = $b_t \cdot l_T$)

2. **Bending:**

   Bending moment $M_b = Q \cdot e$ (e = distance from center of gravity)

   Bending stress $\sigma_b = \dfrac{M_b}{Z}$ ($Z = \dfrac{b_t \cdot L_D^2}{6}$ = section modulus)

3. **Shearing:**

   Shearing stress $\tau = \dfrac{Q}{b_t \cdot L_D}$

4. **Equivalent stress from bending and shearing:**

   Reference stress $\sigma_R = \sqrt{\sigma^2 + (1.73\tau)^2} \cong \sqrt{\sigma^2 + 3\tau^2}$ (according to the strain energy hypotheses) $\sigma_R < \sigma_o$

Fig. 5.36. Design of die with unsupported tongue.

method gives more accurate calculations of the local elastic stresses and strains within the die and the support tooling. In critical cases the shear and bending stresses in the die have to be calculated; Fig. 5.36 and 5.37 give the necessary steps.

5.2.1.2. Determining the Width of the Orifice From the Shrinkage Allowance

The dimensions of the die orifice are larger than those of the section because the product contracts on cooling. In addition to contraction on cooling there is also the problem of incomplete extrusion of the section, particularly of very thin areas. The shrinkage increases as the extrusion speed is increased and is also dependent on the alloy. The expansion of the die during heating to the extrusion temperature also has to be considered (430 to

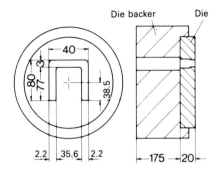

Die: b_{t_1} = 35.6 mm
Die backer: b_{t_2} = 30 mm
Extrusion load: max 27 MN
Container diam: 222 mm
Specific extrusion pressure: p = 700 N/mm^2
L_D = 20 mm
L_B = 175 mm
l_t = 77 mm

1. **Load on the die:**
   $Q = p \cdot b_{t_1} \cdot l_t = 700 \cdot 35.6 \cdot 77 \approx 1\,920\,000$ N

2. **Bending of the tongue of the die backer:**
   $M_b = Q \cdot e = 1\,920\,000 \cdot 3.85 = 7\,390\,000$ Ncm

   $$Z = \frac{b_{t_2} \cdot L_B^2}{6} = \frac{3 \cdot 17.5^2}{6} = 153 \text{ cm}^3$$

   $$\sigma_b = \frac{M_b}{Z} = \frac{7\,390\,000}{153} = 48\,300 \text{ N/cm}^2 = 483 \text{ N/mm}^2$$

3. **Shearing:**

   $$\tau = \frac{Q}{b_{t_2} \cdot L_B} = \frac{1\,920\,000}{30 \cdot 175} = 366 \text{ N/mm}^2$$

4. **Shearing plus bending:**
   $\sigma_R = \sqrt{\sigma^2 + (1.73 \cdot 366)^2} = \sqrt{483^2 + (1.73 \cdot 366)^2} = 796 \text{ N/mm}^2$

   This value of σ_R must be significantly less than the high-temperature yield stress of the steel of the die backer at the working temperature.

Fig. 5.37. Numerical example for a die with an unsupported tongue.

500 °C). Accurate measurements have permitted the aluminum alloys to be classified into two shrinkage groups:

Shrinkage group	Alloy	Contraction of length and width, %	Shrinkage group	Alloy	Contraction of length and width, %
I	Pure Al	1	II	AlMg(3-7% Mg)	1.25
I	AlMn	1	II	AlZnMgCu0.5	1.25
I	AlMgSi	1	II	AlZnMgCu1.5	1.25
I	AlCuMg	1	II	AlZnMgCu2	1.25

The average contraction for brass has been measured at 1.2 to 1.5% and for zinc alloys at 1.4 to 1.6%, but is lower for copper: 0.8 to 1%. Table 5.2

Table 5.2. Dimensional Increases to the Width of Aluminum Sections(a)

(Die size [D] = nominal size [N] + 50% of tolerance + 1% of nominal size; 1% contraction = $23.10^{-6} \cdot 435 \,°C$)

$I^{+0.2}_{-0.1}$ 1 to 10 mm		$II^{+0.3}_{-0.15}$ 10 to 15 mm		$III^{+0.4}_{-0.2}$ 15 to 30 mm		$IV^{+0.6}_{-0.3}$ 30 to 50 mm		$V^{+0.8}_{-0.4}$ 50 to 80 mm		$VI^{+1.0}_{-0.5}$ 80 to 120 mm	
N	D	N	D	N	D	N	D	N	D	N	D
1	1.06	11	11.19	16	16.26	31	31.46	51	51.71	82	83.07
2	2.07	12	12.20	17	17.27	32	32.47	52	52.72	84	85.09
3	3.08	13	13.21	18	18.28	33	33.48	53	53.73	86	87.11
4	4.09	14	14.22	19	19.29	34	34.49	54	54.74	88	89.13
5	5.10	15	15.23	20	20.30	35	35.50	55	55.75	90	91.15
6	6.11			21	21.31	36	36.51	56	56.76	92	93.17
7	7.12			22	22.32	37	37.52	57	57.77	94	95.19
8	8.13			23	23.33	38	38.53	58	58.78	96	97.21
9	9.14			24	24.34	39	39.54	59	59.79	98	99.23
10	10.15			25	25.35	40	40.55	60	60.80	100	101.25
				26	26.36	41	41.56	61	61.81	102	103.27
				27	27.37	42	42.57	62	62.82	104	105.29
				28	28.38	43	43.58	63	63.83	106	107.31
				29	29.39	44	44.59	64	64.84	108	109.33
				30	30.40	45	45.60	65	65.85	110	111.35
						46	46.61	66	66.86	112	113.37
						47	47.62	67	67.87	114	115.39
						48	48.63	68	68.88	116	117.41
						49	49.64	69	69.89	118	119.43
						50	50.65	70	70.90	120	121.45
								71	71.91		
								72	72.92		
								73	73.93		
								74	74.94		
								75	75.95		
								76	76.96		
								77	77.97		
								78	78.98		
								79	79.99		
								80	81.00		

(a) For alloy group I. Alloy group II: 1.25% contraction.

summarizes the factors that must be added to the dimensions of the section (nominal size and shrinkage size) for group I alloys. An addition of 0.25% is made for group II alloys.

In addition to thermal contraction, incomplete extrusion of, in particular, narrow tongues also has to be taken into account in the thickness dimensions. Therefore, more allowance has to be made in the total contraction for the thickness than for the length and width. The amount depends on

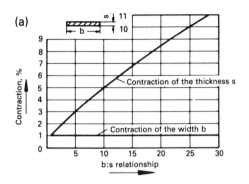

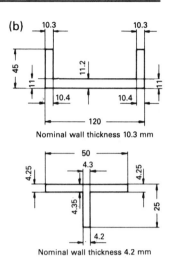

Nominal wall thickness 10.3 mm

Nominal wall thickness 4.2 mm

Fig. 5.38. Dependence of the thickness contraction on the width-to-thickness ratio (a); nominal wall thickness for two sections (b).

the ratio of the width to the thickness. The higher the ratio and the smaller the wall thickness, the greater will be the contraction, although, naturally, the extrusion ratio and flow pattern will play a role. A flat section shrinks more in the middle than at the ends because the material flows more rapidly in the center than at the edges.

The thickness contraction is shown as a function of the width-to-thickness ratio in Fig. 5.38a. The crosspiece will contract more than the two outer legs in U sections, whereas the legs and crosspieces contract uniformly in L and T sections, according to the curve in Fig. 5.38a, but a slight correction of minus 0.1 to 0.2 mm is needed at the ends of the legs. Figure 5.38b shows examples of U and T sections.

5.2.1.3. Die Land Lengths for Uniform Metal Flow

Metal flow through irregular die orifices for sections is controlled by the lengths of the bearing surfaces, which have a braking effect. The length of the die lands should be at least twice the wall thickness for aluminum sections with a minimum value of 2.5 to 3 mm. Die correction is difficult if the length is less than 3 mm. The metal tends to flow faster in the center of the die than at the edges, and the land lengths at the center have to be longer. The metal flow is also faster in the thicker regions of sections of unequal wall thickness, and the length of the land has to be increased accordingly. In solid sections the metal flow can usually be controlled by the different die land lengths. However, there are various methods of correcting hollow dies. The inlets and the mandrel guides are designed to allow alterations after the first trial extrusion.

The shape of the orifice of a heavy metal or steel die is much more complicated. The braking compensation for unsymmetrical shapes comes not only from the die land length but also from the retarding effect of the varying conical entry, which depends on the wall thickness (see Fig. 5.35). Attempts have been made to derive laws to give die land lengths suitable for use in practice. Although such systematic solutions are desirable, the long experience of the designer and die maker and an instinctive "feeling" for the special cases that occur almost daily still provide the only solutions for the alloys under consideration. There must be close cooperation between the designer, die maker and the press operator if satisfactory products are to be produced in all the extrudable metals. There have also been many investigations into empirical mathematical expressions for material flow and contraction. The well-known design rules of Kaiser Aluminum are typical examples.

5.2.2. Manufacture of Extrusion Dies

Extrusion dies with irregular contours are manufactured by the following methods:

(a) Manual machining (drilling, sawing, milling, and filing).
(b) Spark erosion.
(c) Combination of a photoelectric drawing reader with an engraving or duplicate milling machine.

Manual methods are now generally used only for repair work. The most important methods are (b) and (c), and are described in more detail below.

5.2.2.1. Spark Erosion

In this method particles are eroded from the surface of a metal tool blank by electrical energy without any direct contact between the electrode and the material. The periodic discharge of the electrical energy between the positive electrode — the tool blank — and the negative electrode of the desired shape erodes numerous tiny particles from the blank. All the erosion takes place on the blank and only a small fraction — 0.3 to 1.5%, depending on the power — on the die electrode. The spark erosion machine in Fig. 5.39 has the following capabilities and specifications:

(a) The production of a die orifice without the need for pilot holes (i.e., total erosion but only when drilling is impossible).
(b) Preliminary sawing of larger sections slightly undersize to make it possible to rinse with a liquid during the spark erosion process; the rinsing operation has to be carefully controlled.

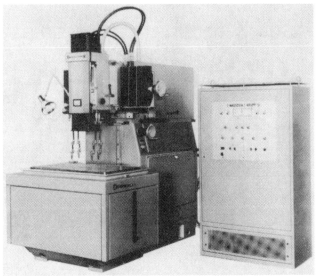

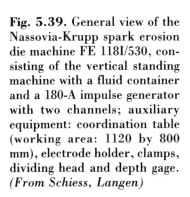

Fig. 5.39. General view of the Nassovia-Krupp spark erosion die machine FE 118I/530, consisting of the vertical standing machine with a fluid container and a 180-A impulse generator with two channels; auxiliary equipment: coordination table (working area: 1120 by 800 mm), electrode holder, clamps, dividing head and depth gage. *(From Schiess, Langen)*

(*c*) The rate of removal varies over a wide range — 250 to 2500 mm^2/min — depending on the power of the generator (input power 3 to 25 kVA).

One important feature is the independence of the erosion rate on the hardness for any given material — that is, it does not matter whether the tool blank has been heat treated or not. Therefore, the process is of considerable importance for extrusion die production, particularly since the introduction of impulse generators and the effective application of graphite electrodes has given significant increases in the output of these machines.

Graphite electrodes (Fig. 5.42a) have a low wear rate, are easy to produce, and allow much higher erosion rates to be used. The electrodes can be automatically produced on a copying milling machine from templates or photoelectrically from drawings.

In addition to standard mechanical die production the spark erosion process must also be capable of the following:

(*a*) Production of dies with one or several identical orifices.
(*b*) Production of dies for very complex sections.
(*c*) Production of one-piece dies for hollow or semihollow sections (especially porthole dies).
(*d*) Correction of hardened dies.
(*e*) Manufacture of replacement dies (the electrodes are reusable).

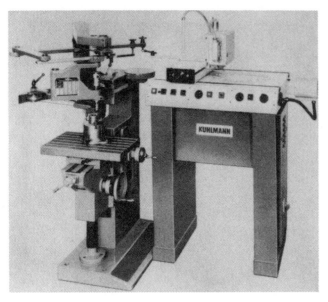

Fig. 5.40. Photoelectric drawing copier with an engraving and copying milling machine. *(From Kuhlmann, Bad Lauterberg)*

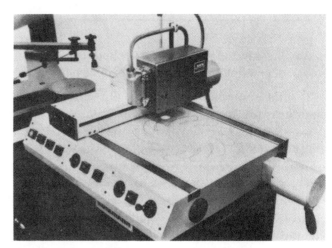

Fig. 5.41. Photoelectric drawing reader FZI; a lifting table with automatic vertical adjustment is used for milling deep tools — for example, electrodes. *(From Kuhlmann, Bad Lauterberg)*

5.2.2.2. Photoelectric Drawing Reader Combined With a Machining Tool

A significant development in the efficient production of extrusion dies is the practical combination of a photoelectric drawing reader with an engraving or duplicate milling machine (Fig. 5.40 and 5.41). Dies of different sizes can be machined directly from a drawing with this process. The scale can be adjusted from 1:1 to 1:100 and the tolerances on the drawing are transferred on a much reduced scale to the die. The method can be used for the direct

Fig. 5.42a. Graphite electrodes produced with a pantograph engraving machine.

Fig. 5.42b. Electrode for spark erosion produced with a photoelectric drawing copier on the engraving and copying milling machine.

production of dies or for producing electrodes for spark erosion (Fig. 5.42b). The production sequence given below underlines the simplified method for die or electrode production that has resulted in significant reductions in cost:

(a) Production of the drawing enlarged to a scale of 1:10.
(b) Fixing the tool blank to a holding plate.
(c) Adjusting the pointer to the milling contour using the dial card switch after locating the drawing.
(d) Trial run with simultaneous adjustment of the automatic vertical feed and alignment of the tool blank.
(e) Working cycle.

The accuracy achieved is given as: contour accuracy, $\pm$ 0.025 mm; accuracy of reproduction, 0.01 mm.

5.2.2.3. Relief Milling

Relief milling is used to adjust the die bearing lengths of the orifices produced mechanically or by spark erosion. This operation used to be carried out in one step with conical milling cutters on simple static milling machines without automatic feed. A direct drive milling spindle is generally used with manual adjustment of the height needed to give the bearing lengths (Fig. 5.43 and 5.44).

Fig. 5.43. Milling the inlets on an extrusion die with a mandrel. *(From Aluminium Matrix N.V., Arcen, Netherlands)*

Fig. 5.44. Relief milling of the mandrel component of an extrusion die. *(From Aluminium Matrix N.V., Arcen, Netherlands)*

More recently, the photoelectric drawing reader has been used to allow dies to be easily milled from the back or provided with conical exits. The drawing and the die are inverted and mirror image contours machined on the rear of the die using a larger milling cutter. Location marks have to be provided on the reader, drawing and tool blank for correct alignment. An important feature of this process is the possibility of automatically controlling the depth to give an automatic working cycle.

5.2.2.4. Electric Discharge Cutting

A new method of producing die orifices accurately and automatically is electric erosion with a wire electrode and numerical path control. This method will gain in importance in die production together with the other processes previously used including spark erosion machining (drilling and engraving), and grinding with rotating electrodes. The process is very suitable for the production of thin-wall architectural sections and for multihole aluminum extrusion using steel and hard metal inserts. The principle of discharge cutting involves cutting a contour with a continually moving wire electrode (copper wire 0.02 to 0.2 mm diam) similar to that made with a band saw. The desired outline is developed by moving the tool blank in two coordinate directions (Fig. 5.45). This spark erosion process requires a

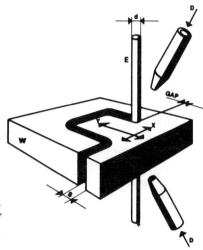

Fig. 5.45. Principle of spark erosion wire cutting: D = dielectric; E = wire; W = die; d = wire diameter; s = width of cut; x and y = movements of the die in the x and y directions. *(From Agie, Losone, Switzerland)*

dependent control of the working gap that cannot be programed and, therefore, a special path control system with a superimposed independent working gap control was developed. A very compact control system of this type can be made using integrated circuits (Agie AG).

5.3. Stresses in Extrusion Tooling

The magnitude of the thermal and mechanical stresses in the tools is one of the major factors in extrusion. However, the properties required by the tooling to withstand the stresses at temperature are not the only factors that have to be considered. It is more important to establish concrete data about the load-carrying capacity of the tool steel, its high-temperature fatigue properties, and the wear of the individual tools in practice.

5.3.1. Mechanical and Thermal Effects

The pressure p applied by the press through the stem must exceed the deformation resistance of the metal and also overcome the friction between the billet and the wall of the container liner in order to extrude the billet.

The most important tools subject to wear are briefly described below. The inner liner of the container holds the hot billet and must resist the high pressures exerted by the billet on its surface during the working cycle. The liner cools down after each cycle in the extrusion of heavy metals and, therefore, has to be insensitive to temperature changes. This cooling between extrusions is desirable because it prevents overheating of the liner at high billet throughputs and excessive wear at continuous stressing above 600 °C. The internal liner surface must remain smooth to keep friction down to a minimum. Therefore, the inner liner has to have a high hot strength and high resistance to wear, be insensitive to temperature changes, and have good thermal conductivity.

When selecting a container diameter, it is important to realize that, for a given press capacity, the specific pressure increases as the internal diameter decreases and vice versa. Consequently, the lower limit of the specific pressure is given by the extrudability of the section and the upper limit by the properties of the tooling.

The maximum specific pressure for heavy metals and aluminum alloys is usually in the range of 1000 to 1250 N/mm^2.

The dummy block must transmit the full extrusion pressure, as must the stem, but the latter does not come into direct contact with the billet. The development of the extrusion of difficult alloys has resulted in very stringent demands being made on the extrusion stem, which is subjected to both compression and buckling.

Die life is very dependent on the design and load-bearing capacity of the die holder and die backers, the importance of which is frequently underrated. The die must be supported as rigidly as possible by the backing tools. The die should not move during prolonged extrusions at high specific pressures.

The extrusion die and the mandrel are the most important tools subject to wear and, at the same time, the most highly stressed tools in extrusion. They must perform the actual change in shape to give wire, sections, rods and tubes, and are in direct contact with the plastically deforming material. The trend to higher extrusion pressures and temperatures means that materials have to be selected for these tools that are capable of withstanding even higher stresses than the inner liner, stem or dummy block. A high tensile strength is needed to withstand the high mechanical stresses, which depend on the specific pressure, friction and the hardness and abrasive effect of the billet.

The mechanical properties selected for these tools are determined by the nature of the metal being extruded, the working temperature and the deformation resistance. The tools heat up during extrusion and have to be cooled after each cycle. This again necessitates adequate insensitivity to temperature fluctuations. Bridge and porthole dies are frequently subjected to even higher stresses, because the thin legs and small mandrels in multihole dies have to withstand exceptionally high loads.

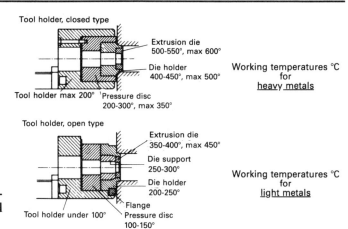

Working temperatures °C
for
heavy metals

Working temperatures °C
for
light metals

Fig. 5.46. Working temperatures for heavy metals and aluminum. *(From Laue)*

This short summary indicates how the extrusion tools that come into direct contact with the billet are the ones that must withstand the highest mechanical and thermal stresses. These tools are subjected to continual temperature cycles, being heated during every extrusion and then having to cool down again. The temperature of the tool at the point of contact with the billet can be so high that the limit of hot strength or resistance to softening of the tool steel is repeatedly exceeded (Fig. 5.46). Forced cooling of these tools is generally possible only after each working cycle and, therefore, the tools have to be capable of withstanding a temperature rise during extrusion. The magnitude of the temperature rise depends on:

(*a*) The temperature gradient between the hot billet and the tool.
(*b*) The contact time between the hot billet and the tool.
(*c*) The area of contact.
(*d*) The volume of the tooling (thermal capacity).
(*e*) The dimensions of the billet and its thermal capacity.
(*f*) The heat transfer (a function of the specific heat and thermal conductivity of the steel).

The decisive factor at high extrusion temperatures is how close the die is heated to its limit or above the annealing temperature of the steel used. In this context, it is important to know the ratio of the surface area of contact and the volume of the die, because this is a measure of the area for conducting a specific quantity of heat.

The temperature profile of a hot working tool is schematically shown in Fig. 5.47 at various stages in the working cycle. Curve *a* shows how the surface is heated to a shallow depth that decreases as the thermal conductivity of the steel is reduced. Heat transfer results in a rapid approach to

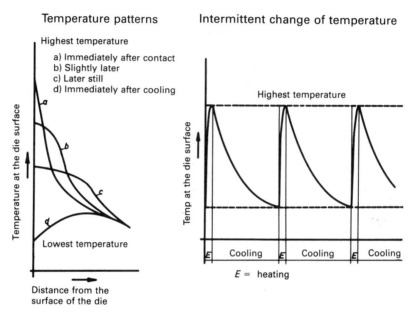

Fig. 5.47. Schematic temperature changes at the surface of the die. *(From Haufe)*

equilibrium — curve *b*. Thus, sufficient heat has to be removed to prevent the temperature from continually rising, resulting in annealing of the steel. Artificial cooling with oil, water or compressed air is beneficial. The right-hand diagram shows the alternate heating and cooling of the die surface. The continual temperature fluctuations result in alternate tensile and compressive stresses in the surface layer and a fine network of cracks forms after long service (Fig. 5.48). Very rapid heat absorption takes place in the die bearing surfaces and is further increased both by the heat developed by friction between the extrusion and die, and by the work of deformation. The increase in temperature can be so high that the inlet edges of the die break up or are softened and the edges deform (Fig. 5.49).

These examples emphasize that it is not only the production of an efficient hot working tool that requires a high degree of technical knowledge and ability, but that the press foreman must also have some technical knowledge, because every alloy extruded has its own special properties including deformation resistance, optimum extrusion temperature and extrusion speed — all parameters that influence the service life of the tooling.

Apart from the correct choice of a suitable tool steel, the steps that can be taken to keep the thermal and mechanical stresses in the tooling within admissible limits include:

Fig. 5.48. Crazing of the surface of a tube mandrel. *(From Ref 59)*

Fig. 5.49. Fractured sections of an extrusion die; plastic distortion of the edges of the orifice resulting from excessive temperature. *(From Laue, unpublished)*

(a) Checking the tool hardness against the specified value.
(b) Slow and uniform heating of the die before loading.
(c) Slow and uniform cooling in potash after use.

Every press must have a suitably controlled electric die heating furnace. Modern press designers have underlined how careful tool arrangements — including die changing mechanisms, internal mandrel cooling, and relative mandrel movement — can play a significant role in reducing tool wear even under strenuous production conditions. It is also advantageous to use several dummy blocks in sequence, according to the thermal conditions.

5.3.2. Die Wear

Aluminum extrusion dies are generally subjected to less wear than those for heavy metals and steels, because of the lower extrusion temperature. The dies used in steel and heavy metal extrusion wear by erosion, cracking, washing out, and plastic deformation. Figure 5.50 diagrams the relative tool wear and temperature range of various heavy metals. The average press output obtained with a mandrel for CuZn37 extrusion was used for the reference line. The press output of the other alloys varies according to the deformation resistance of the material and the thermal stressing of the tooling.

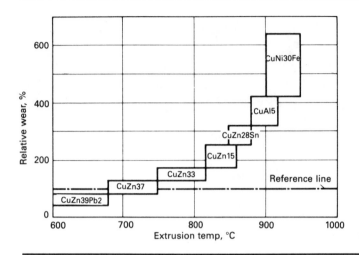

Fig. 5.50. Die wear and temperature limits of different nonferrous heavy metal alloys in reference to CuZn37. *(From Ref 59)*

5.3.3. Design of Containers With Round Bores

Containers are the most expensive of all extrusion tooling because of the large volume of hot working alloy steel needed. The efficiency of the extrusion process depends to a very high degree on the durability of the container, with the life of the inner liner being the most important. Numerous methods of container construction have been adopted in practice during the development of the extrusion process. They have had very different dimensions and design features, depending on the type of press, the alloy being extruded, and the mechanical and thermal stresses.

Calculations are indispensable to obtain the correct dimensions of the container components and to choose the most suitable steels. The mathematical expressions used are given below together with some numerical examples. The following symbols are used in the equations, explanatory diagrams, and the numerical examples:

d_{1i} = Inside diameter of the inner liner and container bore
d_{1a} = Outside diameter of the inner liner
d_{2i} = Inside diameter of the intermediate liner
d_{2a} = Outside diameter of the intermediate liner
d_{3i} = Inside diameter of the mantle
d_{3a} = Outside diameter of the mantle
u_n = Outside diameter/internal diameter = diameter ratio; e.g.: $u_1 = d_{1a}/d_{1i} = r_{1a}/r_{1i}$; $u_2 = d_{2a}/d_{2i} = r_{2a}/r_{2i}$; $u_3 = d_{3a}/d_{3i} = r_{3a}/r_{3i}$; $u = d_{3a}/d_{1i} = r_{3a}/r_{1i}$
F = Press capacity
A_o = Cross sectional area of the container bore

p = F/A_o = specific pressure = stem load/area of container bore

p_{sn} = Shrink-fit pressure between liners or liner and container mantle

p_{ri} = Internal radial pressure on the individual container components

p_{ra} = External radial pressure on the individual container components

σ_t = Tangential service and residual stresses in the container resulting from the working pressure p_{ri} and the shrinkage pressure p_{sn}

σ_r = Radial service and residual stresses in the container resulting from the working pressure p_{ri} and the shrinkage pressure p_{sn}

σ_a = Axial service and residual stresses in the container

σ_{tT} = Effective tangential operating stress from the superimposition of the service and residual stresses

σ_{rT} = Effective radial operating stress from the superimposition of the service and residual stresses

σ_R = Equivalent stress from σ_{tT} and σ_{rT}

E = Modulus of elasticity

ϵ_t = Elastic tensile or compressive strain of the individual container components

ϵ_n = Relative shrinkage allowance

Axial deformation forces act on the stem and the die during extrusion. On the other hand, radial forces act on the container as tangential and radial stresses σ_t and σ_r, which can have very high values. The only axial stresses in the container come from the friction between the billet and the inner liner, but axial thermal stresses also develop during the shrink-fit process and the press operation and, consequently, superimposed axial stresses σ_a cannot be excluded even though they are not considered in the calculations.

A container can withstand higher stresses if it is constructed of several components and if compressive stresses are induced into the more severely stressed inner liner and intermediate liner by shrink fitting. The effective stresses developed in a container during extrusion can be quantitatively assessed only if certain assumptions are made. By assuming symmetrical stressing of the container and its components around its axis, the residual stresses induced by shrink fitting and the stresses developed during extrusion can be calculated. The stresses required — σ_a, σ_r and σ_t — are, by reason of their direction, principal stresses. The temperature distribution is also assumed to be axisymmetric over the full length of the container; local thermal stresses, which cannot be calculated, are neglected. Longitudinal thermal stresses from the temperature variations in the components shrunk together are also excluded, together with the longitudinal stresses developed by the friction between the billet and the container. The materials used for the liners and the mantle are assumed to have the same modulus of elasticity and the state of stress is taken to be purely elastic. A plane stress condition can, therefore, be assumed and the effective service stress can then be calculated from classical elasticity theory superimposing the residual stresses from shrink fitting onto the stresses developed from the deformation loads. The theory of thick-wall cylindrical vessels under internal and external pressure is used to calculate the individual stresses in the container liners and mantle. The equations for the radial and tangential stresses at any arbitrary point r in the hollow body can be determined as a function of the pressure and the dimensions from the equilibrium of forces and the relationships between stress and strain. For a hollow body subjected to an internal pressure:

$$\sigma_r = p_{ri} \frac{r_i^2}{r_a^2 - r_i^2} \left\{ 1 - \frac{r_a^2}{r^2} \right\} = p_{ri} \frac{d_i^2}{d_a^2 - d_i^2} \left\{ 1 - \frac{d_a^2}{d^2} \right\} \qquad \text{(Eq 62)}$$

$$\sigma_t = p_{ri} \frac{r_i^2}{r_a^2 - r_i^2} \left\{ 1 + \frac{r_a^2}{r^2} \right\} = p_{ri} \frac{d_i^2}{d_a^2 - d_i^2} \left\{ 1 + \frac{d_a^2}{d^2} \right\} \qquad \text{(Eq 63)}$$

For a hollow body subjected to an external pressure:

$$\sigma_r = -p_{ra} \frac{r_a^2}{r_a^2 - r_i^2} \left\{ 1 - \frac{r_i^2}{r^2} \right\} = -p_{ra} \frac{d_a^2}{d_a^2 - d_i^2} \left\{ 1 - \frac{d_i^2}{d^2} \right\} \qquad \text{(Eq 64)}$$

$$\sigma_t = -p_{ra} \frac{r_a^2}{r_a^2 - r_i^2} \left\{ 1 + \frac{r_i^2}{r^2} \right\} = -p_{ra} \frac{d_a^2}{d_a^2 - d_i^2} \left\{ 1 + \frac{d_i^2}{d^2} \right\} \qquad \text{(Eq 65)}$$

The stress variation across the container wall is, therefore, hyperbolic and the peak stresses — the maximum stresses — always occur at the inner wall of the hollow body regardless of whether the pressure is applied internally or externally. The initial assumption is that the container is only stressed in two dimensions and, accordingly, the effect of the stresses must be combined into a resultant stress σ_R. The resultant stress implies that flow occurs only in a continuous medium stressed in several dimensions when σ_R exceeds the flow stress determined from uniaxial tensile tests.

The maximum strain criterion was previously used to calculate the equivalent stress σ_R in container calculations. However, experiments have indicated that the strain hypothesis considerably underestimates the danger of fracture. The strain energy hypothesis gives better agreement with the initiation of plastic deformation under multiaxial stresses for materials, including the hot working steels, generally used for container construction. According to this criterion, under a two-dimensional stress system — e.g., the principal stresses σ_r and σ_t — flow occurs when

$$\sigma_R = \sqrt{\sigma_t^2 + \sigma_r^2 - \sigma_t \cdot \sigma_r} = R_{p0.2} \qquad \text{(Eq 66)}$$

σ_R must not exceed the 0.2% proof stress at the operating temperature or the important shrink-fit stresses will not be retained and the container will suffer permanent plastic deformation. Therefore, a safety factor is usually introduced into the calculations:

$$\sigma_R \cdot k < R_{p0.2} - \text{the proof stress at temperature} \qquad \text{(Eq 67)}$$

where the safety factor k should normally be between 1.15 and 1.3. These values will be discussed in more detail later.

It must be remembered that a container is mainly subjected to fatigue stresses, and the stresses in the inner liner and intermediate liners vary from tensile to compressive, whereas the container mantle is only subjected to tensile stresses. The tension-compression fatigue loading of the liners results from the superimposition of the tensile stresses from the extrusion pressure on the compressive residual stresses induced by shrink fitting. The tensile stresses in the mantle result from the superimposition of the tensile service stresses on the residual tensile stresses developed by shrink fitting. The effective tangential stresses at the inner wall of the container liner of a multipart container vary during the press cycle between the compressive stresses from the shrink fitting process and the resultant stress from the addition of the residual compressive stresses and the tensile service stresses when the extrusion load is applied. Fractures in inner and intermediate liners have the characteristic appearance of fatigue failures. However, the most highly stressed component of a container—the inner liner—is only stressed in the limited life area of the fatigue curve ($<10^5$ cycles) and usually fails by wear of the internal wall.

5.3.3.1. Design of Monobloc Containers

In this case the liner and mantle are the same component (Fig. 5.51). Containers of this type are no longer built because the high stress peaks on the inner wall during extrusion restrict the load carrying capacity compared to a compound container. The extrusion pressure induces tensile tangential stresses internally and externally, and the inner wall is also subjected to compressive stresses. The maximum stresses resulting from the extrusion pressure occur at the bore and the minimum at the outer surface. Equations

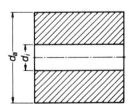

Fig. 5.51. One-piece container.

62 and 63 are used to calculate the stresses induced from the extrusion pressure and these stresses determine the size of the container. At the internal wall:

$$\sigma_r(d_i) = \sigma_{r_{max}} = p_{ri} \frac{d_i^2}{d_a^2 - d_i^2} \left\{ 1 - \frac{d_a^2}{d_i^2} \right\} = -p_{ri} \qquad \text{(Eq 68)}$$

$$\sigma_t(d_i) = \sigma_{t_{max}} = p_{ri} \frac{d_i^2}{d_a^2 - d_i^2} \left\{ 1 + \frac{d_a^2}{d_i^2} \right\} = p_{ri} \frac{u^2 + 1}{u^2 - 1} \qquad \text{(Eq 69)}$$

At the external wall:

$$\sigma_r(d_a) = \sigma_{r_{min}} = p_{ri} \frac{d_i^2}{d_a^2 - d_i^2} \left\{ 1 - \frac{d_a^2}{d_a^2} \right\} = 0 \qquad \text{(Eq 70)}$$

$$\sigma_t(d_a) = \sigma_{t_{min}} = p_{ri} \frac{d_i^2}{d_a^2 - d_i^2} \left\{ 1 + \frac{d_a^2}{d_a^2} \right\} = p_{ri} \frac{2}{u^2 - 1} \qquad \text{(Eq 71)}$$

5.3.3.2. Design of Compound Containers

Only compound containers are used today to reduce the high stress peaks that develop at the bore of a monobloc container under the application of the extrusion pressure. Compressive residual stresses are developed in all the liners by shrink-fitting the liner and, when used, the intermediate liner into the mantle. These compressive stresses must be removed by the applied extrusion pressure before tensile stresses can form. This applies, in particular, to the inner liner. The correct choice of compressive residual stresses permits significantly higher stresses in a prestressed compound container than would be the case for a monobloc container without prestressing.

The friction loads between the mating surfaces resulting from the stresses induced by shrink-fitting and the coefficient of friction must be capable of withstanding the axial loads developed by friction between the billet and the inner liner during extrusion if these axial loads cannot be absorbed elsewhere. Three-piece containers are normally used today but two- or four-piece ones are also found. A further advantage of multicomponent containers is that different grades of steel can be used for the individual sections according to the relevant thermal and mechanical stresses developed during service. The inner liner must, naturally, be manufactured out of the better grade of steels because it has to withstand the greatest stresses and wear.

In the shrink-fitting process a strong bond is formed between the liner, intermediate liner, and mantle by pressing them together. The magnitude of the stresses induced by shrink-fitting can be controlled by the size of the interference fit and this is examined in more detail in the numerical examples. Assembly is usually carried out by pushing the inner liner, which is at room temperature or slightly cooled, into the preheated mantle or intermediate liner. The full shrink-fitting stresses are developed when a uniform temperature is reached. With a three-part container the inner liner and intermediate liner are shrunk together and then fitted into the heated mantle. The outer surface of the intermediate liner is often lightly remachined before this final fitting operation.

The design stress is normally selected to fall below the high-temperature proof stress ($R_{p0.2}$) for the appropriate working range by a specified safety factor. Containers for aluminum are designed with σ_0 approximately 85 to 90% (safety factor k = 1.15 to 1.3) of the high-temperature proof stress, whereas only 75 to 80% (k = 1.25 to 1.3) is used for containers for heavy metals. Prolonged application of the extrusion load with high thermal stresses can result in the residual stresses decreasing by creep of the container material and this must be reflected in the choice of the safety factor.

According to the assumption made, the calculation of the purely elastic behavior of the container components is valid up to the high-temperature yield stress. However, all materials exhibit some permanent deformation at the yield point — elastic behavior only occurs up to the elastic limit. Therefore, it cannot be excluded that some local plastic deformation takes place, at least at the mating surfaces of the components shrunk together. Variations in the interference between the mating surfaces from machining or nonuniform heating must be avoided. The components shrunk together should also be carefully cooled as uniformly as possible. If the cooling rate is too slow relaxation can take place in the highly stressed parts, especially when the selected interference has almost its full effect at high temperatures. The high temperature yield stress is then exceeded in the sections with the highest stresses (stress peaks). This can also result in plastic expansion of the mantle and reduce the residual stresses below those calculated. The relaxation processes are largely suppressed by using faster cooling rates but can instead result in significant variations in the contraction of the parts under tension or compression shrunk together and these variations cannot be balanced out quickly enough at the mating surfaces. Thermal axial loads are also developed between the mating surfaces for the same reason. The net result is an uncontrolled longitudinal stress acting as a third component at the junction of the components shrunk together. This introduces a significant factor of uncertainty in the two-dimensional system assumed for the calculation. The inner liners can, in due course, be moved in the extrusion direction by these axial loads because the friction between the liner and the mantle is insufficient to withstand the additional longitudinal stresses. Considerable experience is, therefore, needed to correctly design and manufacture containers. In general, steel producers should advise the extrusion plant operator of the optimum working conditions for the container.

According to Müller (Ref 27) and also Busch and Schepp (Ref 28) the outside diameter of a container should be approximately four to five times the inside diameter. The wall thickness of the inner liner should not exceed what is necessary to withstand the operating stresses but this condition cannot always be met and the preferred approach for determining the wall thicknesses of the inner liner is based on the practical experience that a multipart container has the optimum resistance to internal pressure if all the components have the same diameter ratio — that is, $u_1 = u_2 = u_3$. However, Busch and Schepp (Ref 28) have considered some practical examples and suggest that this condition is not always valid for containers, especially when the minimum rate of heat removal to prevent heat from accumulating in the container cannot be guaranteed. In this case the inner liner can require a higher diameter ratio than the intermediate liner. Practical considerations can also result in different diameter ratios — for example, a constant outside diameter of the inner liner with varying inside diameters can be selected for several containers for ease of replacement, provided the stresses are satisfactory.

The minimum recommended wall thickness for the inner liners of containers for presses up to 25 MN is 50 to 60 mm to give sufficient heat removal. Thicker liners are needed on larger presses. On the other hand, liners with excessively thick walls should be avoided: they are too stiff and cannot adapt closely enough to the mantle or intermediate liner. Radial cracks have frequently been observed in the center of liners that are too thick; these cracks do not appear if the thick liners are replaced by thinner ones. Adequate heat removal is calculated by the rule of thumb that the transverse section of the inner liner for heavy metals should be at least 1.8 times the cross sectional area of the container bore. This rule is limited by the danger mentioned above of liners becoming too stiff as the wall thickness increases. The factor for aluminum presses should be 1.5, but experience also plays a very important role. In general the diameter ratio of the inner liner is chosen, with due allowance to experience, as follows:

$$u_1 = \frac{d_{1a}}{d_{1i}} = \frac{r_{1a}}{r_{1i}} = 1.5 \text{ to } 2.0.$$

The diameter ratio of the intermediate liner is:

$$u_2 = \frac{d_{2a}}{d_{2i}} = \frac{r_{2a}}{r_{2i}} = 1.6 \text{ to } 1.8.$$

The diameter ratio of the mantle

Fig. 5.52. Principle of induction heating of a three-piece container. (*From Schloemann-SIEMAG*)

$$u_3 = \frac{d_{3a}}{d_{3i}} = \frac{r_{3a}}{r_{3i}}$$

is generally taken to be between 2 and 2.5, for the same reasons.

The intermediate liner has to meet stringent requirements — especially when unalloyed mantles are used. It must withstand a significant part of the stresses developed during extrusion and should be about 1.2 to 1.5 times the thickness of the inner liner. However, the intermediate liner should not be too thick. Arenz (Ref 53) proposed standards for the dimensions of liners and intermediate liners in 1955 but, according to the experience of Busch and Schepp (Ref 28), the recommended wall thicknesses are too small for heavy metals. Special attention also has to be given to ensure that the container mantle is not weakened too severely by the holes for container heating. Almost all containers are now heated electrically with cartridge elements arranged in holes in the mantle parallel to the container axis (Fig. 5.52 and 5.63). Both resistance and induction heating are used.

The axial heating element holes act as notches in the cross section of the mantle, and stress concentrations that can result in localized overstress-

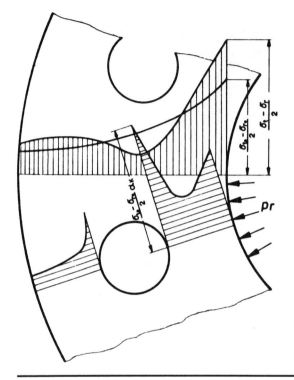

Fig. 5.53. Detrimental effect of heating element holes on the stress profile in the container mantle. *(From Ref 29)*

ing of the mantle steel develop under load. According to Grüning (Ref 29) the stress profile across the mating surfaces is also influenced, in addition to the characteristic discontinuities in the profile in the neighborhood of the holes as expected with any notch. The removal of the load-carrying sections represented by the heating element holes results in higher stress peaks at the mantle inner wall from both the shrink-fitting operation and the extrusion load, and this can give lower residual stresses in the intermediate liner or the inner liner in a two-piece container. Figure 5.53 illustrates the stress profile around a heating hole and between the mating surfaces together with half the difference of the two principal stresses: $\sigma_t - \sigma_r/2$. This situation is reflected in the design of a container mantle by selecting a suitably large diameter ratio u_3, often higher than the ratios used for the other container components.

In the following sections, especially in the calculated examples, the terms service stresses, residual stresses and operating stresses are used. Service stresses result from the radial component p_{ri}, of the extrusion pressure p in all cross sections of the solid containers. Residual stresses are formed in all the components of the compound container by the pressures

p_{sn} developed in the shrink-fitting operation. The operating stresses are the effective stresses in all the cross sections of the compound container resulting from the superimposition of the absolute values of the service and residual stresses.

5.3.3.2.1. Two-Piece Containers

The effective operating stresses used to select the dimensions are obtained by superimposing the service and residual stresses:

At the inner wall of the liner:

$$\sigma_{rT} (r_{li}) = \sigma_r (p_{ri}) + \sigma_r (p_s) = -p_{ri} \pm 0 \qquad \text{(Eq 72)}$$

$$\sigma_{tT} (r_{li}) = \sigma_t (p_{ri}) + \sigma_t (p_s) = p_{ri} \frac{u^2 + 1}{u^2 - 1} - p_s \frac{2u_1^2}{u_1^2 - 1} \qquad \text{(Eq 73)}$$

At the external wall of the liner, at the shrinkage interface:

$$\sigma_{rT} (r_{la}) = \sigma_r (p_{ri}) + \sigma_r (p_s) = -p_{ri} \frac{u_3^2 - 1}{u^2 - 1} - p_s \qquad \text{(Eq 74)}$$

$$\sigma_{tT} (r_{la}) = \sigma_t (p_{ri}) + \sigma_t (p_s) = p_{ri} \frac{u_3^2 + 1}{u^2 - 1} - p_s \frac{u_1^2 + 1}{u_1^2 - 1} \qquad \text{(Eq 75)}$$

At the inner wall of the mantle, at the shrinkage interface:

$$\sigma_{rT} (r_{3i}) = \sigma_r (p_{ri}) + \sigma_r (p_s) = -p_{ri} \frac{u_3^2 - 1}{u^2 - 1} - p_s \qquad \text{(Eq 76)}$$

$$\sigma_{tT} (r_{3i}) = \sigma_t (p_{ri}) + \sigma_t (p_s) = p_{ri} \frac{u_3^2 + 1}{u^2 - 1} + p_s \frac{u_3^2 + 1}{u_3^2 - 1} \qquad \text{(Eq 77)}$$

At the external wall of the mantle:

$$\sigma_{rT} (r_{3a}) = \sigma_r (p_{ri}) + \sigma_r (p_s) = 0 \pm 0 \qquad \text{(Eq 78)}$$

$$\sigma_{tT} (r_{3a}) = \sigma_t (p_{ri}) + \sigma_t (p_s) = p_{ri} \frac{2}{u^2 - 1} + p_s \frac{2}{u_3^2 - 1} \qquad \text{(Eq 79)}$$

The pressure p_s developed between the inner liner and the mantle by shrink-fitting is:

$$p_s = \frac{E \cdot \epsilon}{2} \cdot \frac{(u_3^2 - 1)(u_1^2 - 1)}{u^2 - 1} \qquad \text{(Eq 80)}$$

where ϵ is the relative interference.

5.3.3.2.2. Three-Piece Containers

The effective operating stresses used to design the container are again obtained by superimposing the service and residual stresses.

At the inner wall of the inner liner:

$$\sigma_{rT}(r_{li}) = \sigma_r(p_{ri}) + \sigma_r(p_{s_1}) + \sigma_r(p_{s_2}) = -p_{ri} \pm 0 \pm 0 \tag{Eq 81}$$

$$\sigma_{tT}(r_{li}) = \sigma_r(p_{ri}) + \sigma_r(p_{s_1}) + \sigma_r(p_{s_2}) = p_{ri}\frac{u^2+1}{u^2-1} - p_{s_1}\frac{2u_1^2}{u_1^2-1} - p_{s_2}\frac{2u_2^2u_1^2}{u_2^2u_1^2-1}$$
$$\tag{Eq 82}$$

At the shrinkage interface 1 at the external wall of the internal liner:

$$\sigma_{rT}(r_{1a}) = -p_{ri}\frac{u_3^2u_2^2-1}{u^2-1} - p_{s_1} - p_{s_2}\frac{u_2^2u_1^2-u_2^2}{u_2^2u_1^2-1} \tag{Eq 83}$$

$$\sigma_{tT}(r_{1a}) = p_{ri}\frac{u_3^2u_2^2+1}{u^2-1} - p_{s_1}\frac{u_1^2+1}{u_1^2-1} - p_{s_2}\frac{u_2^2u_1^2+u_2^2}{u_2^2u_1^2-1} \tag{Eq 84}$$

At the internal shrinkage interface 1 of the intermediate liner:

$$\sigma_{rT}(r_{2i}) = -p_{ri}\frac{u_3^2u_2^2-1}{u^2-1} - p_{s_1} - p_{s_2}\frac{u_2^2u_1^2-u_2^2}{u_2^2u_1^2-1} \tag{Eq 85}$$

$$\sigma_{tT}(r_{2i}) = p_{ri}\frac{u_3^2u_2^2+1}{u^2-1} + p_{s_1}\frac{u_3^2u_2^2+1}{u_3^2u_2^2-1} - p_{s_2}\frac{u_2^2u_1^2+u_2^2}{u_2^2u_1^2-1} \tag{Eq 86}$$

At the external shrinkage interface 2 of the intermediate liner:

$$\sigma_{rT}(r_{2a}) = -p_{ri}\frac{u_3^2-1}{u^2-1} - p_{s_1}\frac{u_3^2-1}{u_3^2u_2^2-1} - p_{s_2} \tag{Eq 87}$$

$$\sigma_{tT}(r_{2a}) = p_{ri}\frac{u_3^2+1}{u^2-1} + p_{s_1}\frac{u_3^2+1}{u_3^2u_2^2-1} - p_{s_2}\frac{u_2^2u_1^2+1}{u_2^2u_1^2-1} \tag{Eq 88}$$

At the internal shrinkage interface 2 of the mantle:

$$\sigma_{rT}(r_{3i}) = -p_{ri}\frac{u_3^2-1}{u^2-1} - p_{s_1}\frac{u_3^2-1}{u_3^2u_2^2-1} - p_{s_2} \tag{Eq 89}$$

$$\sigma_{tT}(r_{3i}) = p_{ri}\frac{u_3^2+1}{u^2-1} + p_{s_1}\frac{u_3^2+1}{u_3^2u_2^2-1} + p_{s_2}\frac{u_3^2+1}{u_3^2-1} \tag{Eq 90}$$

At the outer wall of the mantle:

$$\sigma_{rT}(r_{3a}) = \pm 0 \pm 0 \pm 0 \tag{Eq 91}$$

$$\sigma_{tT}(r_{3a}) = p_{ri}\frac{2}{u^2-1} + p_{s_1}\frac{2}{u_3^2u_2^2-1} + p_{s_2}\frac{2}{u_3^2-1} \tag{Eq 92}$$

The pressures p_{s_1} and p_{s_2} from the shrink-fitting operation are obtained from:

$$p_{s_1} = \frac{E \cdot \epsilon_1}{2} \cdot \frac{(u_3^2 \cdot u_2^2 - 1)(u_1^2 - 1)}{u^2 - 1} \tag{Eq 93}$$

and

$$p_{s_2} = \frac{E \cdot \epsilon_2}{2} \cdot \frac{(u_2^2 \cdot u_1^2 - 1)(u_3^2 - 1)}{u^2 - 1} \tag{Eq 94}$$

where ϵ_1 is the relative interference between the inner liner and the intermediate liner, and ϵ_2 the relative interference between the intermediate liner and the mantle.

5.3.3.2.3. Numerical Examples

The 180 and 224 mm containers of a 25 MN extrusion press equipped with inside diameters 180, 200, 224 and 250 mm, had to be restored. The press was used only for extruding aluminum and its alloys.

The calculations are given for one- and two-piece containers and also, in the case of very high stresses, for a three-piece design. After determining the type of construction from the maximum operating stresses, suitable hot working steels are selected for each component. The mathematical relationships in sections 5.3.3.2.1 and 5.3.3.2.2, which are the usual ones for container design, are used to determine the service, residual and effective operating stresses. The working pressure p_{ri} at the inner liner wall of the container was taken to be less than the full specific pressure p because there is no hydrostatic stress distribution in the container. Metallic materials do not behave as a fluid even when they are very plastic. Similarly, axisymmetric distribution of the radial stresses along the length of the container mentioned in section 5.3.3 is also assumed. This simplifies the calculation but does not agree exactly with the true radial stresses on the inner wall of the container. As well as being dependent on the deformation resistance of the individual alloys, the radial pressure is also a function of the friction between the billet and the container liner. The radial pressure p_{ri} decreases with increasing friction. Usually, p_{ri} is taken to be 0.6 to 0.8 p, with the maximum radial pressure being used for the design of the containers for alloys extruded with little friction between the billet and the container and vice versa. Higher loads from friction are normally developed during aluminum extrusion than with copper, because of the method of extrusion. Containers for aluminum are, therefore, designed with lower radial pressures, whereas higher pressures are used for the heavy metals. In the following examples $p_{ri} = 0.7$ p is assumed because only containers for aluminum alloys are considered.

The general numerical method for container design using the expressions above is described below. A detailed description of container design

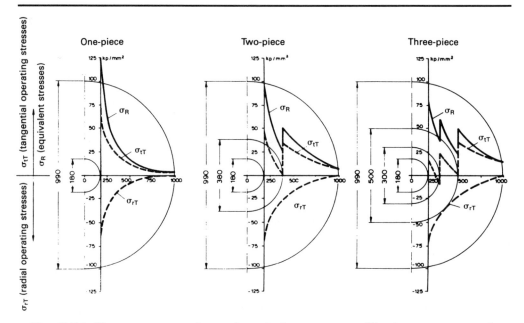

Fig. 5.54. Transverse operating and equivalent stress profiles in one-, two- and three-piece containers with a 180 mm bore. *(From Ref 24)*

using numerical examples by Sauer (Ref 24) has been given in the DGM report No. 29/1275.

Design of the Container With a Bore of 180 mm (Fig. 5.54)

The specific pressure is: $\dfrac{2.5 \cdot 10^7 \cdot 4}{1.8^2 \cdot 10^4 \cdot \pi} = 983$ N/mm^2 and $p_{ri} = 0.7 \, p = 688$ N/mm^2. The outside mantle diameter of all the containers is: $d_{3a} = 990$ mm, and the diameter ratio is then: $u = d_{3a}/d_{1i} = 990/180 = 5.5$.

One-Piece Container

Internal wall:

$$\sigma_r \, (r_{li}) = \sigma_{r_{max}} = -p_{ri} = -688 \text{ N/mm}^2$$

$$\sigma_t \, (r_{li}) = \sigma_{t_{max}} = p_{ri} \frac{u^2 + 1}{u^2 - 1} = 688 \, \frac{31.25}{29.25} = 735 \text{ N/mm}^2$$

External wall:

$$\sigma_r \, (r_{3a}) = \sigma_{r_{min}} = 0 \text{ N/mm}^2$$

$$\sigma_t \, (r_{3a}) = \sigma_{t_{min}} = p_{ri} \frac{2}{u^2 - 1} = 688 \, \frac{2}{29.25} = 47 \text{ N/mm}^2$$

Therefore the equivalent stress at the internal container wall is:

$$\sigma_{Ri} = \sqrt{\sigma_t^2 + \sigma_r^2 - \sigma_r \cdot \sigma_t} = \sqrt{735^2 + 688^2 + 735 \cdot 688} = 1233 \text{ N/mm}^2$$

and at the external wall:

$$\sigma_{Ra} = \sqrt{47^2} = 47 \text{ N/mm}^2$$

There is no hot working steel for containers that can withstand a stress as high as 1223 N/mm^2 without plastic deformation at the operating temperatures of 500 to 550 °C found in aluminum extrusion. The maximum equivalent stress cannot exceed the high temperature yield stress and, therefore, the container must be prestressed and constructed of several components.

Two-Piece Container

The outside diameter of the inner liner was chosen at 380 mm. The diameter ratios are then:

$$u_1 = d_{1a}/d_{1i} = 380/180 = 2.11; \quad u_3 = d_{3a}/d_{3i} \approx d_{3a}/d_{1a} = 2.61;$$
$$u = d_{3a}/d_{1i} = 990/180 = 5.5$$

The modulus of elasticity of the inner liner is assumed to be approximately equal to that of the mantle even at the working temperature:

$$E_{\text{ liner}} \approx E_{\text{ mantle}} = 183\,000 \text{ N/mm}^2 \text{ at } 500 \text{ °C}$$

The relative interference allowance is taken as $\epsilon = 1.8\%\!o$; the shrink fitting pressure is therefore:

$$p_s = \frac{E \cdot \epsilon}{2} \cdot \frac{(u_3^2 - 1)(u_1^2 - 1)}{u^2 - 1} = \frac{183\,000 \cdot 1.8 \cdot 10^{-3}}{2} \cdot \frac{5.81 \cdot 3.45}{29.25} = 113 \text{ N/mm}^2$$

The service stresses = the stresses under the working pressure in the one-piece container:

Inner wall of inner liner:

$$\sigma_r(r_{1i}) = -p_{ri} = -688 \text{ N/mm}^2$$

$$\sigma_t(r_{1i}) = p_{ri} \frac{u^2 + 1}{u^2 - 1} = 688 \frac{31.25}{29.25} = 735 \text{ N/mm}^2$$

At the shrinkage interface:

$$\sigma_r \left(\begin{matrix} r_{1a} \\ r_{3i} \end{matrix} \right) = -p_{ri} \frac{u_3^2 - 1}{u^2 - 1} = -688 \frac{2.61^2 - 1}{5.5^2 - 1} = -688 \frac{5.81}{29.25} = -137 \text{ N/mm}^2$$

$$\sigma_t \left(\begin{matrix} r_{1a} \\ r_{3i} \end{matrix} \right) = p_{ri} \frac{u_3^2 + 1}{u^2 - 1} = 688 \frac{7.81}{29.25} = 184 \text{ N/mm}^2$$

External wall of the mantle:

$$\sigma_r(r_{3a}) = 0 \text{ N/mm}^2$$

$$\sigma_t(r_{3a}) = p_{ri}\frac{2}{u^2 - 1} = 688\,\frac{2}{29.25} = 47 \text{ N/mm}^2$$

Residual stresses = stresses from shrink fitting:
Inner wall of inner liner:

$$\sigma_r(r_{li}) = 0 \text{ N/mm}^2$$

$$\sigma_t(r_{li}) = p_s\frac{2u_1^2}{u_1^2 - 1} = -11.298\,\frac{2 \cdot 2.11^2}{2.11^2 - 1} = -291 \text{ N/mm}^2$$

External wall of the liner:

$$\sigma_r^{\cdot}(r_{la}) = -p_s = -113 \text{ N/mm}^2$$

$$\sigma_t(r_{la}) = -p_s\frac{u_1^2 + 1}{u_1^2 - 1} = -113\,\frac{2.11^2 + 1}{2.11^2 - 1} = -113\,\frac{5.45}{3.45} = -178 \text{ N/mm}^2$$

Inner wall of the mantle:

$$\sigma_r(r_{3i}) = -p_s = -113 \text{ N/mm}^2$$

$$\sigma_t(r_{3i}) = p_s\frac{u_3^2 + 1}{u_3^2 - 1} = 113\,\frac{2.61^2 + 1}{2.61^2 - 1} = 113\,\frac{7.81}{5.81} = 152 \text{ N/mm}^2$$

External wall of the mantle:

$$\sigma_r(r_{3a}) = 0 \text{ N/mm}^2$$

$$\sigma_t(r_{3a}) = p_s\frac{2}{u_3^2 - 1} = 113\,\frac{2}{2.61^2 - 1} = 113\,\frac{2}{5.81} = 39 \text{ N/mm}^2$$

Operating stresses = service stresses plus residual stresses:
Internal wall of the liner:

$$\sigma_{rT} = -p_{ri} = -688 \text{ N/mm}^2$$

$$\sigma_{tT} = p_{ri}\frac{u^2 + 1}{u^2 - 1} - p_s\frac{2u_1^2}{u_1^2 - 1} = 735 - 291 = 444 \text{ N/mm}^2$$

$$\sigma_R = \sqrt{444^2 + 688^2 + 444 \cdot 688} = 988 \text{ N/mm}^2$$

External wall of the liner:

$$\sigma_{rT}(r_{la}) = -p_{ri}\frac{u_3^2 - 1}{u^2 - 1} - p_s = -137 - 113 = -250 \text{ N/mm}^2$$

$$\sigma_{tT}(r_{la}) = p_{ri}\frac{u_3^2 + 1}{u^2 - 1} - p_s\frac{u_1^2 + 1}{u_1^2 - 1} = 184 - 178 = 6 \text{ N/mm}^2$$

$$\sigma_R = \sqrt{6^2 + 250^2 + 6 \cdot 250} = 253 \text{ N/mm}^2$$

Internal wall of the mantle:

$$\sigma_{rT}(r_{3i}) = -p_{ri}\frac{u_3^2 - 1}{u^2 - 1} - p_s = -137 - 113 = -250 \text{ N/mm}^2$$

$$\sigma_{tT}(r_{3i}) = p_{ri}\frac{u_3^2 + 1}{u^2 - 1} + p_s\frac{u_3^2 + 1}{u_3^2 - 1} = 184 + 152 = 336 \text{ N/mm}^2$$

$$\sigma_R = \sqrt{336^2 + 250^2 + 336 \cdot 250} = 509 \text{ N/mm}^2$$

External wall of the mantle:

$$\sigma_{rT}(r_{3a}) = 0 \text{ N/mm}^2$$

$$\sigma_{tT}(r_{3a}) = p_{ri}\frac{2}{u^2 - 1} + p_s\frac{2}{u_3^2 - 1} = 47 + 39 = 86 \text{ N/mm}^2$$

$$\sigma_R = \sqrt{86^2} = 86 \text{ N/mm}^2$$

Naturally, the internal wall of the liner has to withstand the highest operating stresses and, in spite of the considerable residual stresses from a relatively high shrinkage allowance of 1.8%, the maximum operating stress is 988 N/mm². None of the hot working steels generally used for containers has a high-temperature yield stress capable of preventing plastic deformation under this applied stress and a three-part construction must be used to reduce the magnitude of the operating stresses.

Three-Piece Container

The high equivalent stress at the internal wall of the liner of the two-piece container indicates that the relative shrinkage allowances ϵ_1 and ϵ_2 for the three-part container must be selected to give residual stresses of suitable magnitude. It has also been shown numerically that the inner liner must have a relatively thin wall for the same reasons. In this example the following values are used:

$u = d_{3a}/d_{1a} = 990/180 = 5.5$
$u_1 = d_{1a}/d_{1i} = 300/180 = 1.67$; $s_{\text{inner liner}} = 60$ mm
$u_2 = d_{2a}/d_{1a} = 500/300 = 1.67$; $s_{\text{intermediate liner}} = 100$ mm
$u_3 = d_{3a}/d_{2a} = 990/500 = 1.98$; $s_{\text{mantle}} = 245$ mm
$\epsilon_1 = 1.8‰$; $\epsilon_2 = 1.8‰$; $E = 183\ 000$ N/mm² at 500 °C

Thus:

$$p_{s_1} = \frac{E \cdot \epsilon_1}{2} \cdot \frac{(u_3^2 u_2^2 - 1)(u_1^2 - 1)}{u^2 - 1} = \frac{183\ 000 \cdot 1.8 \cdot 10^{-3}}{2} \frac{(1.98^2 \cdot 1.67^2 - 1)(1.67^2 - 1)}{5.5^2 - 1}$$

$$= 164.7 \frac{9.94 \cdot 1.79}{29.25} = 100 \text{ N/mm}^2$$

$$p_{s_2} = \frac{E \cdot \epsilon_2}{2} \cdot \frac{(u_2^2 u_1^2 - 1)(u_3^2 - 1)}{u^2 - 1} = \frac{183\,000 \cdot 1.8 \cdot 10^{-3}}{2} \frac{(1.67^4 - 1)(1.98^2 - 1)}{5.5^2 - 1}$$

$$= 164.7 \frac{6.78 \cdot 2.92}{29.25} = 112 \text{ N/mm}^2$$

Service stresses = stresses under the applied pressure in a one-piece container:

Internal wall of the inner liner:

$$\sigma_r(r_{li}) = -p_{ri} = 688 \text{ N/mm}^2$$

$$\sigma_t(r_{li}) = p_{ri} \frac{u^2 + 1}{u^2 - 1} = 688 \frac{31.25}{29.25} = 735 \text{ N/mm}^2$$

Shrinkage interface 1 between the outside surface of the inner liner and the internal wall of the intermediate liner:

$$\sigma_r \binom{r_{1a}}{r_{2i}} = -p_{ri} \frac{u_3^2 u_2^2 - 1}{u^2 - 1} = -688 \frac{1.98^2 \cdot 1.67^2 - 1}{5.5^2 - 1} = -688 \frac{9.93}{29.25}$$

$$= -234 \text{ N/mm}^2$$

$$\sigma_t \binom{r_{1a}}{r_{2i}} = p_{ri} \frac{u_3^2 u_2^2 + 1}{u^2 - 1} = 688 \frac{1.98^2 \cdot 1.67^2 + 1}{5.5^2 - 1} = 688 \frac{11.94}{29.25}$$

$$= 281 \text{ N/mm}^2$$

Shrinkage interface 2 between the outside surface of the intermediate liner and the internal wall of the mantle:

$$\sigma_r \binom{r_{2a}}{r_{3i}} = -p_{ri} \frac{u_3^2 - 1}{u^2 - 1} = -688 \frac{1.98^2 - 1}{5.5^2 - 1} = -688 \frac{2.92}{29.25}$$

$$= -69 \text{ N/mm}^2$$

$$\sigma_t \binom{r_{2a}}{r_{3i}} = p_{ri} \frac{u_3^2 + 1}{u^2 - 1} = 688 \frac{4.92}{29.25} = 116 \text{ N/mm}^2$$

External wall of the mantle:

$$\sigma_r(r_{3a}) = 0 \text{ N/mm}^2$$

$$\sigma_t(r_{3a}) = p_{ri} \frac{2}{u^2 - 1} = 688 \frac{2}{29.25} = 47 \text{ N/mm}^2$$

Residual stresses "1" from the shrink-fit pressure p_{s_1}:

Internal wall of the inner liner:

$$\sigma_r(r_{li}) = 0 \text{ N/mm}^2$$

$$\sigma_t(r_{li}) = -p_{s_1} \frac{2u_1^2}{u_1^2 - 1} = -100 \frac{2 \cdot 1.67^2}{1.67^2 - 1} = -100 \frac{5.58}{1.79} = -312 \text{ N/mm}^2$$

Shrinkage interface 1: external wall of the inner liner:

$$\sigma_r(r_{1a}) = -p_{s_1} = -100 \text{ N/mm}^2$$

$$\sigma_t(r_{1a}) = -p_{s_1} \frac{u_1^2 + 1}{u_1^2 - 1} = -100 \frac{3.79}{1.79} = -212 \text{ N/mm}^2$$

Shrinkage interface 1: inside surface of the intermediate liner:

$$\sigma_r(r_{2i}) = -p_{s_1} = -100 \text{ N/mm}^2$$

$$\sigma_t(r_{2i}) = p_{s_1} \frac{u_3^2 u_2^2 + 1}{u_3^2 u_2^2 - 1} = 100 \frac{1.98^2 \cdot 1.67^2 + 1}{1.98^2 \cdot 1.67^2 - 1} = 100 \frac{11.94}{9.94}$$

$$= 120 \text{ N/mm}^2$$

Shrinkage interface 2: external wall of the intermediate liner and internal wall of the mantle:

$$\sigma_r \binom{r_{2a}}{r_{3i}} - p_{s_1} \frac{u_3^2 - 1}{u_3^2 u_2^2 - 1} = -100 \frac{2.92}{9.94} = -29 \text{ N/mm}^2$$

$$\sigma_t \binom{r_{2a}}{r_{3i}} = p_{s_1} \frac{u_3^2 + 1}{u_3^2 u_2^2 - 1} = 100 \frac{4.92}{9.94} = 50 \text{ N/mm}^2$$

External wall of the mantle:

$$\sigma_r(r_{3a}) = 0 \text{ N/mm}^2$$

$$\sigma_t(r_{3a}) = p_{s_1} \frac{2}{u_3^2 u_2^2 - 1} = 100 \frac{2}{9.94} = 20 \text{ N/mm}^2$$

Residual stresses "2" from the shrink-fit pressure p_{s_2}:
Internal wall of the inner liner:

$$\sigma_r(r_{li}) = 0 \text{ N/mm}^2$$

$$\sigma_t(r_{li}) = -p_{s_2} \frac{2u_2^2 u_1^2}{u_2^2 u_1^2 - 1} = -112 \frac{2 \cdot 1.67^4}{1.67^4 - 1} = -256 \text{ N/mm}^2$$

Shrinkage interface 1 between the external wall of the inner liner and the internal wall of the intermediate liner:

$$\sigma_r \binom{r_{1a}}{r_{2i}} = -p_{s_2} \frac{u_2^2 u_1^2 - u_2^2}{u_2^2 u_1^2 - 1} = -112 \frac{1.67^4 - 1.67^2}{1.67^4 - 1} = -82 \text{ N/mm}^2$$

$$\sigma_t \binom{r_{1a}}{r_{2i}} = -p_{s_2} \frac{u_2^2 u_1^2 + u_2^2}{u_2^2 u_1^2 - 1} = -112 \frac{1.67^4 + 1.67^2}{1.67^4 - 1} = -174 \text{ N/mm}^2$$

Shrinkage interface 2: external wall of the intermediate liner:

$$\sigma_r(r_{2a}) = -p_{s_2} = -112 \text{ N/mm}^2$$

$$\sigma_t(r_{2a}) = -p_{s_2} \frac{u_2^2 u_1^2 + 1}{u_2^2 u_1^2 - 1} = -112 \frac{1.67^4 + 1}{1.67^4 - 1} = -144 \text{ N/mm}^2$$

Shrinkage interface 2: internal wall of the mantle:

$$\sigma_r(r_{3i}) = p_{s_2} = -112 \text{ N/mm}^2$$

$$\sigma_t(r_{3i}) = p_{s_2} \frac{u_3^2 + 1}{u_3^2 - 1} = 112 \frac{1.98^2 + 1}{1.98^2 - 1} = 188 \text{ N/mm}^2$$

External wall of the mantle:

$$\sigma_r(r_{3a}) = 0 \text{ N/mm}^2$$

$$\sigma_t(r_{3a}) = p_{s_2} \frac{2}{u_3^2 - 1} = 112 \frac{2}{1.98^2 - 1} = 76 \text{ N/mm}^2$$

Operating stresses = service stresses plus residual stresses:
Internal wall of the inner liner:

$$\sigma_{rT}(r_{li}) = -p_{ri} + 0 + 0 = -688 \text{ N/mm}^2$$

$$\sigma_{tT}(r_{li}) = p_{ri} \frac{u^2 + 1}{u^2 - 1} - p_{s_1} \frac{2u_1^2}{u_1^2 - 1} - p_{s_2} \frac{2u_2^2 u_1^2}{u_2^2 u_1^2 - 1}$$

$$= 735 - 312 - 256 = 167 \text{ N/mm}^2$$

$$\sigma_R = \sqrt{\sigma_t^2 + \sigma_r^2 - \sigma_t \cdot \sigma_r} \quad \sqrt{167^2 + 688^2 + 167 \cdot 688} = 785 \text{ N/mm}^2$$

Shrinkage interface 1: external wall of the inner liner:

$$\sigma_{rT}(r_{la}) = -p_{ri} \frac{u_3^2 u_2^2 - 1}{u^2 - 1} - p_{s_1} - p_{s_2} \frac{u_2^2 u_1^2 - u_2^2}{u_2^2 u_1^2 - 1}$$

$$= -234 - 100 - 82 = -416 \text{ N/mm}^2$$

$$\sigma_{tT}(r_{la}) = p_{ri} \frac{u_3^2 u_2^2 + 1}{u^2 - 1} - p_{s_1} \frac{u_1^2 + 1}{u_1^2 - 1} - p_{s_2} \frac{u_2^2 u_1^2 + u_2^2}{u_2^2 u_1^2 - 1}$$

$$= 281 - 212 - 174 = -105 \text{ N/mm}^2$$

$$\sigma_R = \sqrt{105^2 + 416^2 - 105 \cdot 416} = 375 \text{ N/mm}^2$$

Shrinkage interface 1: external wall of the intermediate liner:

$$\sigma_{rT}(r_{2i}) = -p_{ri} \frac{u_3^2 u_2^2 - 1}{u^2 - 1} - p_{s_1} - p_{s_2} \frac{u_2^2 u_1^2 - u_2^2}{u_2^2 u_1^2 - 1}$$

$$= -234 - 100 - 82 = -416 \text{ N/mm}^2$$

$$\sigma_{rT}(r_{2i}) = p_{ri} \frac{u_3^2 u_2^2 + 1}{u^2 - 1} + p_{s_1} \frac{u_3^2 u_2^2 + 1}{u_3^2 u_2^2 - 1} - p_{s_2} \frac{u_2^2 u_1^2 + u_2^2}{u_2^2 u_1^2 - 1}$$

$$= 281 + 120 - 174 = 227 \text{ N/mm}^2$$

$$\sigma_R = \sqrt{227^2 + 416^2 + 227 \cdot 416} = 565 \text{ N/mm}^2$$

Shrinkage interface 2: external wall of the intermediate liner:

$$\sigma_{rT}(r_{2a}) = -p_{ri}\frac{u_3^2 - 1}{u^2 - 1} - p_{s_1}\frac{u_3^2 - 1}{u_3^2 u_2^2 - 1} - p_{s_2}$$

$$= -69 - 29 - 112 = -210 \text{ N/mm}^2$$

$$\sigma_{tT}(r_{2a}) = p_{ri}\frac{u_3^2 + 1}{u^2 - 1} + p_{s_1}\frac{u_3^2 + 1}{u_3^2 u_2^2 - 1} - p_{s_2}\frac{u_2^2 u_1^2 + 1}{u_2^2 u_1^2 - 1}$$

$$= 116 + 50 - 144 = 22 \text{ N/mm}^2$$

$$\sigma_R = \sqrt{22^2 + 210^2 + 22 \cdot 210} = 222$$

Shrinkage interface 2: internal wall of the mantle:

$$\sigma_{rT}(r_{3i}) = -p_{ri}\frac{u_3^2 - 1}{u - 1} - p_{s_1}\frac{u_3^2 - 1}{u_3^2 u_2^2 - 2} - p_{s_2}$$

$$= -70 - 29 - 112 = -211 \text{ N/mm}^2$$

$$\sigma_{tT}(r_{3i}) = p_{ri}\frac{u_3^2 + 1}{u^2 - 1} + p_{s_1}\frac{u_3^2 + 1}{u_3^2 u_2^2 - 1} + p_{s_2}\frac{u_3^2 + 1}{u_3^2 - 1}$$

$$= 116 + 50 + 188 = 354 \text{ N/mm}^2$$

$$\sigma_R = \sqrt{353^2 + 210^2 + 353 \cdot 210} = 493 \text{ N/mm}^2$$

External wall of the mantle:

$$\sigma_{rT}(r_{3a}) = 0 + 0 + 0 = 0 \text{ N/mm}^2$$

$$\sigma_{tT}(r_{3a}) = p_{ri}\frac{2}{u^2 - 1} + p_{s_1}\frac{2}{u_3^2 u_2^2 - 1} + p_{s_2}\frac{2}{u_3^2 - 1}$$

$$= 47 + 20 + 76 = 143 \text{ N/mm}^2$$

$$\sigma_R = \sqrt{143^2} = 143 \text{ N/mm}^2$$

All the operating and equivalent stresses are compared in Table 5.3 for the one-, two- and three-piece containers.

Figure 5.54 (page 364) shows the operating and equivalent stress profiles across the container cross section in each of the different designs.

Material Selection for the Three-Part 180 mm Container According to the Stresses That Are Encountered

The most severe calculated equivalent stresses occur at the internal wall of the liner ($\sigma_R = 785$ N/mm^2), at the inside surface of the intermediate liner ($\sigma_R = 565$ N/mm^2) and at the inside surface of the mantle ($\sigma_R = 493$ N/mm^2).

Table 5.3. Comparison of Operating and Equivalent Stresses for One-, Two- and Three-Piece Containers

Container		Operating and equivalent stresses (N/mm²)					
		Inner liner		Intermediate liner		Mantle	
		r_{li}	r_{la}	r_{2i}	r_{2a}	r_{3i}	r_{3a}
One-piece	σ_{tT}	735	. .	. .	. .	. .	47
	σ_{rT}	−688	. .	. .	. .	. .	0
	σ_R	1233	. .	. .	. .	. .	47
Two-piece	σ_{tT}	444	5	. .	. .	336	86
	σ_{rT}	−688	−250	. .	. .	−250	0
	σ_R	988	252	. .	. .	509	86
Three-piece	σ_{tT}	167	−105	227	21	353	144
	σ_{rT}	−688	−416	−416	−210	−210	0
	σ_R	785	375	565	221	493	144

These three maximum stresses have to be considered in the selection of suitable hot working steels for the individual container components. The following steels are, accordingly, considered suitable:

For the liner: steel X32CrMoV33, alloy number 1.2365, heat treated to $R_m = 1600$ N/mm², with a high-temperature proof stress of:

Safety factor $R_{p0.2}/\sigma_R$

$R_{p0.2} \approx 980$ N/mm² at 500 °C   k = 1.25

$R_{p0.2} \approx 820$ N/mm² at 550 °C   k = 1.04

Intermediate liner and mantle: steel 45CrMoV67, alloy number 1.2323, heat treated to $R_m = 1300$ N/mm², with a high-temperature proof stress of:

Safety factor $R_{p0.2}/\sigma_R$

$R_{p0.2} \approx 750$ N/mm² at 500 °C   k = 1.33

$R_{p0.2} \approx 600$ N/mm² at 550 °C   k = 1.06

As mentioned previously, $(\sigma_R \cdot k)$ should be less than or equal to $R_{p0.2}$ at the appropriate working temperature. The safety factors k for the assumed working temperatures are given above for both the liner and intermediate liners, together with the high-temperature proof stresses. The factors k for the mantle are 1.22 and 1.52 at temperatures of 550 and 500 °C, respectively.

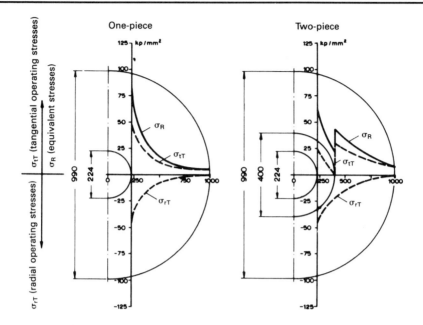

Fig. 5.55. Transverse operating and equivalent stress profiles in one- and two-piece containers with a 224 mm bore (see Fig. 5.54). *(From Ref 24)*

Design of the Container With a 224 mm Bore (Fig. 5.55)

The specific pressure for this container is:

$$p = \frac{2.5 \cdot 10^7 \cdot 4}{2.24^2 \cdot \pi \cdot 10^4} = 635 \text{ N/mm}^2$$

and gives a radial pressure on the container of:

$$p_{ri} = 0.7 \cdot p = 0.7 \cdot 635 = 444 \text{ N/mm}^2$$

The mantle diameter is constant at 990 mm giving a diameter ratio u of:

$$u = d_{3a}/d_{li} = 990/224 = 4.42$$

One-Piece Container

Internal wall:

$$\sigma_r(r_{li}) = \sigma_{r_{max}} = -p_{ri} = -444 \text{ N/mm}^2$$

$$\sigma_t(r_{li}) = \sigma_{t_{max}} = p_{ri}\frac{u^2 + 1}{u^2 - 1} = 444\,\frac{20.54}{18.54} = 492 \text{ N/mm}^2$$

External wall:

$$\sigma_r(r_{3a}) = 0 \ \text{N/mm}^2$$

$$\sigma_t(r_{3a}) = \sigma_{t_{min}} = p_{ri} \frac{2}{u^2 - 1} = 444 \frac{2}{18.54} = 48 \ \text{N/mm}^2$$

At the internal wall:

$$\sigma_{Ri} = \sqrt{493^2 + 444^2 + 493 \cdot 444} = 812 \ \text{N/mm}^2$$

At the external wall:

$$\sigma_{Ra} = \sqrt{48^2} = 48 \ \text{N/mm}^2$$

Practically no hot working steel can withstand the high equivalent stress σ_{Ri} of 812 N/mm^2 at the internal wall of the container without plastic deformation. Therefore a multipiece container — having at least two pieces — must be designed.

Two-Piece Container

The outside diameter of the liner is assumed to be 400 mm with a wall thickness of 88 mm. The wall thickness of the mantle is 295 mm. The diameter ratios are then:

$$u = 990/224 = 4.42; \ u_1 = 400/224 = 1.79; \ u_3 = 990/400 = 2.48$$

As in the previous example it is assumed that:

$$E_{liner} \approx E_{mantle} = 183\,000 \ \text{N/mm}^2 \ \text{at} \ 500 \ °C$$

A relative interference fit of 1.5‰ is selected to give a shrink-fit pressure of:

$$p_s = \frac{E \cdot \epsilon}{2} \cdot \frac{(u_3^2 - 1)(u_1^2 - 1)}{u^2 - 1} = \frac{183\,000 \cdot 1.5 \cdot 10^{-3}}{2} \cdot \frac{(2.48^2 - 1)(1.79^2 - 1)}{4.42^2 - 1}$$

$$= 137.25 \frac{5.15 \cdot 2.20}{18.54} = 84 \ \text{N/mm}^2$$

Service stresses = stresses under the applied pressure in a one-piece container:

Internal wall of the liner:

$$\sigma_r(r_{li}) = -p_{ri} = 444 \ \text{N/mm}^2$$

$$\sigma_t(r_{li}) = p_{ri} \frac{u^2 + 1}{u^2 - 1} = 444 \frac{20.54}{18.54} = 492 \ \text{N/mm}^2$$

At the shrinkage interface:

$$\sigma_r \left(\frac{r_{la}}{r_{3i}} \right) = -p_{ri} \frac{u_3^2 - 1}{u^2 - 1} = -444 \frac{5.15}{18.54} = -123 \text{ N/mm}^2$$

$$\sigma_r \left(\frac{r_{la}}{r_{3i}} \right) = p_{ri} \frac{u_3^2 + 1}{u^2 - 1} = 444 \frac{7.15}{18.54} = 171 \text{ N/mm}^2$$

External wall of the mantle:

$$\sigma_r(r_{3a}) = 0 \text{ N/mm}^2$$

$$\sigma_t(r_{3a}) = p_{ri} \frac{2}{u^2 - 1} = 44.43 \frac{2}{18.54} = 48 \text{ N/mm}^2$$

Residual stresses = stresses from the shrink-fit operation:
Internal wall of the liner:

$$\sigma_r(r_{li}) = 0 \text{ N/mm}^2$$

$$\sigma_t(r_{li}) = -p_s \frac{2u_1^2}{u_1^2 - 1} = -84 \frac{2 \cdot 1.79^2}{1.79^2 - 1} = -84 \frac{2 \cdot 3.20}{2.20} = -244 \text{ N/mm}^2$$

External wall of the liner:

$$\sigma_r(r_{la}) = -p_s = -84 \text{ N/mm}^2$$

$$\sigma_t(r_{la}) = -p_s \frac{u_1^2 + 1}{u_1^2 - 1} = -84 \frac{4.20}{2.20} = -160 \text{ N/mm}^2$$

Internal wall of the mantle:

$$\sigma_r(r_{3i}) = -p_s = -84 \text{ N/mm}^2$$

$$\sigma_t(r_{3i}) = p_s \frac{u_3^2 + 1}{u_3^2 - 1} = 84 \frac{7.15}{5.15} = 117 \text{ N/mm}^2$$

External wall of the mantle:

$$\sigma_r(r_{3a}) = 0 \text{ N/mm}^2$$

$$\sigma_t(r_{3a}) = p_s \frac{2}{u_3^2 - 1} = 84 \frac{2}{5.15} = 32 \text{ N/mm}^2$$

Operating stresses = service stresses plus residual stresses:
Internal wall of the liner:

$$\sigma_{rT}(r_{li}) = -p_{ri} = -444 \text{ N/mm}^2$$

$$\sigma_{tT}(r_{li}) = p_{ri} \frac{u_2 + 1}{u_2 - 1} - p_s \frac{2u_1^2}{u_1^2 - 1} = 492 - 242 = 250 \text{ N/mm}^2$$

$$\sigma_R = \sqrt{250^2 + 444^2 + 250 \cdot 444} = 609 \text{ N/mm}^2$$

External wall of the liner:

$$\sigma_{rT}(r_{la}) = -p_{ri}\frac{u_3^2 - 1}{u^2 - 1} - p_s = -123 - 83 = -206 \ \text{N/mm}^2$$

$$\sigma_{tT}(r_{la}) = p_{ri}\frac{u_3^2 + 1}{u_2 - 1} - p_s\frac{u_1^2 + 1}{u_1^2 - 1} = 171 - 159 = 12 \ \text{N/mm}^2$$

$$\sigma_R = \sqrt{12^2 + 206^2 + 12 \cdot 206} = 212 \ \text{N/mm}^2$$

Internal wall of the mantle:

$$\sigma_{rT}(r_{3i}) = -p_{ri}\frac{u_3^2 - 1}{u^2 - 1} - p_s = -123 - 83 = -206 \ \text{N/mm}^2$$

$$\sigma_{tT}(r_{3i}) = p_{ri}\frac{u_3^2 + 1}{u^2 - 1} + p_s\frac{u_3^2 + 1}{u_3^2 - 1} = 171 + 116 = 287 \ \text{N/mm}^2$$

$$\sigma_R = \sqrt{287^2 + 206^2 + 287 \cdot 206} = 429 \ \text{N/mm}^2$$

External wall of the mantle:

$$\sigma_{rT}(r_{3a}) = 0 \ \text{N/mm}^2$$

$$\sigma_{tT}(r_{3a}) = p_{ri}\frac{2}{u^2 - 1} + p_s\frac{2}{u_3^2 - 1} = 48 + 32 = 80 \ \text{N/mm}^2$$

$$\sigma_R = \sqrt{80^2} = 80 \ \text{N/mm}^2$$

Table 5.4 summarizes the operating and equivalent stresses in both one- and two-piece containers and clearly shows how the high equivalent stress at the bore of the one-piece container can, according to the calculations, be sufficiently decreased with a two-piece design. A two-piece container can, therefore, be used. The operating and equivalent stress profiles across the container wall are depicted in Fig. 5.55 for both designs.

Material Selection for the 224 mm Two-Piece Container

The maximum equivalent stress in the bore resulting from the superimposed working and residual stresses is $\sigma_R = 609 \ \text{N/mm}^2$. The corresponding equivalent stress at the inside surface of the mantle is $\sigma_R = 429 \ \text{N/mm}^2$. The following steels were, therefore, selected:

A 38CrMoV51 steel, alloy number 1.2343, for the inner liner, heat treated to $R_m = 1600 \ \text{N/mm}^2$, with a high-temperature proof stress of:

$$R_{p0.2} \approx 980 \ \text{N/mm}^2 \ \text{at} \ 500 \ °C$$

safety factor: $k = R_{p0.2}/\sigma_R = 1.61$

$$R_{p0.2} \approx 700 \ \text{N/mm}^2 \ \text{at} \ 550 \ °C$$

safety factor: $k = R_{p0.2}/\sigma_R = 1.15$

Table 5.4 Comparison of Operating and Equivalent Stresses for One- and Two-Piece Containers

Container		Stress (N/mm²)			
		Inner liner		Mantle	
		r_{li}	r_{la}	r_{3i}	r_{3a}
One- piece	σ_{tT}	492	. .	. .	48
	σ_{rT}	−444	. .	. .	0
	σ_R	−811	. .	. .	48
Two- piece	σ_{tT}	250	−12	286	80
	σ_{rT}	−444	−206	−206	0
	σ_R	609	212	428	80

A 45CrMoV67 steel, alloy number 1.2323, for the mantle, heat treated to R_m = 1300 N/mm², with a high-temperature yield stress of:

$R_{p0.2} \approx 750$ N/mm² at 500 °C

safety factor: $k = R_{p0.2}/ \sigma_R = 1.75$

$R_{p0.2} \approx 600$ N/mm² at 550 °C

safety factor: $k = R_{p0.2}/ \sigma_R = 1.40$

Comments on the Examples

The examples illustrate how correct design can give a favorable distribution of the operating stresses in a container. The most important feature is the reduction of the high stress peaks by superimposing residual stresses of sufficient magnitude in a compound container that the maximum equivalent stresses calculated from the operating stresses, using the shear strain energy hypothesis, do not reach or exceed the high-temperature yield stress of the hot working steel used.

The reduction of the high stress peaks in a container by making it of several parts shrunk together to develop residual stresses was introduced at a relatively late date. As late as 1934 a well-known German extruder was using containers of several steel cylinders inside each other but separated by insulating layers to keep them cool, following Dick's patent 83590 of 1894. Technical developments and the need to reduce tooling costs have brought about a fundamental change. No container manufacturer today, whether the press builder or the steel works, would argue against the necessity of using prestressed compound containers, even if the design and method of calculation vary from producer to producer.

5.3.4. Containers With Rectangular Bores

For some years now there has been increasing interest in containers with rectangular bores. Wider sections, which could normally be extruded only in much larger presses with round containers, can be produced on aluminum presses with these containers. A rectangular container also provides a more favorable metal flow for flat sections than that developed in a correspondingly larger round container and, as a result, the extrusion pressure is reduced. However, the introduction of these containers has been associated with considerable problems. It was quickly realized that the service life of a flat container was significantly less than that of a standard round container. The rounded corners at the transition from the vertical to the horizontal sides of the bore usually cracked after relatively few extrusions. Even semicircular sides in the bore did not prevent cracks from forming at the apex of the semicircles. Metal then forced its way into the cracks during extrusion and they rapidly increased in size.

The shrink-fitting and operating stresses for round containers were initially used for rectangular ones, but this assumes, among other things, an axisymmetrical load and stress distribution, which is not applicable to rectangular containers where stress concentrations occur, particularly at the rounded corners. The stresses that develop in these regions during extrusion can be so high that the liner deforms or cracks. Consequently, many investigations have recently been undertaken to try to cope with the particular stresses that form in rectangular containers. Whereas efforts concentrated on a compound liner in the United States, more attention was paid in Europe to minimizing the local stress concentrations by varying the shape of the bore.

Shrink-fitting is used for both the one-piece and compound liners to develop residual compressive stresses. Thus, two types of rectangular containers need be considered:

(a) Those with a one-piece liner (Fig. 5.56).
(b) Those with a compound liner (Fig. 5.57).

Time will show which liner will prevail in the future. The one-piece design is preferred in Germany and the compound liner in the United States. In the latter case, the liner is constructed of four unequal segments and this necessitates a three-piece container because the segments must be held together by the intermediate liner. The size of the container bore, therefore, has to be reduced in a press if a rectangular container is used. Nevertheless, containers with compound liners have proved to be so successful on small presses in the United States that a container of this design has been built for an 80 MN press.

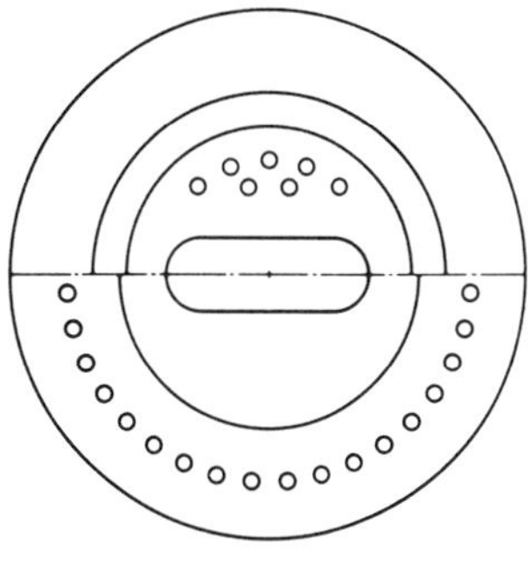

Fig. 5.56. Two- and three-piece flat container with a one-piece liner and different arrangements of the heater element holes. *(From Ref 33)*

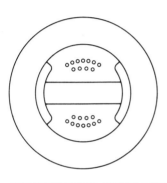

Fig. 5.57. Flat container with the liner consisting of four segments; the heating element holes are in the two larger sections. *(From Ref 33)*

Finite-element methods have been used with some success by universities and container manufacturers in Germany to calculate the optimum stress distribution in rectangular containers. There have also been some attempts to verify the calculated results by photoelastic analysis of container models. These methods gave the actual stresses that develop in the container without load and under the extrusion load to a good approximation (Fig. 5.58). It is not possible to calculate the stresses by an analytical approach analogous to the method used for round containers. These investigations have revealed, among other things, that the stress concentrations at the critical areas in flat containers are reduced to a minimum if the narrow side of the bore is designed as a compound curve with large blending radii with the long sides (Fig. 5.59). According to these results a rectangular bore with rounded corners is just as unfavorable as one with semicircular narrow sides (Fig. 5.60). Stress concentrations form at the rounded zones as well as at the apex of the circular arcs in these containers and the resultant strains formed in the steel are so high that cracks form in these regions after relatively few extrusions. These cracks usually have the characteristic appearance of fatigue cracks with beach markings. They propagate rapidly as the metal is forced into them.

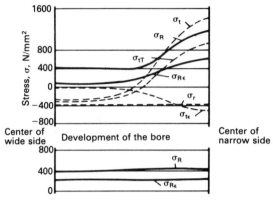

Development of the shrinkage gap

σ_t = tangential service stresses from the internal pressure p_{ri}
σ_r = radial service stresses from the internal pressure p_{ri}
σ_{te} = tangential residual stresses from p_s
σ_{Re} = radial residual stresses from p_s
σ_t = tangential operating stress
σ_r = radial operating stress
σ_R = equivalent stress calculated from the operating stresses σ_t and σ_r

Relative interference fit $\epsilon = 2\%_0$; internal pressure $p_{ri} = 400$ N/mm²; width-to-height ratio of the bore B:H = 3; referred shrinkage gap diameter D_s:B = 1.5; referred mantle diameter d_{3a}:B = 2.5.

Fig. 5.58. Stresses in the liner of a flat container at the bore and in the mantle at the shrinkage gap with a semicircular narrow side in the bore. The curves show that the highest stresses occur at the inner wall of the liner in the middle of the narrow side. *(From Ref 33)*

The three-piece design is also preferred for stress reasons for rectangular containers. Usually, only architectural sections in the easily extruded or moderately difficult alloys are produced with these containers and the container temperature can be limited. Given a sufficiently high temperature flow stress and design strength, the relief of residual stresses by creep can be almost completely suppressed if the temperature is not allowed to exceed 500 °C. The high-temperature flow stress of a hot working steel decreases very rapidly as the operating temperature is raised. Rapid heating from the cold or after an alloy change with steep temperature gradients must be avoided to a much greater extent with rectangular containers than with round ones. Consequently, particular attention has to be paid to the arrangement of the heating element holes in the mantle because the liner life of rectangular containers is directly related to the load-carrying capacity of the mantle.

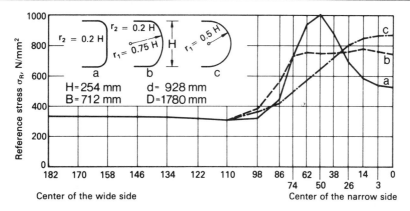

Fig. 5.59. Maximum reference stresses σ_R on the internal wall of the bore of a two-piece flat container with different designs of the narrow side as a function of the specific pressure p = 500 N/mm² and the resultant radial pressure p_{ri} = 0.7 · p = 350 N/mm² = outside diameter of the liner; inside diameter of the mantle = 928 mm; D = outside diameter of the mantle = 1780 mm. The profiles clearly reveal that design (b) has the lowest stress concentration, whereas design (a) exhibits a particularly high stress peak at the transition from the wide to the narrow side. Develop- of the bore over the nodes resulting from the finite element stress analysis. (*From Ref 33*)

Fig. 5.60. Flat container for a 35 MN extrusion press with semicircular narrow sides.

The following rules can be applied to the optimum design of rectangular containers:

(*a*) Three-piece construction.
(*b*) One-piece liner with the narrow sides in the form of a compound curve.
(*c*) Heating element holes related to the stress distribution.
(*d*) Restricted operating temperature.

5.3.4.1. Containers with Round and Rectangular Bores in Service

The container is an expensive tool and extrusion plants have long recognized that profitability is closely related to the service life of the tooling. Accordingly, the container must be treated with special care to prevent damage and premature failure. Considerable damage can arise from incorrect handling, including the common problem of movement of the inner liner and, occasionally, also the intermediate liner. A common cause of these problems is incorrect preheating of the container before installation into the press or when the alloy is changed. Uncontrolled external heating — that is, from the mantle towards the bore — which is still used in many plants, can result in excessive temperature gradients and overheating of the container mantle. Occasionally, the high-temperature yield stress is exceeded and creep processes are initiated in the steel of the mantle by the residual stresses induced by the shrink-fitting process. The residual stresses in the whole container are thus reduced by processes similar to those that can occur during incorrect cooling after shrink-fitting. A further consequence of over-heating the mantle — especially when it occurs frequently — is the gradual decrease in the high-temperature yield stress and tensile strength if the local temperature reaches or exceeds the annealing temperature of the steel. If there is a sudden rise in the temperature of the liner by heating or loading hot billets — for example, in heavy metal extrusion — the shrink-fit residual stresses can deform the liner, which also reduces the magnitude of the residual stresses.

An investigation into containers for heavy metal extrusion presses by the Extrusion Committee of the German Metallurgical Society (DGM) revealed how dangerous incorrect heat treatment can be. The mechanical properties of the container mantles in some presses had decreased by 30% or more compared with their initial condition, although this was after many years of service. The decrease in mechanical properties is associated with a reduction in the high-temperature flow stress and, accordingly, the associated residual stresses from the shrink-fitting process are also reduced. A container is by no means continuously stressed to the high value for which it is designed, but is always more highly stressed at the die end: the pressure and temperature are applied here for longer times because the billet length decreases during the extrusion cycle. This is particularly true for containers for steel and heavy metals; the localized relaxation processes initiated — creep — can be sufficient to give a continual reduction in the residual stresses. In general, the thermal stresses from the billet temperature in the extrusion of iron or copper alloys are more dangerous than the stresses induced by the extrusion pressure, especially at the die end of the container. In extreme cases the liner can completely soften (Fig. 5.61 and 5.62).

Fig. 5.61. Plastic deformation, caused by overloading,
at the front face of a container.

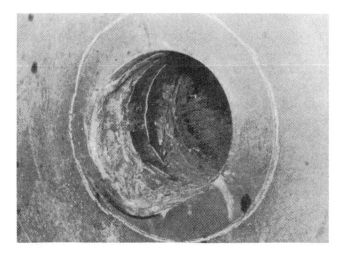

Fig. 5.62. Container softened
by overheating on the exit
side.

High liner temperatures are developed at extrusion temperatures above
800 °C with alloys that are extruded slowly but also with high-speed alloys at
high outputs. The liner can become red hot during the extrusion of copper
alloys for condenser tubes or copper-nickel alloys and in these cases the
containers have to be carefully cooled during extrusion. They have to be
heated with as much care. The cooling must be effective but not too severe,
because thermal shocks must be avoided at all costs, to prevent cracking.
Thus heavy metal containers must be cooled continuously whereas aluminum
containers are heated continuously, between 250 and 500 °C, generally, to
ensure trouble-free press operation. These containers are normally maintained at temperature by heating elements in the mantle. This requires, on

the one hand, a not too rapid temperature-controlled heating of aluminum containers — and also those for heavy metal and steel extrusion presses — to avoid reaching the annealing temperature of the steel at any point. Internal heating is very effective in this respect, but resistance or induction heated containers connected to an appropriate electrical supply outside the press have also proved to be satisfactory. On the other hand, temperature-controlled cooling is also required for containers for heavy metals. Temperature control is imperative for trouble-free operation. Obviously, there are basic differences between the design and operation of containers for steel and heavy metal extrusion and those for aluminum, and it is a serious mistake to use the same container for extruding both aluminum and copper alloys. Containers should never be used to preheat billets or a billet to heat the liner. Sticking extrusion billets are particularly dangerous because of the associated prolonged thermal and mechanical stressing. If excessive temperatures at, for example, the die end of the container have resulted in a slight movement of the liner, there is a danger of cracking when the press is shut down because the liner will attempt to regain its original position but is restrained by the solidly fitted intermediate liner or mantle. Obviously, soft liners for heavy metal extrusion have a lower resistance to wear and the service life is decreased, in some cases significantly, whereas liners made of a suitable hot working steel with its associated high resistance to softening and fitted in a correctly designed container can withstand 30 000 to 40 000 extrusions. Soft liners frequently last only for 8000 to 10 000 cycles.

Liners and intermediate liners should be changed only by container manufacturers: they usually have better equipment and more experience. If, however, this operation is carried out by the extrusion plant personnel, they should not rely on their own experience but get advice from the steel producer. Steel manufacturers are always trying to improve the methods of calculating the residual and service stresses, as well as improving the shrinkage bond and the hot working steels. New knowledge about the creep behavior of the steels used is also contributing to a reassessment of the stress limits now used in container design. The following rules summarize the points to be watched in using containers:

(a) The container should be slowly heated at program or alloy changes; there must be no direct contact with gas flames.
(b) It should be carefully but effectively cooled; thermal shocks must be avoided.
(c) A container should be used at the lowest possible operating temperature, to ensure trouble-free extrusion; the container should not be used for billet heating.
(d) The temperature monitoring equipment and its connections should be continually maintained and checked for inaccurate readings.

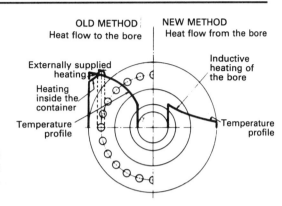

OLD METHOD
Heat flow to the bore

NEW METHOD
Heat flow from the bore

Externally supplied heating

Inductive heating of the bore

Heating inside the container

Temperature profile

Temperature profile

Fig. 5.63. Temperature distribution in a container heated by induction cartridge heating (right) and mantle heating (left). *(From Ref 58)*

The inductive cartridge heating system introduced by Loewy has proved to be effective for heating the liner internally before installing the container or after a long downtime without thermal shocks or relief of the shrinkage bond (Fig. 5.52 and 5.63).

5.4. Steel Selection for Extrusion Tooling

5.4.1. Development and Present State of Hot Working Steels

The correct selection of the correct grade of steel for extrusion tooling requires experience and continual observation of the tooling by the press operator. As well as the design and quality of machining, the selection of the steel and its heat treatment are decisive factors in the performance of the tooling, which is often highly stressed. This is particularly true in the extrusion of very difficult alloys, the working of which has been continuously improved by the experience and knowledge gained from research into steels. Metal extruders are increasing their investigations into the relationships between the type of steel, heat treatment, and service life because of the economical advantages.

There are numerous publications available from steel producers on steel selection for extrusion tooling. Planckensteiner (Ref 34) produced the first comprehensive report on the extrusion process including a survey of the stresses in the tools and the most suitable steels with mechanical properties after heat treatment. Hohage, Rollet (Ref 35), and Treppschuh (Ref 36) have reported on "Tools for Metal Extrusion." Useful data on the technology of hot working steels and tooling for metal tube and rod extrusion can be found in the technical literature. The comprehensive works of Houdrement (Ref 37), Rapatz (Ref 38) and Pattermann (Ref 39) are of particular relevance.

Throughout the last world war extrusion experts were occupied with the problem of using low-alloy steels for extrusion. The first comprehensive survey of steels for extrusion tooling was published by the Association of German Steel Manufacturers in cooperation with the extrusion plants following directive E24 then in operation to save expensive alloying elements. This list was later extended to the Steel Application List 195-59, which is still applicable, although a new edition for extrusion is planned (edited January 1972) and this should simplify the selection of hot working steels. The papers by Hiller (Ref 44), Höpken (Ref 45, 46), Heinen (Ref 47), Braun and Schulte (Ref 48), published in the last decade, are of particular relevance because they are also mainly concerned with the correct application of extrusion tooling.

Catalogs of the different steel producers provide valuable information.

5.4.2. Characteristics of Hot Working Steels

The steels used for extrusion press tooling should, depending on the actual application, have the following properties to withstand the high mechanical and thermal stresses:

(a) Good resistance to softening and good toughness.
(b) Adequate high-temperature strength and good resistance to wear.
(c) Resistance to distortion and cracking from tensile stresses developed during heat treatment as well as the stresses resulting from temperature changes which can initiate hot cracking.
(d) High thermal conductivity to rapidly remove heat from the area of contact with the hot billet.

These properties are usually required simultaneously and it is frequently difficult to determine the dependence of the service life on the individual properties.

The resistance to softening is the most important requirement for steels operating at high temperatures and is primarily controlled by the addition of tungsten, molybdenum and vanadium. Typical hot working steels are the chromium-tungsten steels with vanadium, molybdenum and cobalt or the chromium-molybdenum steels with vanadium, tungsten and cobalt. The cobalt addition, in particular, gives an additional increase in the resistance to softening because additions up to 2% retard the precipitation processes. The higher the alloy content in the steels containing tungsten (up to 10%), the greater is the resistance of the tooling to softening at high operating temperatures. However, these tools must be quenched from high temperatures well above the Ac3 point to retain as much carbide in solution in the matrix as possible. On the other hand, these high-alloy chromium-tungsten steels are very sensitive to sudden temperature changes and significantly more brittle in the working temperature range of 400 to 600 °C. They cannot withstand any water cooling. Chromium reduces the critical rate of cooling and thus increases the hardenability of hot working steels. At higher chromium contents (up to 5%) the resistance to softening and to wear are also increased, because of the carbide precipitates. Additions of silicon (up to 1%) further increase the resistance to softening, whereas manganese is found only in normal amounts in hot working steels. The crack sensitivity of high alloy hot working steels is increased by raising the carbon content (above 0.3%.

The thermal conductivity of chromium-tungsten steels decreases as the tungsten content is increased, and these steels have to be carefully heated for forging and hardening. The influence of the thermal conductivity on the service life of the hot working tooling, which is subjected to large temperature variations, is well-known from practical experience. It is known that the thermal conductivity decreases more at higher temperature as the total alloy content is increased. Therefore, the chromium-molybdenum steels offer a more favorable thermal conductivity, because the total alloy content for the same high-temperature mechanical properties is far less (up to 3%) than that of the chromium-tungsten steels (3 to 10%). Vanadium also has a favorable influence on the thermal conductivity, and low additions (up to 0.8%) can considerably lengthen the service life.

The toughness of the steel depends to a large degree on the heat treatment used. If the hardening temperature is too high, grain growth occurs and the toughness decreases. The correct heat treatment is the decisive factor in matching the high-temperature strength and toughness to the operating conditions. The toughness of chromium steels containing tungsten, molybdenum or vanadium is significantly improved by nickel, and tools of these steels are used at lower temperatures (up to 400 °C).

The most important property for a long service life is the susceptibility to thermal cracking, which can be reduced only if the stresses induced by temperature variations are lowered by suitable precautionary measures. The thermal conductivity plays an important role in this context because it determines the rate of heat removal from the areas in direct contact with the hot billet. The increased toughness is just as important because it governs the ability of the steel to withstand plastic deformation at high temperatures.

The hot working steels used for extrusion tooling are given in the Steel Application List 195-59 (new edition 1972) by the Association of German Steel Manufacturers and the German Metallurgical Society (DGM) in 1958–59.

Table 5.5 summarizes all the hot working steels given in the old list (a) and compares them with those recommended by the extrusion working party in the new list (b).

From the user's point of view, it would be better if the new publication follows the suggestion of the steel experts and is significantly shortened. However, the extruders do not want the well-tried and tested steels 1.2581 and 1.2606, nor the recently developed heavy-duty steels 1.2678 and 1.2758, which have given very good results, excluded. If the steel list is to have any practical use, it must include all those steels that can be held in stock in the standard sizes. Those marked c in the table are the most important steels used in extrusion, including steels 1.2581 and 1.2606. The two steels 1.2678 and 1.2758, which will also be included as standard steels in the new list, are included among the special materials for high-temperature deformation (d) along with the well tested chromium-nickel steel 1.2731. This steel was specially developed in the 1930's for the Singer tube presses and one firm has produced about a million tonnes of tube with dies of this material. The characteristics of this type of steel, which reaches 600 °C during production, necessitates the recalibration of the die with a mandrel every 15 to 20 tube extrusions. However, this operation only takes 8 to 10 seconds and does not interrupt production.

Figure 5.64 gives the operating temperature ranges of different steels and compares them with the hot working temperatures. The following summary can be drawn up for the different alloys extruded:

(a) *Aluminum and aluminum alloys:* few problems and the choice of steel is limited more by the static stresses than by thermal considerations.

(b) *Copper and copper alloys:* high extrusion temperatures above the annealing temperature result in rapid softening, which can be prevented by cooling. The throughput, therefore, decreases as the extrusion temperature is increased.

(c) *Steel:* the different properties of the hot working steels containing tungsten and molybdenum have to be considered in the selection of the most suitable steel according to the following comparison:

Molybdenum Steels	*Tungsten Steels*
Better thermal conductivity, not susceptible to thermal cracking.	Better fatigue properties at high tool temperatures.
Better toughness because of the more favorable structure from martensitic hardening, whereas tungsten steels have a high volume of bainite.	Low toughness with a long service life.
Start to deform after a short period in service but fracture only after high deformations.	

The high-temperature mechanical properties of the tungsten-containing steels (on the left) are compared in Fig. 5.65 with the tungsten-free steels

Table 5.5. Hot Working Steels for Extrusion

No.	Alloy No.	Type of steel (abbreviation)	Nominal composition, % C	Si	Mn	Cr	Mo	Ni	V	W	Co	Footnote references
1	1.2243	61CrSiV5	0.61	0.9	0.8	1.2	...	...	0.1	...	...	(a)
2	1.2311	40CrMnMo7	0.40	0.3	1.5	2.0	0.2	...	...	...	...	(a)(b)
3	1.2323	48CrMoV67	0.48	0.3	0.7	1.5	0.7	...	0.3	...	...	(a)(b)
4	1.2343	X38CrMoV51	0.38	1.0	0.4	5.3	1.1	...	0.4	...	...	(a)(b)(c)
5	1.2344	X40CrMoV51	0.40	1.0	0.4	5.3	1.4	...	1.0	...	...	(b)(c)
6	1.2365	X32CrMoV33	0.32	0.3	0.3	3.0	2.8	...	0.5	...	...	(a)(b)(c)
7	1.2367	X40CrMoV53	0.40	0.4	0.45	5.0	3.0	...	0.9	...	...	
8	1.2542	45WCrV7	0.45	1.0	0.3	1.0	...	...	0.2	2.0	...	(a)
9	1.2547	45WCrV77	0.45	1.0	0.3	1.7	...	...	0.2	2.0	...	(a)
10	1.2564	X30WCrV41	0.30	1.0	0.4	1.0	...	...	0.2	4.0	...	(a)
11	1.2567	X30WCrV53	0.30	0.2	0.3	2.4	...	...	0.6	4.3	...	(a)(b)(c)
12	1.2581	X30WCrV93	0.30	0.2	0.3	2.5	...	...	0.4	9.0	...	(a)
13	1.2603	45CrVMoW58	0.45	0.6	0.4	1.5	0.5	...	0.8	0.5	...	(a)(b)(c)
14	1.2606	X37CrMoW51	0.37	0.9	0.6	4.8	1.5	...	0.2	1.4	...	(a)(c)
15	1.2622	X60WCrMoV94	0.60	0.3	0.3	4.0	0.9	...	0.7	9.0	...	(a)
16	1.2625	X33WCrVMo1212	0.33	0.2	0.3	12.0	0.5	...	1.0	12.0	...	
17	1.2662	X30WCrCoV93	0.30	0.2	0.3	2.5	...	...	0.3	9.0	2.0	(a)(d)
18	1.2678	X45CoCrWV555	0.45	0.4	0.4	4.5	0.5	...	2.0	4.5	4.5	(b)(d)
19	1.2710	45CrNi6	0.45	0.3	0.7	1.4	...	1.7	...	...	...	(a)
20	1.2713	55NiCrMoV6	0.55	0.3	0.6	0.7	0.3	1.7	0.1	...	...	(a)
21	1.2714	56NiCrMoV7	0.56	0.3	0.7	1.0	0.5	1.7	0.1	...	...	(a)(b)(c)
22	1.2731	X50NiCrWV1313	0.50	1.3	0.7	13.0	...	13.0	0.5	2.5	...	(a)(b)(c)(d)
23	1.2758	X50WNiCrVCo1212	0.50	1.4	0.6	4.0	0.7	11.5	1.1	12.5	1.6	(b)(d)
24	1.2767	X45NiCrMo4	0.45	0.2	0.5	1.3	0.2(e)	4.0	...	...	...	(a)
25	1.2826	60MnSi4	0.60	1.0	1.0	...	...	...	...	...	...	(a)
26	1.2888	X20CoCrWMo109	0.20	0.3	0.5	10.0	2.0	...	...	5.5	10.0	(d)
27	1.4980	X5NiCrTi2615(f)	0.05	0.5	0.8	15.0	1.3	25	0.3	...	...	(d)

(a) *Stahleinsatzliste 195-59*, 1st ed., Apr 1959. (b) *Stahleinsatzliste 195*, 2nd ed., Jan 1972. (c) A steel in major extrusion press use. (d) A special alloy for high-temperature extrusion. (e) Or 0.5% W. (f) 2% Ti.

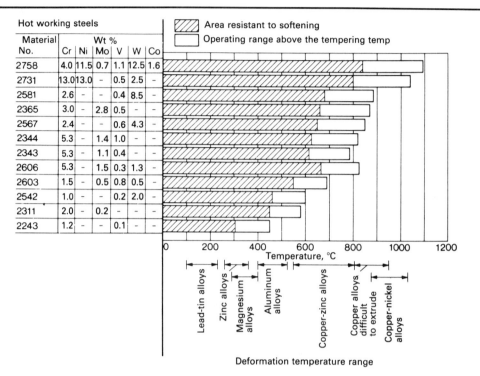

Fig. 5.64. Thermal operating ranges of different hot working steels compared with the deformation temperature. *(From Ref 59)*

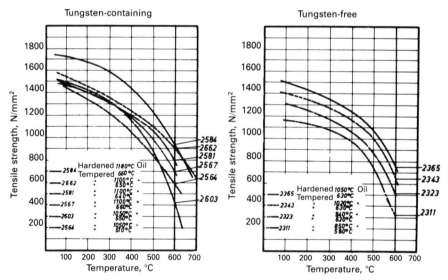

Fig. 5.65. High-temperature tensile strength of tungsten-containing and tungsten-free hot working steels.

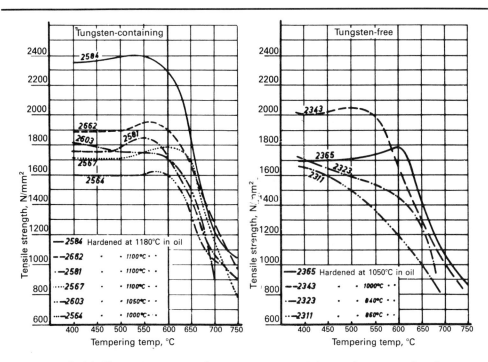

Fig. 5.66. Tempering curves for tungsten-containing and tungsten-free hot working steels.

(right). The hardness of all steels gradually decreases at high temperatures but those containing tungsten are generally stronger at high temperatures than those without. However, the steels without tungsten are particularly suitable for extrusion tooling, because tools made of the chromium-molybdenum hot working steels have a higher thermal conductivity and do not increase in temperature to the same extent as those containing tungsten under identical conditions.

Figure 5.66 compares the annealing curves for steels with and without tungsten. The favorable behavior of the steels 1.2343 and 1.2365 stands out and in many cases they are more suitable than the 4.5% tungsten steels, because of the slower heating. It was previously thought that this behavior was directly attributable to the higher thermal conductivity of the chromium-molybdenum steels. However, it is now believed that the heating depends on the thermal diffusivity, which is defined as the thermal conductivity divided by the density and the specific heat.

The higher thermal conductivity of the molybdenum steels is directly related to the lower alloy content because molybdenum is about three times as effective as, for example, tungsten from the point of view of increasing the

Table 5.6. Thermal Conductivity of Different Hot Working Steels

Alloy No.	Composition, wt %						Thermal conductivity (W/cm · K)
	C	Cr	Mo	V	W	Co	
2581	0.30	2.65	. .	0.35	8.50	. .	0.23
2662	0.30	2.30	. .	0.25	8.50	2.0	0.26
2567	0.30	2.35	. .	0.60	4.25	. .	0.27
2365	0.32	3.00	2.80	0.55	. .	. .	0.32
2344	0.40	5.30	1.30	1.00	. .	. .	0.33
2343	0.38	5.30	1.10	0.40	. .	. .	0.34

thermal conductivity. The thermal conductivity of several hot working steels is given in Table 5.6. However, the tungsten steels are preferred to the molybdenum steels at very high tool temperatures, although, depending on the stresses that occur, the lower toughness must be kept in mind. Knowledge about the behavior of steels at high temperatures is completed by creep tests.

Conclusions about the load-carrying capacity at high temperatures cannot be drawn entirely from the high-temperature tensile strength. The 0.2% proof stress is the critical factor. This is illustrated in Fig. 5.67, in which two steels are compared, the 4.5% tungsten hot working steel 1.2567 and the familiar molybdenum hot working steel 1.2343. Both were initially heat treated to a tensile strength of about 1400 N/mm^2 but the second steel was also hardened to 1600 N/mm^2. The properties of the steels hardened to 1400 N/mm^2 illustrate the effect of the total alloying content. Not only does the tungsten steel (W + Mo + V = 5.1%) have a higher high-temperature strength than the molybdenum steel (W + Mo + V = 1.8%) but also a higher 0.2% proof stress and a higher ratio of tensile strength to proof stress. However, the molybdenum steel is clearly better with the second heat treatment. The molybdenum steel also offers technological advantages for extrusion tooling, including reduced susceptibility to cracking from changes in temperature (e.g., water-cooling) and a lower tendency to stick than the tungsten steels.

5.4.3. Hot Working Steels for the Individual Tooling

The tooling for vertical and horizontal presses is depicted in Fig. 5.1 to 5.15 and listed in Tables 5.7 and 5.8, along with details about the most suitable steels, including the material number and the approximate initial hardness and tensile strength. The behavior of the tooling, from the point of view of dimensional stability and guidance, varies considerably from press to press and depends on the metal being extruded and the complexity

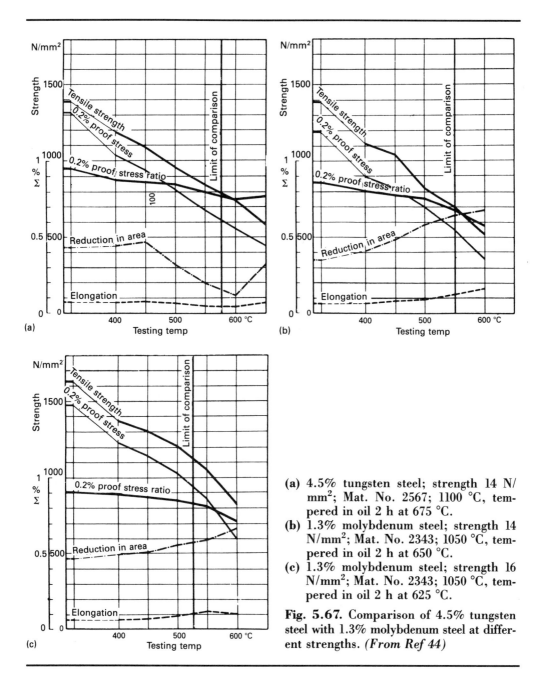

(a) 4.5% tungsten steel; strength 14 N/mm^2; Mat. No. 2567; 1100 °C, tempered in oil 2 h at 675 °C.

(b) 1.3% molybdenum steel; strength 14 N/mm^2; Mat. No. 2343; 1050 °C, tempered in oil 2 h at 650 °C.

(c) 1.3% molybdenum steel; strength 16 N/mm^2; Mat. No. 2343; 1050 °C, tempered in oil 2 h at 625 °C.

Fig. 5.67. Comparison of 4.5% tungsten steel with 1.3% molybdenum steel at different strengths. *(From Ref 44)*

of the section. This applies, in particular, to the tooling that actually deforms the metal—the die and the mandrel. The most important factor in efficient production is the correct design, construction and handling of the tooling.

Table 5.7.　Hot Working Steels for Tooling Subjected to Wear and Containers for Rod and Tube Extrusion Presses (From *Stahleinsatzliste 195*, VDEh, 1972)

Type of steel, abbreviation	Alloy No.	Nominal values in initial temper		Extruded alloy	Application
		Hardness (HB)	Tensile strength (N/mm²)(a)		
Extrusion, Bridge, Porthole and Spider Dies and Inserts					
48CrMoV67..............	1.2323	405 to 455	1400 to 1600	Zinc and lead alloys	Rods, tubes and sections
X38CrMoV51	1.2343	405 to 455	1400 to 1600	Aluminum alloys	Rods, tubes and sections at normal pressure
X40CrMoV51	1.2344	405 to 455	1400 to 1600	Aluminum alloys	Special sections and tubes at normal pressure
X32CrMoV33	1.2365	405 to 455	1400 to 1600	Aluminum alloys	Special sections and tubes at high pressure
X32CrMoV33	1.2365	405 to 455	1400 to 1600	Copper alloys(b)	Rods and sections at normal pressure
X30WCrV53..........	1.2567	405 to 455	1400 to 1600	Copper alloys(b)	Rods and sections at normal pressure
X50NiCrWV1313	1.2731	> 300	..	Copper alloys(b)	Sections, wire and tubes at high pressure
X45CoCrWV555.........	1.2678	405 to 455	1400 to 1600	Copper alloys(b)	Sections, wire and tubes at high pressure
X38CrMoV51..........	1.2343	405 to 455	1400 to 1600	Steel	Sections
X38CrMoV51..........	1.2343	405 to 455	1400 to 1600	Steel	Tubes
X50NiCrWV1313	1.2731	> 300	..	Steel	Tubes
Extrusion Mandrels and Centering Mandrels					
X40CrMoV51..........	1.2344	430 to 480	1500 to 1700	Zinc and lead alloys	Mandrels

Material	No.	Temp. (°C)	Temp. (°F)	Work material	Application
X38CrMoV51	1.2343	430 to 480	1500 to 1700	Aluminum alloys	Mandrels >50 mm diam
X40CrMoV51	1.2344	430 to 480	1500 to 1700	Aluminum alloys	Mandrels >50 mm diam
X32CrMoV33	1.2365	430 to 480	1500 to 1700	Aluminum alloys	Mandrels <50 mm diam
X40CrMoV51	1.2344	405 to 455	1400 to 1600	Copper alloys(c)	With water cooling
X32CrMoV33	1.2365	405 to 455	1400 to 1600	Copper alloys(c)	With water cooling
X30WCrV53	1.2567	430 to 480	1500 to 1700	Copper alloys(c)	With oil cooling
X45CoCrWV555	1.2678	430 to 480	1500 to 1700	Copper alloys(c)	With oil cooling
X40CrMoV51	1.2344	430 to 480	1500 to 1700	Steel(c)	General
X32CrMoV33	1.2365	430 to 480	1500 to 1700	Steel(c)	General
Dummy Blocks, Ejection and Cleaning Discs					
56NiCrMoV7	1.2714	375 to 430	1300 to 1500	Zinc and lead alloys	General
45CrVMoW58	1.2603	405 to 455	1400 to 1600	Aluminum alloys	Normal pressure
X38CrMoV51	1.2343	405 to 455	1400 to 1600	Aluminum alloys	High pressure
X38CrMoV51	1.2343	405 to 455	1400 to 1600	Copper alloys	Normal pressure
X32CrMoV33	1.2365	405 to 455	1400 to 1600	Copper alloys	High pressure and water cooling
X30WCrV53	1.2567	405 to 455	1400 to 1600	Copper alloys	High pressure and oil cooling, air cooling
X40CrMoV51	1.2344	405 to 455	1400 to 1600	Steel	General
X32CrMoV33	1.2365	405 to 455	1400 to 1600	Steel	General

(continued)

Table 5.7 (continued). Hot Working Steels for Tooling Subjected to Wear and Containers for Rod and Tube Extrusion Presses (From *Stahleinsatzliste 195*, VDEh, 1972)

Type of steel, abbreviation	Alloy No.	Nominal values in initial temper		Extruded alloy	Application
		Hardness (HB)	Tensile strength (N/mm²)(a)		
Inner Liners					
48CrMoV67........	1.2323	350 to 405	1200 to 1400	Zinc and lead alloys	..
48CrMoV67........	1.2323	375 to 430	1300 to 1500	Aluminum alloys	Normal thermal conditions
45CrVMoW58........	1.2603	375 to 430	1300 to 1500	Aluminum alloys	Normal thermal conditions
X38CrMoV51	1.2343	375 to 430	1300 to 1500	Aluminum alloys	Severe thermal conditions
45CrVMoW58........	1.2603	375 to 430	1300 to 1500	Copper alloys(b)	Normal thermal conditions
X32CrMoV33	1.2365	375 to 430	1300 to 1500	Copper alloys(b)	Severe thermal conditions
X30WCrV53	1.2567	375 to 430	1300 to 1500	Copper alloys(b)	Severe thermal conditions
48CrMoV67........	1.2323	375 to 430	1300 to 1500	Steel	Normal thermal conditions
X38CrMoV51........	1.2343	375 to 430	1300 to 1500	Steel	Severe thermal conditions
X40CrMoV51	1.2344	375 to 430	1300 to 1500	Steel	Severe thermal conditions
Intermediate Liners					
40CrMnMo7........	1.2311	320 to 375	1100 to 1300	..	Normal thermal conditions
48CrMoV67........	1.2323	320 to 375	1100 to 1300	..	Severe thermal conditions
Mantles					
40CrMnMo7	1.2311	280 to 320	950 to 1100	..	Normal thermal conditions

48CrMoV67................	1.2323	290 to 350	1000 to 1200	..	..	Severe thermal conditions
X38CrMoV51...............	1.2343	290 to 350	1000 to 1200	..	..	Very severe thermal conditions

(a) Tensile strengths determined from hardness measurements (1 kp/mm² ≈ 10 N/mm²).   (b) Can be extruded with hard alloys or high alloyed steels.   (c) Can be extruded with hard alloys.

Table 5.8. Hot Working Steels for Extrusion Stems, Stem Heads and Auxiliary Tooling of Rod and Tube Extrusion Presses

Type of steel, abbreviation	Alloy No.	Nominal values in initial temper		Application
		Hardness (HB)	Tensile strength (N/mm²)(a)	
Stem Heads				
X32CrMoV33...........	1.2365	430 to 505	1500 to 1800	Preferred for aluminum
X30WCrV53............	1.2567	430 to 480	1500 to 1700	Preferred for copper alloys
X45CoCrWV555........	1.2678	430 to 480	1500 to 1700	Preferred for copper alloys
X40CrMoV51...........	1.2344	430 to 480	1500 to 1700	Preferred for steel
Rod and Tube Extrusion Stems				
X38CrMoV51...........	1.2343	430 to 505	1500 to 1800	For aluminum and copper alloys
X40CrMoV51...........	1.2344	430 to 505	1500 to 1800	For aluminum and copper alloys
X40CrMoV51...........	1.2344	430 to 505	1500 to 1800	For steel

(continued)

Table 5.8 (continued). Hot Working Steels for Extrusion Stems, Stem Heads and Auxiliary Tooling of Rod and Tube Extrusion Presses

Type of steel, abbreviation	Alloy No.	Nominal values in initial temper		Application
		Hardness (HB)	Tensile strength (N/mm²)(a)	
Die Holders				
40CrMnMo7	1.2311	370 to 430	1300 to 1500	General(b)
48CrMoV67	1.2323	370 to 430	1300 to 1500	General(b)
45CrVMoW58	1.2603	370 to 430	1300 to 1500	General(b)
X38CrMoV51	1.2343	370 to 430	1300 to 1500	General(b)
X30WCrV53	1.2567	370 to 430	1300 to 1500	General(b)
Die Backers				
X38CrMoV51	1.2343	350 to 430	1200 to 1500	General(b)
56NiCrMoV7	1.2714	320 to 375	1100 to 1300	General(b)
Bolsters				
56NiCrMoV7	1.2714	350 to 430	1200 to 1500	General
Die Holder Carriers				
56NiCrMoV7	1.2714	320 to 405	1100 to 1400	General
Mandrel Holders				
56NiCrMoV7	1.2714	350 to 405	1200 to 1400	General
Compaction Stems, Shearing Stems, Shearing Mandrels				
X40CrMoV51	1.2344	375 to 455	1300 to 1600	General(c)
45CrVMoW58	1.2603	375 to 455	1300 to 1600	General(c)
X30WCrV53	1.2567	375 to 455	1300 to 1600	General(c)

(a) Tensile strengths determined from hardness measurements (1 kp/mm² ≈ 10 N/mm²).   (b) Depending on the thermal stresses and on the choice of die material.   (c) Depending on the thermal stresses.

The reduction of the dead cycle time and the faster throughput of billets in modern presses have resulted in higher stresses. In critical cases it is advisable to select a more highly alloyed steel and this also applies if very long billets are extruded or in billet-to-billet extrusion. The increasing demands on surface finish and very narrow tolerances also necessitate careful handling of the tools and control of the press operation. The average working temperatures of the tooling generally fall within the limits given in Fig. 5.46. These values are taken from numerous practical measurements in several presses for both heavy metals and aluminum. The press operator must realize that the mechanical properties are affected every time the tooling is heated above the annealing temperature of the steel. Therefore, the time above this temperature must be kept to a minimum. Hiller (Ref 44) has given a simple definition for handling hot working steels in practice: in general — assuming 1000 hours to be a tolerable working life — tempered tooling made of hot working steels can be stressed to the 0.2% limit up to 100 °C below the tempering temperature without any loss in strength or permanent deformation. In other words, depending on the alloy content, the steels can either withstand high thermal stresses or have a longer service life at lower temperatures. However, the decisive factor for the stresses in the steel is not the room-temperature hardness but the high-temperature tensile strength or 0.2% proof stress. As already emphasized in Fig. 5.64, which gives the thermal operating ranges of the hot working steels, service temperatures below 500 °C with aluminum and brasses do not require any special technical preventive measures other than the correct heat treatment. However, apart from the austenitic steels and the Stellites, there are no steels that do not suffer a loss in strength in the temperature range 600 to 700 °C.

Before discussing the special steels for high-temperature deformation, the hot working steels normally used for the different tooling will be summarized. The eight hot working steels in Table 5.5 labeled "c" will fulfill most of the normal requirements needed to guarantee economic production (see Tables 5.6 and 5.7).

The design of containers is particularly critical for high service temperatures and mechanical stressing. The resistance to wear at high temperatures, the high-temperature strength, and the thermal conductivity are decisive factors in the selection of the hot working steel, especially for the liner. The following steels are, depending on the stresses, suitable for the liner (the group number 1 designates iron-base alloys): 1.2603, 1.2343, 1.2344 and 1.2365, the last three being for high thermal stresses; for the intermediate liner: 1.2311, 1.2323; for the mantle: 1.2311, 1.2323. Steel 1.2344 was not included in the steel list 195-59 but the properties from the increased vanadium should not be underrated, particularly for the inner liner.

The extrusion stem (solid or hollow) is subjected to compressive, buckling, and, depending on the process, also thermal stresses. The steels used are 1.2714, 1.2343, 1.2344. The heads of stems that come into direct contact with the hot billet can be made of 1.2344, 1.2365 and also 1.2581 for vertical presses.

Mandrels for piercing and extrusion can be cooled internally or externally. A new addition to the steel list is 1.2367, which has a slightly higher chromium and molybdenum content than the usual steel 1.2343, and has replaced the more highly alloyed steel 1.2365, which forms more bainite in large dimensions without passing through an embrittling phase during annealing. The steels for internally cooled mandrels are: 1.2343, 1.2344 and 1.2365, as well as 1.2344 with a higher molybdenum content and, for externally cooled mandrels, 1.2365, 1.2367 and 1.2581.

Pressure pads can be classified according to the thermal stresses they have to withstand and this depends on whether they are reused after each extrusion or used in series. The steels that have proved satisfactory are 1.2603, 1.2343, 1.2344, 1.2365 and 1.2567. The die holder, die backer and die carrier, and the like, which are usually subjected only to low thermal stresses, can be made of the following steels: 1.2311, 1.2713, 1.2714, 1.2323; at higher thermal stresses: 1.2603, 1.2343. Steels 1.2365 and 1.2567 are used for die holders in special cases.

Two steels have recently been developed for the most highly stressed tooling and in particular for metals with high deformation temperatures and steels. Steels 1.2625, with 12 Cr, 12 W, 0.5 Mo and 1 V, and 1.2758, with 11.5 Ni, 12.5 W, 1.6 Co, 0.7 Mo, 1.1 V and 4.0 Cr, have proved to be suitable for extrusion dies.

These hot working steels are given a precipitation hardening heat treatment. Steel 1.2758, in particular, has an excellent high-temperature strength and resists softening up to 850 °C. Extensive tests have shown that these steels are very suitable for the extrusion of brass strip: they have a high wear-resistance especially at corners. The second steel demonstrates the influence of cobalt, which increases the solubility of the carbide-forming elements in the austenite. Thus, in this case, the increased resistance to softening is governed by the cobalt.

The selection of steels for dies extends from the normal stress range to very high deformation resistances and temperatures, as shown in the chart on the opposite page.

5.4.4. Development Trends

The alloy steel producers are always trying to develop new types of steel and methods of treatment, with the hope that the higher tooling costs of the special steels will be less important than the loss in production when a tool

Selection of Hot Working Steels for Dies

Material No.

1.2343 ⎤
1.2344 ⎥ For aluminum, depending on the thermal ⎤
1.2606 ⎥ stressing and difficulty of the section   ⎥
1.2364 ⎦   ⎥
                                                                       ⎥
1.2365 ⎤ For easily extruded alloys and   ⎥ For
1.2567 ⎦ uncomplicated shapes   ⎥ heavy
                                                                       ⎥ metals
1.2581   For high thermal stresses   ⎥
                                                                       ⎥
1.2731 ⎤   ⎥
1.2758 ⎬ For copper and copper alloys with   ⎦
1.2678 ⎦ prolonged thermal stressing

1.2343 ⎤ For cast dies with reduced carbon and   ⎤ For heavy
1.2731 ⎦ nickel content (X35CrNiWV136), Stellite, ⎬ metals and
                ceramic material   ⎦ steel

prematurely breaks. This approach, however, includes the danger of a trend to even more expensive materials, even though the eight main steels in Table 5.5 are only slightly inferior even under high thermal stresses and do have the advantage of lower costs. In addition, the special materials developed for high-temperature deformation are, almost without exception, used only for dies and, therefore, do not represent large volumes.

5.4.4.1. Special Materials

Table 5.9 summarizes the special materials available for high-temperature extrusion together with recently developed steels. The austenitic steel 1.2731 (6 in the table), containing 13% chromium, 13% nickel and 2.5% tungsten, has been used for highly stressed dies for tube and wire in nonferrous metal extrusion. Important additions to the special materials for heavy-metal extrusion at high temperatures or prolonged thermal stressing are the recently developed die materials (1 to 8 in Table 5.9). The steels 1.2758 (7), containing 11.5% nickel and 12.5% tungsten, and 1.2678 (3), with 4.5% tungsten and 4.5% cobalt, have brought significant improvements.

According to Table 5.9, the cobalt-base alloys with good high-temperature mechanical properties are increasing in importance because they can now be vacuum melted and forged. In the past few years extensive investigations with some promising results have been made into these special materials (with alloy contents from 20 to 30% chromium, 4 to 5% molybdenum, up to 25% nickel, and 20 to 60% cobalt). Significant successes have

Table 5.9. Special Materials for High-Temperature Extrusion

Type of steel	Alloy No.	No.	Abbreviation	Nominal composition, %										Application
				C	Cr	Mo	W	V	Co	Ni	Ti	Al	Other	
Heat treatable steels	1	1.2625	X33WCrVMo1212	0.3	12.0	0.5	12.0	1.0	...	...	...	...	...	Strip dies
	2	1.2887	X31CrWCoMoV129	0.3	11.5	0.8	9.0	0.45	1.25	...	...	...	...	Section dies
	3	1.2678	X45CoCrWV555	0.45	4.5	0.5	4.5	2.0	4.5	...	...	...	...	Section dies
	4	1.2888	X20CoCrWMo109	0.2	10.0	2.0	6.0	...	10.0	...	...	...	...	Section dies, higher performance
	5	2.4989	X40CoCrNiMoWNb432020	0.4	20.0	4.0	4.5	...	43.0	20.0	...	...	Nb 4.0 Fe≤5.0	Highest thermal performance
Austenitic steels	6	1.2731	X50NiCrWV1313	0.5	13	...	2.5	0.5	...	13	...	...	...	Wire dies
	7	1.2758	X50WNiCrVCo1212	0.5	4	0.7	12.5	1.1	1.6	11.5	...	...	...	Wire dies, higher performance
	8	1.4980	X5NiCrTi2615	0.2	15	1.4	...	0.3	...	25	2	0.2	...	Highest performance
Cobalt alloys	9	...	ALX	2	33	...	16.5	...	50	...	...	...	...	Die inserts
	10	...	Akrit Co 50	2.2	27	...	14	...	55	...	...	...	...	Die inserts
	11	...	Celsit P	2.5	31	...	13.5	...	50	...	...	...	...	Die inserts
	12	...	Revolta	0.29	28	5.9	...	...	55	...	...	...	...	Die inserts
	13	...	Platit PZ	1.4	28	...	5	...	67	...	...	...	...	Die inserts
Stellite	14	...	Cast	2.5	32	2.5	17	...	48	...	...	...	...	Section, bridge and porthole dies, difficult profiles
	15	...	Forged	0.3	28	5	...	...	60	...	...	...	...	Section, bridge and porthole dies, difficult profiles
Nickel alloys	16	2.4632	NiCr20Co18Ti	0.1	20	...	...	...	18	rem	2.4	1.5	...	For copper(a)
	17	...	NiCo15Cr15MoAlTi	0.2	11	4	...	...	16	rem	4	5	...	For copper inserts(b)
Molybdenum alloys	18	...	TZM	0.01 to 0.03	...	99.25 min	...	...	...	...	0.4 to 0.55	...	Zr 0.06 to 0.12	Steel dies
Sinter alloys	19	...	Cermotherm	0.01	...	80 to 85	...	...	...	...	...	...	(c)	Dies

(a) Nimonic 90.   (b) Nimonic 115.   (c) ZrO_2 15.0 to 20.0.

been achieved with the special steel 1.2888 (4), in which the high cobalt content raises the annealing temperature by 60 to 70 °C at an initial tensile strength of about 1400 N/mm^2.

The high-alloy nickel alloys Nimonic 90 and 115 (16 and 17) should also be included in this series as well as the Stellites (14 and 15), which are used in both cast and forged forms for highly stressed dies for the production of sections in large quantities. The cast dies, naturally, offer advantages for bridge dies. Stellites have a very high resistance to wear but must be held in support tooling because of their low toughness.

All these very highly alloyed special steels do, however, have the disadvantage of inferior physical properties, including thermal expansion, thermal conductivity and machinability (Stellite). Braun and Schulte (Ref 48) have correctly pointed out that in changing from the standard hot working steels to the very highly alloyed special materials, unsatisfactory changes in the material properties that determine the behavior of a material for hot working must be accepted. Every extruder is aware that increasing the alloy content decreases the thermal conductivity, raises the thermal expansion to undesirable levels, and considerably impairs the machinability. There is, therefore, great interest in developing new materials that do not suffer from these disadvantages to such an extent. The researchers mentioned above (Ref 48) undertook this task; numerous extrusion trials with different steel sections on a horizontal hydraulic 18 MN press verified that the material TZM (molybdenum alloy 2) has a significantly longer life than the usual hot working steels if it is used for simple to moderately difficult alloys. This alloy has properties needed for efficient use as a die material: good high-temperature strength, good thermal conductivity, very low coefficient of expansion, and good machinability. The major constituent of the TZM alloy is molybdenum, with 0.5% titanium, 0.12% zirconium and up to 0.02% carbon (Table 5.9, No. 18).

Figure 5.68 illustrates the considerable differences between the high-temperature strengths of the different die materials at temperatures up to 1000 °C. The comparison between the standard steel (1.2567) and the nickel alloy Nimonic 90 is of interest. The tensile strength of 1.2567 is 800 N/mm^2 at 640 °C and the strength of the austenitic alloy Nimonic 90 falls below this value at a temperature only 80 °C higher. The surface temperature of a die of this austenitic alloy can exceed this temperature interval because of the lower thermal conductivity and, thus, be more susceptible to softening than the 5% tungsten steel. TZM is clearly superior to all other materials at temperatures above 900 °C.

Fundamental investigations into the service life of different die materials for extruding stainless steels have been carried out by Braun and Schulte (Ref 48). The appearances of the usual cast steel dies of steel 1.2343, a high-quality cast Stellite die and a solid die of TZM from a milled bar are

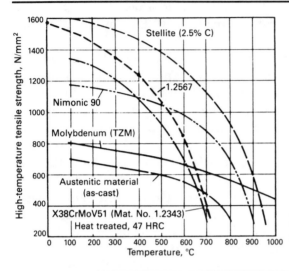

Fig. 5.68. High-temperature tensile strength of different die materials up to 1000 °C (*Compiled by Stenger*)

compared in 5.69. Whereas the steel die can be rewelded up to ten times after every two or three extrusions to bring it back to an "as-new" condition, the periphery of the Stellite die was wavy after only one extrusion and a projecting tongue had been washed out — possibly the result of exceeding the solidus temperature of the alloy. The TZM alloy die exhibited no change in the radii after 145 extrusions although it was rough and had suffered some washout along the long leg.

Bensmann (Ref 50) has pointed out that there is no material commercially available that even approaches a satisfactory high-temperature strength at extrusion temperatures of 1200 to 1300 °C and that can also be machined without any great difficulty. The molybdenum dies now being developed will, in his opinion, play an important role in the future.

5.4.4.2. Methods of Manufacture

The process of compound centrifugal casting that makes it possible to use the austenitic steels with their better resistance to wear at high temperatures for inner liners is of particular interest to extruders. Thick-wall cylinders are centrifugally cast and a second layer added before the first has completely solidified. This method is used to produce liners of a heat treatable high-strength hot working steel with the bore plated with an austenitic steel resistant to wear at high temperatures. These liners have a much longer service life associated with good dimensional stability and a low tendency to wear at the die end. The application of ready-to-use cast dies similar to die castings for complicated inserts in welding chamber or bridge dies is also growing in importance. Sintered materials with a metal or metal-ceramic

Fig. 5.69. Comparison of the service life of dies for extruding sections. *(From Ref 48)*

base as well as cast Stellite inserts have been used for heavy metal dies with considerable success because of their good high-temperature strength.

Certain properties of the hot working steels have been improved in the past few years by developments in the methods of steel production including the electroslag refining (ESR) process. Kösters (Ref 51) has described how the toughness of the hot working steels has been improved by the more homogeneous and segregation-free ingots obtained from the electroslag refining process. Almost constant properties are obtained over the entire ingot cross section, especially in the transverse direction, and the die maker can use discs sawn from the bar without any loss in quality, whereas, previously, only individually forged discs could be used. This represents a significant economical advance.

A special development in the field of surface hardening that has given a significant increase in the life of extrusion dies, mandrels and hollow section dies is bath nitriding (Tenifer process, section 5.4.5.5) and this is now extensively used for the extrusion of aluminum and aluminum alloys. According to results obtained in several extrusion plants, this process increases the die output by three to four times, with improved retention of the shape and dimensions. The extrusion speed can also be significantly increased and the product surface improved.

5.4.5. Heat Treatment and Maintenance of Extrusion Tooling

It is not possible to discuss all the numerous methods and practical skills in the heat treatment of hot working steels in this book. The heat treatment methods that give the most suitable properties for extrusion are, however, of interest. The possibilities for controlling the structure by heat treatment should be known and their correct application understood, because every steel user can control the service life of his tooling by the selection of the optimum heat treatment. It is advisable for an extrusion plant to limit its range of hot working steels to a few specific steels and to optimize the heat treatments applied.

5.4.5.1. Heat Treatments

The individual properties of the steels are mainly determined by the alloying elements present. Iron dissolves almost all the elements used in iron alloys to form solid solutions. If carbon is present, the effect of the alloying element depends to a large degree on whether they tend to form carbides — for example, chromium, vanadium, tungsten — or dissolve in the matrix. The volume of carbides formed in an alloy steel is a function of the carbon content and, therefore, the alloy content of the matrix decreases as the carbon content is raised. However, the solubility of carbon in the matrix increases at higher temperatures and, consequently, the alloy content of the matrix also increases. The resistance of the carbides to dissolution controls the resistance to softening of a hot working steel. After the initial decrease in hardness during tempering with increasing temperature, which is caused by the precipitation of Fe_3C, there is an increase in hardness resulting from the very fine precipitates of the previously dissolved special carbides (precipitation hardening). The hardness starts to decrease again only at higher annealing temperatures — e.g., 550 °C — because of the increasing coagulation of the precipitated special carbides.

Special carbides dissolve less readily than iron carbide. Therefore, maximum solubility requires sufficient time at the high hardening temperatures used for hot working steels, usually between 1000 and 1200 °C. The optimum hardening conditions depend on the composition of the steel. Some of the most important points of heat treating hot working steels are described below, without giving the exact hardening specifications for the various steels with the most favorable hardening and tempering temperatures and times — these data are available from the steel manufacturers.

5.4.5.2. Thermal Stress Relieving

Thermal stress relieving after rough machining is recommended to avoid distortion or even cracking in the finished die by the release of residual stresses. The most effective reduction in residual stresses is obtained by thermal stress relieving but the residual stresses developed during machining, with or without swarf, are never completely eliminated and some stresses are always present. In some special cases the hot working steel has to be subjected to austenitizing treatment followed by annealing to obtain sufficient stress relief. Thermal stress relieving is usually carried out between 550 and 650 °C. The time at temperature should last several hours, depending on the cross sectional ratios in the die. A thermal stress relieving treatment can be almost completely negated by the formation of new residual stresses formed by incorrect, too rapid cooling. Furnace cooling at a controlled rate should, therefore, be used.

The reduction or elimination of residual stresses is always associated with changes in shape or crack formation. Consequently, the stresses present problems in dies, because stress relieving is always accompanied by dimensional changes. Therefore, in critical cases the die should be reworked or finish machined after stress relieving. Rapid heating to the stress relieving temperature should always be avoided, particularly with complicated dies of varying cross section. Slow heating is just as important as slow cooling. This also applies to the handling of extrusion tooling after extrusion and is discussed below. Very careful cooling is also important in this case to prevent the formation of residual stresses from too rapid cooling. If residual stresses are induced during cooling, they can be released when the die is reused and the dimensional changes make it necessary to scrap the die. These residual stresses can also initiate cracking when the die is placed under load.

5.4.5.3. Hardening

Hardening commences with slow heating. The thermal conductivity of hot working steels usually decreases as the alloy content is raised and this, together with the development of significant thermal stresses during the heating of complicated dies with large variations in cross section, necessitates the slow heating. Usually, the tools are first heated in an air circulating furnace to about 300 to 400 °C to thoroughly and uniformly heat the die through to its core. The die must, therefore, be held at this temperature long enough for complete soaking. The subsequent heating to the hardening temperature is normally carried out in two stages: a preheat to 850 °C with a soaking time sufficient to give a uniform temperature and complete structural transformation, followed by interrupted heating to the hardening temperature. The holding time at this temperature must be sufficient to ensure a uniform temperature and sufficient dissolution of the special carbides. Prolonged soaking times should be avoided as far as possible, as well as excessive temperatures, to prevent the formation of coarse grains and a decrease in the toughness. The following rules should, therefore, be observed: tools that need a high toughness should be hardened at the lower limit of the temperature range, and those that must have a high resistance to softening must be hardened at the upper limit.

Extrusion dies are best hardened in a salt-bath furnace. The dies are heated in a liquid salt in the complete absence of air; this minimizes distortion. The good thermal transfer between the liquid salt and the steel ensures thorough heating more rapidly than in other furnaces. This prevents excessive soaking time at the corners and along the edges of large sections — that is, the danger of grain coarsening is significantly reduced in a salt bath. The hot quenching bath is, for similar reasons, preferred for quenching very complex extrusion dies of suitable steels. The distortion associated with hardening is not completely eliminated but greatly reduced with the hot quenching bath.

5.4.5.4. Tempering

Tempering transforms the tetragonal martensite retained after quenching to a cubic structure. This increases the toughness of the steel and reduces its susceptibility to cracking. The required resistance to softening is obtained only with the optimum volume of dissolved special carbides. The tempering temperature should, as a general rule, be 30 to 50 °C above the operating temperature of the tool. If the surface is to be nitrided, the tempering temperature must also be above the nitriding temperature, otherwise tempering can occur during nitriding. The tool would then distort and have to be scrapped.

Double or triple tempering is always advisable for the more highly alloyed steels. The temperature for the first tempering is higher than that for the subsequent treatments. These steels have to undergo multiple tempering to remove the residual austenite retained after every hardening treatment. Residual austenite is usually an unstable component of the structure after hardening that partly transforms to martensite during cooling after the first tempering process. Martensite has a larger volume than austenite and the tool distorts under the high residual stresses formed. The martensite formed by the transformation of the residual austenite can itself be completely converted to a cubic structure in a subsequent tempering operation, the residual stresses from the austenite-to-martensite transformation reduced, and the steel toughness improved. It must also be remembered that the residual austenite is present as a very soft structural component surrounded by much harder ones. The transformation of the residual austenite to martensite is associated with a simultaneous increase in the hardness of the steel and positive dimensional changes. Both effects can be easily measured.

Tempering is best carried out in a liquid bath and the correct temperature can be obtained from tempering diagrams. Slow heating and cooling are important to avoid residual stresses.

5.4.5.5. Surface Treatment of Hardened and Tempered Extrusion Tooling to Increase Production

Nitrogen diffusion hardening in the temperature range 400 to 550 °C is the most important of the surface treatment processes used in aluminum extrusion. The surface hardness and, hence, the resistance to wear can be significantly increased by nitriding. Hardness values of over 1000 HV can be attained, but nitriding also embrittles the surface. The thickness of the nitrided layer that can be attained—that is, the diffusion depth of the nitrogen—is low for the alloy steels containing special nitride-forming elements. All alloying elements that have a high affinity for nitrogen hinder the diffusion, and the result is a shallow diffusion layer. Salt baths are very suitable for the nitriding process.

The service life of nitrided dies is far superior to that of untreated dies and very good results have been obtained, in particular in aluminum extrusion. A die life of three to six times that of unnitrided dies has been realized. Tolerances can also be maintained more easily with nitrided dies. The hardness of the nitrided surface slowly decreases as the number of extrusions increases, because the temperatures attained by the die lands in contact with the flowing metal are in the range of the nitriding temperatures. Nitrogen then diffuses towards the center of the die, reducing the concentration at the surface and the hardness. This softening of the surface results in a decrease in the surface quality of the product in the extrusion of aluminum alloys (die lines on the surface). The dies, therefore, have to be removed and cleaned after 150 to 250 extrusions and can then be successfully renitrided. This operation can be repeated several times, provided the die does not have to be taken out of service because of cracks.

Nitriding cannot be used for metals extruded above 550 °C for the reasons given above, but research is in progress to try to develop wear resistance films by special surface treatments that can be used at the higher temperatures.

5.4.5.6. Wear of Tooling on Rod and Tube Extrusion Processes

Investigations were carried out by various steel experts during the last world war to determine the decisive factors in the selection of suitable steels for hot working tooling capable of high outputs in spite of the shortage of alloying elements, particularly tungsten and molybdenum. The low-alloy steels (including 1.2343 and 1.2344) had already proved themselves at this time and are still widely used. The working party for heavy metal extrusion of the extrusion group of the DGM initiated detailed investigations in 1972–73 into the service life of the tooling used for the heavy metals. The results largely confirmed earlier studies but special materials had since been successfully developed for the alloys difficult to extrude and the dies subjected to high thermal stresses (Table 5.9). The output obtained today from the tooling that comes into direct contact with the billet during heavy metal extrusion is given in Table 5.10. These include dies, mandrels, dummy blocks and liners. Only the characteristic alloys are compared. Comparisons with the service life of the tooling in aluminum extrusion are meaningless, because the low thermal stressing gives very high outputs, provided the tool design is correct for the mechanical stress involved. Exceptions are very complicated sections with long thin legs, etc.

5.5. Standardization of Extrusion Tooling

It would be an important step forward if all the practical experience and knowledge available were gathered together and combined into a single set of standards. A proposal for standardization of extrusion tooling was drawn up by the predecessor of the present extrusion working party of the Nonferrous Metal Tool Committee of the DGM in the 1950's. The working party for tooling of the Extrusion Committee extended this to a more comprehensive proposal for aluminum extrusion tooling that also extensively applies to tooling for heavy metal extrusion.

Data about the existing tooling from 98 presses in 19 plants were collected and analyzed. As expected, the results indicated a bewildering range of different dimensions. The differences were frequently minimal.

A new proposal has been drawn up from these data and published in the *Zeitschrift für Metallkunde*. The aims of the proposal are:

(a) Meaningful progression of press capacities following a standard series.
(b) Standardization of container bores and lengths according to press capacity and adequate specific pressure.
(c) The establishment of standard billet dimensions from (b). The imperial units still in use today correspond almost exactly to the metric system.
(d) Suitable graduation of die and support tooling dimensions according to statistical data to give a tool stack of adequate dimensions.

Table 5.10. Typical Service Life of Heavy Metal Extrusion Tooling for Rods and Wires, and for Tubes

Rods and Wires(d) — avg billet diam, 180 mm

Material	Press, MN(a)	Extruded diam range, mm	Min thickness, mm	Extrusion dies(b) Steel alloy No.	Extrusion dies(b) No. of extrusions	Pressure pads Steel alloy No.	Pressure pads No. of extrusions	Inner liner(c) Steel alloy No.	Inner liner(c) No. of extrusions, 1000's
Cu................	20	5 to 180	4	.	200	.	600	.	20
CuZn38Pbl	20	3 to 120	2	2731	500	2603	3000	2603	70
	20	3 to 120	2	2581	500	2343	3000	2343	70
CuZn37	20	4 to 130	3	2888(e)	300	2344	1500	2344	40
	20	4 to 130	3	2888(e)	300	2365	1500	2567	40

Tubes — avg billet diam, 200 mm

Material	Press, MN(a)	Avg tube diam, mm	Min wall thickness, mm	Extrusion dies(b) Steel alloy No.	Extrusion dies(b) No. of extrusions	Mandrels Steel alloy No.	Mandrels No. of extrusions	Inner liner(c) Steel alloy No.	Inner liner(c) No. of extrusions, 1000's
CuZn40Pb2	20	43 to 48	2.5	2344	500	2365	300	2603	>1000
	20	43 to 48	2.5	2731	500	2367	300	2603	>1000
Cu	25	50 to 58	4	2731	250	2581	200	2344	40
	25	50 to 58	4	2367	250	2367	200	2365	40
	25	50 to 58	4	2581	250	2367	200	2365	40
CuZn20Al	25	50 to 60	5	2758(e)	300	2344	150	.	300
	25	50 to 60	5	2758(e)	300	2367	150	2343	300
CuSn8	25	55 to 70	7.5	2758(e)	350	2567	250	2344	300
CuNi10Fe	25	54 to 68	7	2731	150	2344	100	2365(f)	8
	25	54 to 68	7	2581	150	2367	100	2365(f)	8
CuNi30Fe..........	25	50 to 65	7.5	2662(e)	100	2567	70	2365(f)	6
	25	50 to 65	7.5	2662(e)	100	2581	70	2365(f)	6

(a) Extrusion presses from 6.3 to 35 MN were used for the alloys listed. (b) Also inserts of Stellite, Co alloys, Ni alloys, Mo alloys and cermotherm. (c) The service life can be affected if different alloys are extruded in the same liner. (d) Also sections of simple form. (e) And inserts. (f) And fused.

Bibliographic References

1. Sauer, G., and Bielen, J.: Terminologie der Strangpreßwerkzeuge. Fachausschuß Strangpressen DGM (1970-1976).
2. National Engineering Laboratory: Research in Metal Extrusion. Metallurgia 60 (1959) p. 160.
3. Arenz, M.: Konstruktive Arbeiten zur Gestaltung und Berechnung von Strangpreßwerkzeugen. Fachausschuß Strangpressen DGM (1950-1955).
4. Heinen, B.: Herstellung und Behandlung von Strangpreßwerkzeugen. Z. f. Metallkunde 58 (1967) p. 215/217.
5. Baugh, R. and Lyons, J.: Extrusion Press Tooling. Light Metal Age 15 (1957) p. 19/20.
6. Möckli, F. and Locher, M.: Heutiger Stand der Technik im Bau von Strangpreßmatrizen. Aluminium 41 (1965) p. 629/633.
7. Bergmaier, W.: Gedanken zur Gestaltung von neuen Aluminium-Strangpreßprofilen. Schweiz. Schlosser 13 (1967).
8. Aalberts, J.: Herstellung und Gestaltung von Werkzeugen für das Strangpressen von Leichtmetallprofilen. Z. f. Metallkunde 62 (1971) p. 191/196.
9. Kursetz, E.: Herstellung von Spezial-Strangpreßprofilen in amerikanischen Halbzeugwerken. Aluminium 36 (1960) p. 323/329.
10. Kursetz, E.: Aluminium im Bauwesen in den USA. Aluminium 40 (1964) p. 53/58.
11. Buige de, C.: Design and Manufacturing of Aluminum Extrusion. International Extrusion Technology Seminar, New Orleans (1969).
12. Neumann, H.: Aluminium-Strangpreßprofile für Gerätekonstruktionen. Siemens-Mitt. (1964).
13. Laue, K.: Neuerungen auf dem Strangpreßgebiet. Metall 19 (1965) p. 922/928.
14. Schrimer, W. D.: Werkzeuge zum Strangpressen von Stahl. Bänder-Bleche-Rohre 12 (1971) p. 409/410.
15. Bielen, J.: Grundlagen der Werkzeuggestaltung für das Strangpressen von Leichtmetallprofilen. Paper presented at the conference "Strangpressen von Aluminium-Werkstoffen," Iserlohn (1974).
16. Bijl de, A.: Herstellung von Werkzeugen für das Strangpressen von Leichtmetallprofilen. Paper presented at the conference "Strangpressen von Aluminium-Werkstoffen," Iserlohn (1974).
17. Kleinow, F.: Herstellung und Behandlung von Strangpreßwerkzeugen. Behandlung der Strangpreßwerkzeuge im Preßbetrieb. Z. f. Metallkunde 58 (1967) p. 217/220.
18. Flicker, D.: To Correct Extrusion Dies. Modern Metals 14 (1958) p. 38/42.
19. Laue, K. and Keller, H.: Werkzeugaufgaben im Halbzeugwerk. Aluminium 38 (1962) p. 725/728.
20. Dahlheimer, R. and Dieterle, K.: Die Berechnung elastischer Formänderungen von belasteten Strangpreßmatrizen. Industrie Anzeiger 92 (1970), No. 65.
21. Gönner, H.: Praktische Merkmale für die Werkzeugkonstruktion. VDM-Werkzeugnotizen (1964).
22. Bender, W.: Verfahrenstechnik beim funkenerosiven Herstellen von Schneidwerkzeugen. Werkstatt und Betrieb 106 (1973).
23. Kursetz, E.: Die Entwicklung der Warmstrangpreßtechnik von Aluminium, Stählen und Sondermetallen. Blech (1968), No. 2, p. 8/11; No. 3, p. 12/16.
24. Sauer, G.: Berechnungsmethoden von Rezipienten mit runden Durchbrüchen. DGM-Report 29/1275 (1975).
25. Peiter, A.: Der Einfluß der Abmessungen auf die Spannungen in Schrumpfpassungen ist bedeutend. Maschinemarkt 79 (1973).
26. Peiter, A.: Einfluß und Fügebedingungen auf die Spannungen in Schrumpfpassungen. Maschinenmarkt 79 (1973).

27. Müller, E.: Hydraulische Pressen und Druckflüssigkeitsanlagen. Vol. 3, Springer Verlag, Berlin (1959).
28. Busch, F. and Schepp, W.: Werkzeuge und Werkzeugstähle für das Strangpressen. Handbuch der Edelstahlwerke Buderus AG., Wetzlar (1966).
29. Grüning, K.: Der Einfluß achsparalleler Heizbohrungen auf die Tragfähigkeit von Blockaufnehmern von Strangpressen. Forschungsbericht Land Nordrhein-Westfalen, No. 966.
30. Vater, M. and Rathjen, C.: Untersuchungen über die Größe der Stempelkraft und des Innendrucks im Aufnehmer beim Strangpressen. Forschungsbericht VDI, Series 2, No. 9 (1966).
31. Satorius, K.: Blockaufnehmer für das Strangpressen breiter Flachprofile. Röchling, Techn. Mitt. No. 17 (1970).
32. Bühler, H., Piesberger E., Reich W. and Schepp, W.: Berechnung und Auslegung von Blockaufnehmern mit flachem Büchsendurchbruch für Metallstrangpressen. Werkstatt und Betrieb 106 (1973) p. 10.
33. Reich, W. and Schepp, W.: Ausführungsformen bei Blockaufnehmern mit flachem Durchbruch (1973).
34. Plankensteiner, S.: Metallstrang- und Rohrpresse und ihre Werkzeuge. Stahl und Eisen 56 (1936) p. 1497/1504.
35. Hohage, R. and Rollet, R.: Werkzeuge in Metallstrangpressen. Werkstoffhandbuch, Stahl und Eisen, 3rd ed. (1953).
36. Treppschuh, H.: Stähle für Warmarbeitswerkzeug. Stahl und Eisen 93 (1973).
37. Houdremont, E.: Handbuch der Sonderstahlkunde, 3rd ed. (1956). Verlag Stahleisen, Düsseldorf.
38. Rapatz, F.: Die Edelstähle. Springer Verlag, Berlin (1940).
39. Pattermann, O.: Werkzeugstähle. Poldi-Hütte, Kladno (1934).
40. Houdremont, E.: Die Sonderstahlentwicklung unter Berücksichtigung der Rohstofflage. Techn. Mitt. Krupp 5 (1937) p. 153/173.
41. Assmann, H.: Sonderstähle zur Formung von Warmpreßteilen aus Kupfer-Zink-Legierung. Part II: Austauschstähle. Metallwirtschaft 20 (1941) p. 82/88.
42. Rapatz, F.: Die neuzeitlich hochwertigen Stähle. Berg- u. Hütténm. Mon. H. 88 (1940) p. 109/115.
43. Treppschuh, H.: Stähle für Warmarbeitswerkzeuge. Werkstoffhandbuch Stahl und Eisen, 3rd ed. (1953).
44. Hiller, H.: Neuzeitliche Warmarbeitsstähle. (a) für Werkzeuge zur Warmumformung von NE-Metallen. Metall 14 (1960) p. 310/317. (b) Zur Frage der Wärmebehandlung von Warmarbeitsstählen. Paper presented at the conference "Hardening," Nürnberg (1964).
45. Höpken, H.: Werkzeuge für Stahl, Buntmetall und Leichtmetall unter besonderer Berücksichtigung der geeigneten Stahlauswahl und konstruktive Besonderheiten. Techn. Report Stahlwerke Südwestfalen.
46. Höpken, H.: Hinweise zur Werkstoffauswahl für Strangpreßwerkzeuge. Ingenieur Digest (1967), Part 1: No. 9, p. 64/66; Part 2: No. 10, p. 61/63; Part 3: No. 11, p. 59/64.
47. Heinen, H.: (a) Die Teniferbehandlung als verzugsarme Werkzeug- und Oberflächenbehandlung zur Erreichung optimaler Werkzeughärtung. (b) Die Badnitrier-Behandlung in ihrer Anwendung für die Kaltverformung von Metallen. Z. W. F. No. 59 (1964) p. 110/115.
48. Braun, H. and Schulte, W.: Molybdänmatrizen für das Strangpressen von Stahlprofilen. Stahl und Eisen 86 (1966) p. 967/980.
49. Braun, H.: Metallisches Molybdän. Metall 16 (1962) p. 646/655, 990/999.
50. Bensmann, K.: Probleme beim Strangpressen schwer umformbarer Werkstoffe bei hohen Temperaturen. Presented at the "Extrusion Conference," TH Berlin (1973).

51. Kösters, R.: Neue Entwicklungstendenzen auf dem Gebiet der Warmarbeitsstahl-werkzeuge. Deutsche Edelstahlwerke, Krefeld (1973).

52. Sauer, G.: Herstellung und Behandlung von Strangpreßwerkzeugen. Erhöhung der Standzeiten von Preßmatrizen durch Badnitrieren. Z. f. Metallkunde 58 (1967) p. 289/296.

53. Arenz, M.: Die Normung der Strangpreßwerkzeuge. Z. f. Metallkunde 46 (1955) p. 172/179.

54. Ames, A., Bielen, J., and Sauer, G.: Vorschlag zur Normung von Werkzeugen für Leichtmetallstrangpressen in Abhängigkeit der Preßkräfte. Z. f. Metallkunde 62 (1971) p. 716/720.

55. Laue, K.: Erfahrungen mit Strangpreßwerkzeugen. Z. f. Metallkunde 62 (1971) p. 350/354.

56. Laue, K. and Arenz, M.: Über die Normung der Strangpreßwerkzeuge. Z. f. Metallkunde 45 (1954) p. 461/464.

57. Keller, R.: Tool Production, Alsdorf.

58. Elkan, R. M. L.: Extrusion Presses and Ancillary Equipment. Metal Industry 100 (1962) p. 506/509, 101 (1962) p. 7/8.

59. Laue, K.: Thermische und mechanische Beanspruchung der Strangpreßwerkzeuge. Z. f. Metallkunde 46 (1955) p. 1/6.

6. Economics of Extrusion

6.1. General Analysis

The principle on which this general analysis is based is the need to produce extruded components with the minimum of material and the shortest production time on suitable extrusion presses in economic quantities with efficient tooling. Obviously, accurate cost control must be used in a well-organized plant to ensure profitability. Production costs and tooling costs are significantly influenced by the method of production and the volume of orders in any plant as material-dependent as an extrusion works. The economical lot size is the point on the cost curve (Fig. 6.1) at which the gradient changes to a flatter profile.

(a) Large press: High tool and plant costs, therefore expensive for small orders. However, the production costs for large orders are less than those of a small press, because of the heavier billets.
(b) Small press: Lower tool and plant costs for small orders but higher production costs on large orders, because of the lighter billets.

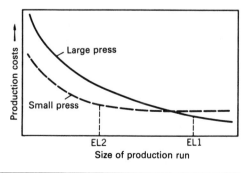

Fig. 6.1. Production costs as a function of the size of the production run. EL1 = production run for a large press; EL2 = production run for a small press.

The variety of production costs for the individual production steps, the influence of tooling costs and the indirect production costs are decisive factors for any plant. Technology and costs are, therefore, closely interconnected and an objective statement about the profitability of the production process must be drawn from a technical and analytical comparison of the various production steps.

6.2. Productivity Comparison

Useful comparisons between the productivity of German and non-German producers of sheet, strip, tube, rod and sections have been made in the last decade by the European Wrought Aluminium Association (EWAA; Ref 2). A recent comparison of tube production revealed significant differences between the various types of press and different billet dimensions used for the various alloys, which resulted in large differences between the methods of production and the output of individual plants. Table 6.1 compares the production of tubes from three different alloys in three different plants. The extrusion speeds and production times differ considerably and the time required on press 3 exceeds those on presses 1 and 2 by:

Alloy	Compared with press 1	Compared with press 2
Al99.5	110%	66%
AlMgSi1	129%	79%
AlMg3	335%	276%

The figures underline the advantage of using a modern fully automatic 20 MN press (No. 1) for all three alloys. The efficient 12.5 MN press (No. 2) gave a higher production rate, but the billets were too small. In comparison, the nonautomatic 18 MN press (No. 3), built before World War II, was very unprofitable. A further comparison by the EWAA can be drawn on to answer the question, whether the inefficiency of the old press was due to its control system or the lack of auxiliary equipment (Table 6.2). Tubes of AlMgSi0.5 were extruded on three 30 MN presses, all over ten years old, using approximately the same billet diameter. According to the data in Table 6.2, there were considerable differences between the monthly outputs. If these results are compared with Table 6.1, it is obvious that even older presses can operate economically, and the most important factor is to determine the optimum press parameters for the production program.

Table 6.3 compares the production of a wide, relatively thin AlMgSi0.5 section in three extrusion presses of different ages. The billet weights and

Table 6.1. Productivity Comparison for the Extrusion of Aluminum Tubes From Diverse Alloys (From Ref 2) (Tube dimensions: diam 30 mm; wall thickness 1.25 mm)

Alloy	Press No.	Press capacity, MN(a)	Dimensions of billet, diam·length	Wt, kg	Extrusion process	Dimensions of billet, diam·length	Extrusion ratio	Extrusion speed, m/min	Extrusions per h	No. of workmen	Direct work hours per t — Press	Direct work hours per t — Total
Al99.5....	1	20	195·700	56.4	Porthole die	40·35	107	60	42	8	4.9	68.4
	2	12.5	135·370	14.5	Bridge die	34·30	77	60	40	4	20	86.5
	3	18	220·280	28.1	Piercing mandrel	35·31	200	30	18	10	40	144
AlMgSi1...	1	20	172·450	28.3	Piercing mandrel	45·40	70	24	23	4	9.8	78.8
	2	12.5	135·400	14.5	Hollow billet, mandrel	38·33	53	18	18	2	22	104.9
	3	18	220·280	28.1	Piercing mandrel	36.5·31.7	153	8	12	10	60	187
AlMg3.....	1	20	172·350	22	Piercing mandrel	45·40	70	8.5	17	4	17.8	87.1
	2	12.5	135·400	14.5	Hollow billet, mandrel	38·33	52	6	12	2	28	105.1
	3	18	260·305	39	Piercing mandrel	47·40.5	124	2.5	4	10	130	396

(a) The 20 MN press is fully automatic; the 12.5 MN press is semiautomatic; the 18 MN press is an older, manual-operation version.

Table 6.2. Comparison of the Performance of Three Older 30 MN Extrusion Presses for AlMgSi0.5 Tube Production (From Ref 2) (Tube dimensions: diam 25 mm; wall thickness 2 mm)

Factor	Press A	B	C
Billet length, mm	760	475	320
Billet diam, mm	228	225	220
Billet, kg	82.5	47.5	32
No. of strands	6	4	3
Extrusion ratio	47	69	88
Length of extruded product, m	6·33	4·25.7	5·25
Extrusion speed, m/min	25	15.3	10.7
Extrusions per h	19	23.2	13
Dead cycle time, s	27	54	60
To Produce 500 kg of Finished Tubing:			
Downtime, h	0.37	0.65	1.29
Direct work hours	2.65	10.43	23
Total work hours	3.29	12.61	28.5
Calculated monthly output, t	320	232	50

Table 6.3. Productivity Comparison for the Production of AlMgSi0.5 Sections (From Ref 2)

Section Profile and Dimensions
Wt: 0.5 kg/m

Press	Press capacity, MN	Age class, yr	No. of workmen	Billet data diam · length, mm	Wt, kg	Extrusion speed, m/min	Extrusions per h	Work hours per 1000 kg of finished product			Output comparison, t	
								Production time	Down-time	Total	At 400 h, eff.	From Table 6.4
A	20	< 5	5	176 · 340	21	38.8	38.6	9.64	0.25	9.89	220	243
B	25	5 to 10	7	200 · 800	68	20	8	25	3	28	145	310
C	25	>10	6	245 · 600	76	15.3	5.7	36.1	7.2	43.3	120	310

press outputs vary considerably. The results are given in man hours per 1000 kg of finished product. The output comparison clearly shows that the following factors are important for economical production:

(a) The choice of press according to the size of the section — that is, optimum extrusion ratio, correct billet weight and fastest production cycle with the highest possible extrusion speed.

(b) High efficiency in plant utilization — that is, low setting-up times and dead cycle times.

(c) Trouble-free operation of the die with very little die correction.

Table 6.4 illustrates the normal output that can be achieved with modern presses extruding easy and moderately difficult aluminum alloys. If this table is compared with the values for the 31.5 MN press in Table 6.2, it can be seen that plant A with a monthly output of 320 tonnes almost attains the normal output of AlMgSi0.5 tubes of approximately 350 tonnes per month. In the productivity comparison in Table 6.3, the normal output for aluminum sections given in Table 6.4 is only just attained by plant A, whereas plants B and C fall well below the normal output. However, this thin section has to be extruded very slowly and the output from plant A is, in fact, excellent. The basic requirements of a modern extrusion press are described in detail in Chap. 4. If such extreme variations in output occur as those evaluated by the EWAA (Ref 2), there is a strong indication of defects in the equipment or method of production.

Table 6.4. Standard Output of New Extrusion Presses in Tonnes per Month for Aluminum Alloys Easy and Moderately Difficult To Extrude (Compiled by Stenger)

Datum		Extrusion presses (standard series) Press capacity, MN											
		6.3	8	10	12.5	16	20	25	31.5	40	50	63	80
Avg container diam, mm		125	140	160	180	200	224	250	280	315	355	400	450
Specific pressure, N/mm²		513	520	497	491	509	508	509	512	513	505	501	503
Container length, mm		450	450	500	630	710	800	900	1000	1120	1250	1400	1600
Avg billet length, mm		300	300	350	450	600	700	750	800	850	900	1000	1000
Avg billet wt, kg		8.7	14.8	17.2	22	37	54.5	73	98.5	167	177	251	320
Extruded wt, kg		7.4	12.6	14.6	18.7	31.5	46.5	62	84	141	150	213	272
No. of extrusions per work h	(a)	50	48	44	40	37	31	27	25	21	20	18	16
	(b)	30	28	26	24	22	18	16	15	12	12	11	10
Theoretical output, kg/h	(a)	374	600	650	750	1170	1460	1670	2100	2800	3000	3810	4350
	(b)	222	350	380	450	700	830	1000	1180	1690	1800	2350	2720
Effective output, kg/h	(a)	300	480	520	600	870	1170	1370	1570	2100	2250	2650	3270
	(b)	178	270	304	360	490	665	800	890	1260	1530	1620	1900
Monthly output, t/400 h	(a)	120	188	208	240	348	457	545	630	840	900	1060	1300
	(b)	71	108	122	144	196	261	320	355	500	540	640	760
Finished product, 75% bar and sections, t/month	(a)	90	140	150	180	260	350	410	475	630	675	800	1000
	(b)	53	81	91	108	147	196	240	270	375	400	480	570
Finished product, 60% tube, t/month	(a)	72	113	125	144	209	274	321	380	500	540	630	780
	(b)	43	65	73	87	118	157	192	210	300	320	380	450
Output of semifinished products, t/month	(a)	81	127	137	160	235	310	365	428	565	610	715	890
	(b)	48	73	82	97	133	177	216	240	335	360	430	510
	avg	65	100	130	135	184	243	300	335	450	480	575	700

(a) 100% alloys easy to extrude: Al99.5, AlMn, AlMgSi0.5. (b) 70% alloys easy to extrude; 30% alloys moderately difficult and difficult to extrude: AlMg3, AlZnMg1, AlCuMg1 and 2.

6.3. Methods of Increasing Efficiency

Ferguson (Ref 5) once described the equipment in aluminum extrusion plants as varying in quality "from very old, poorly designed, and badly maintained equipment to the most modern plant that can be built with modern technology and financing. I have never seen a plant in which some of the equipment could not be improved."

The sources of wastage that continually occur in extrusion and the details that have to be frequently and systematically examined are given below and are based on the paper by Ferguson (Ref 5). Five key areas have to be studied in a systematic cost analysis:

> (a) Equipment.
> (b) Operating crew.
> (c) Utilization of equipment and crew.
> (d) Scrap losses.
> (e) Operating practices.

Anyone who wants to improve the productivity of his extrusion plant has to concern himself with each of these areas in turn.

6.3.1. Equipment

(a) Is the material flow efficient?

(b) Is there adequate space for packing and shipping?

(c) Billet handling: billet saw before the heating furnace or a billet shear after the furnace to cut the billets to the most suitable length.

(d) Speed of die changing: e.g., with a single-position die slide (die change time of approximately 4 minutes) compared with a two-position die slide.

(e) Billet heating: which is more efficient, gas or induction heating? Does it make sense to use taper heating to develop a temperature gradient along the billet length (isothermal extrusion)?

(f) Is the press tooling designed for the stresses encountered and are the dies ready for use without excessive die trials?

(g) Is sufficient use made of the technology available to increase the die life — for example, nitriding, tungsten carbide coating, and the like — in addition to systematic retreatment after a given number of extrusions?

(h) Are the die furnaces correctly designed from the point of view of capacity and heating capability? Correct preheating increases the die life and reduces costs.

(i) Is the discard separation and dummy block return automated and is this automation suitable?

(j) Is the equipment that is needed for die maintenance and inspection available near the press?

(k) Are the dies that are under the responsibility of the die man methodically stored near the press, so that they can be found easily when required?

6.3.2. Operating Crew

(*a*) Given the same degree of automation and press program, the size of the crew is independent of the press size. The output increases with press capacity and, thus, the labor costs per kg of extrusion decrease with increasing press size.

(*b*) A modern aluminum section press has the following typical crew for each shift:

> 1 press driver
> 1 die man (maintenance, no correction)
> 1 stretcher operator
> 1 stretcher assistant
> 1 saw operator
> 1 saw assistant
> 1 die corrector (not required if all the dies are corrected on
>   a special shift)
> _____
> 7 men

The crew size can be reduced on heavy metal presses or aluminum rod and tube presses if the products are not stretched. The functions of the individual crew members must be precisely laid down in the plant regulations.

6.3.3. Utilization of Equipment and Crew

A modern plant and a good crew are not enough; both must be coordinated to produce the maximum output and this is attained only if the following steps are systematically undertaken:

(*a*) The theoretical maximum capacity is calculated from the press cycle, assuming no downtime. This theoretical maximum is rarely reached in practice because of inevitable delays attributable to die changes, mechanical breakdowns, and the like, but must be known in order to recognize the target.

(*b*) A practical mean capacity for the plant is then established, which includes the time lost by breakdowns and die changes — that is, the effective utilization standard or "par" production rates can then be given for each shift (Table 6.4).

(*c*) Bottlenecks (for example, die preparation, billet heating, stretcher and saw) must be located and eliminated; the press should be the "bottleneck."

(*d*) Always use the fastest extrusion speed possible.

(*e*) The actual production should be continually compared with the "par" production in order to increase profitability.

Table 6.5 lists 14 interruptions that can result in production losses and suggests methods of coping with them. The list in Table 6.6 gives an example of how a few of these interruptions built up to a loss in production of 25% in

Table 6.5. Common Causes of Production Interruptions (From Ref 5)

No.	Nature of interruption	Comments	Solution
1 ..	Changing dies	10 changes/8 h shift typical with double die slide, 1 min/die; with single die slide, 4 min/die	Plan more billets/run; organize die changing operation to reduce time; install double die slide
2 ..	Cutting porthole hollows and multiple-length solids at die head	Learn to cut with extrusions moving	Reduce number of cuts or cut moving extrusion
3 ..	Extrusions filling table ahead of stretcher or saw	Stretcher or saw may be too slow, causing press to stop	Schedule fast stretching and sawing sections before and after slow ones
4 ..	Slow starting or early stopping of shifts	Ideally press should operate full 8 h	Organize shift time better
5 ..	Press operator attending to other matters	Press idle	Have alternate operator ready when needed
6 ..	Waiting for billet, aging racks, etc.	May indicate inadequate planning or equipment	Reorganize work assignments
7 ..	Polishing dies in press	Poor die design, operating practices, billet or die maintenance	Change die design practices, billet or die maintenance; nitride the dies
8 ..	Die trials	Usually necessary to try one or two billets with each new die	Use dies that do not need trials except in special cases
9 ..	Extrusions snarl in canister or fall off runout table	Metal does not emerge from die straight	Proper die correction and support tooling
10 ..	Billets "flashing" near end of push	Time wasted prying butt loose	Correct worn pressure ring or inadequate sealing pressure
11 ..	Failure of shear to completely sever butt	Time wasted prying butt loose	Usually a mechanical maintenance problem
12 ..	Failure of lift-off or transfer equipment, billet heater, or press to function properly	Usually indicates inadequate mechanical, electrical or hydraulic maintenance	Institute a good program of preventive maintenance
13 ..	Billet heater, stretcher or saw unable to keep up with press	Necessitates stopping press to overcome such bottlenecks	Better planning of section sequence; overhaul or replace equipment
14 ..	Waiting for runout table men to get back to die head	A basic problem with long, stationary runout tables	Install automated runout table with independently operated pullers

Table 6.6. Unproductive Time in a Sample Operation (From Ref 5)

Cause	Frequency per 8 h shift	Average time lost	
		Per occurrence, min	Per 8 h shift, min
Changing dies	6	8	48
Time to polish die	2	5.5	11
Dummy block or ingot falls to floor....................	6	0.83	5
Ingot or dummy block jammed	6	0.5	3
Waiting for dummy block	5	0.17	1
Waiting for ingot.....................................	3	0.33	1
Checking thermocouple on furnace	3	0.33	1
Extrusions fall off runout table.......................	6	0.33	2
Extrusions caught up on cooling table	1	2	2
Lift-off arms caught on runout table...................	1	1	1
Paperwork by press operator	3	1.75	5
Press operator loading billets	0.5	8	4
Changing oxyacetylene cylinder	0.5	10	5
Malfunction of press (out of cycle)	2	1	2
Miscellaneous(a).....................................	..	..	29
Typical time loss per 8 h shift	..	..	120

(a) Included here are die trials on new dies; occasional maintenance on billet heater, press and runout table; time lost due to cutting multiple-length sections; time lost at beginning and end of shift.

an 8-hour shift in a plant that assumed it had no serious production problems. Individually, the interruptions do not appear to be very significant but it is the total effect that is important. Other events cannot be described as interruptions but do result in production losses for reasons that might not be obvious. Table 6.7 gives nine common examples and it suggests how to overcome them.

If the press production is constantly less than 50 to 60% of the theoretical capacity, the equipment or crew is not functioning correctly. The following measures can be recommended:

(a) In a prominent place, put up a chart of the number of billets processed and the production rate per shift.
(b) Install a recorder to monitor production, dead cycle and breakdown times, and also a billet temperature recorder.
(c) Initiate a daily analysis of the charts by plant superintendents with copies forwarded to the plant management and, depending on the results, praise or admonish those responsible (especially the foreman and chief operator).

6.3.4. Scrap Losses

Scrap is expensive because it ties up capital and requires nonprofitmaking expenditure on reprocessing. Aluminum extrusion plants operate with a

Table 6.7. Common Causes of Slow Production Rates and How To Overcome Them (From Ref 5)

No.	Problem	Comments	Solution
		BILLETS	
1 . . .	Using billets that inherently extrude slower than necessitated by the die	Extrudability of various kinds of billets varies as much as 50%	Use the fastest extruding billets that will give the hardness and finish required for each section
2 . . .	Using low-quality billets to make extrusions that are to be polished and anodized	With such billets, acceptable finish attainable only when extruded very slowly	No false economies: use billets suited to quality of product being produced
		PROCEDURES	
3 . . .	Using billets or containers that are too hot	Excessive extrusion temperatures generate pickup and tearing that cause press operator to reduce extrusion speed	Follow production instructions, check new dies at various temperatures before deciding which is best
4 . . .	Using too many short billets	Gross production per hour inevitably decreases as billet length decreases	Use longest billets possible, cutting multiple-lengths, using longer runout table
5 . . .	Excessive break-through pressures	Press operator may hold back or slow down such sections to avoid breaking die or damaging pump	Change billet type; increase billet or container temperature; increase number of holes in die
		DIES	
6 . . .	Correcting dies at less than top speed	Deflection on dies generally increases as speed of extrusion increases	Be sure die corrections are made to reflect top extrusion speeds
7 . . .	Poor die design	Long bearings, thick bridges and small ports slacken production; hollow dies are no longer the low productivity factors they once were	Avoid excessive bridge thickness on bridge dies, larger ports on porthole dies, shorter die bearings
8 . . .	Problem dies	Slow-running problem dies often need to be redesigned, adding more holes, reducing bearings changing feeds	Tell die supplier when a die performs poorly; arrange for further trials
		EXTRUSION PRESS	
9 . . .	Inadequate oil volume	If most sections can be run as fast as press will go, oil is probably being delivered to cylinder too slowly	Especially with older presses, consider installing an additional pump

Table 6.8. Production Methods for Copper Tubes (From Ref 6)

Method	Tube roll piercing	Normal extrusion	Thin-wall tube extrusion	Tube casting
A...............	Casting of rolling ingots	Casting of extrusion billets	Casting of extrusion billets	Casting of tubes
B..............	Roll piercing of tubes	Extrusion	Thin-wall tube extrusion	Cold Pilger rolling
C..............	Cold Pilger rolling or drawing	Cold Pilger rolling or drawing	(No intermediate process)	(Multiple Pilger rolling)
D	Drum drawing	Drum drawing	Drum drawing	Drum drawing
	Rolled Ingot	**Feed Tube**	**Extruded Tube**	**Cast Tube**
Dimensions	3 to 4 in.; 50 to 60 kg coils	60 to 90 mm diam; 120 to 200 kg coils	55 mm diam × 2.5 mm; 200 to 250 kg coils	113 mm diam × 15 mm; 800 kg coils
Advantages	100% workable, lowest waste, average surface quality	Heavy feed tube, thus high coil weight, good extruded surface, fine grain size	Most economical production, high extrusion speed, good surface (depending on die quality), fine grain size	Economical production, large weights, low capital cost
Disadvantages....	Danger of surface defects, coarse grain size, low coil weight, high capital cost	High scrap rate, expensive finishing processes, high capital cost	Danger of larger variations in wall thickness; very high extrusion speeds, necessitating frequent die changes	High defect rate, coarse grain size, extremely long lengths, danger of damage
Machinery	Roll piercing mill, improved by Stiefel-type rolling mill, Discher-type rolling mill; cold Pilger mill, drum drawing machine	Cold Pilger mill, drum drawing machine	50 MN extrusion press (60 MN press in preparation), drum drawing machine	Cold Pilger mill, e.g., <51 mm × 2.5 mm, several drum drawing machines

scrap percentage ranging from 17 to 27% in relation to the billets used. The scrap percentage used to be even higher, notwithstanding the less stringent requirements of sections. A plant that has higher scrap percentages than its competitors can reduce costs significantly by finding and eliminating the causes of scrap.

6.3.5. Operating Practices

All technical production data — including billet preparation, billet temperature, container temperature, extrusion speed, method of cooling the product — are part of the operating practice and must be used to give the maximum extrusion speed, together with satisfactory product quality. Given sufficient press capacity and volume of hydraulic fluid, the maximum extrusion speed is governed by the formation of surface cracks, roughness, and die lines on the extruded product. The most suitable billet composition and heat treatment (homogenization or heterogenization) must be selected to attain this maximum extrusion speed, particularly with aluminum alloys. In certain cases (for example, architectural AlMgSi0.5 sections) special high-speed alloys have been developed for very competitive production.

The extrusion operation is, however, not the only factor governing the competitiveness of the finished product. The finishing operations play an equally important role in production. The path to profitable finishing is directly related to the alloy and the quality required, especially in the case of tubes that have to be subjected to a relatively large number of operations after extrusion. The decision to extrude thin heavy metal tubes for processing on drum drawing machines (bull blocks) or to extrude pierced rolled ingots for a stretch reduction line can be made from the economical viewpoint only if the full production program is known.

Tuschy (Ref 6) has compared four different methods of producing copper tubes (Table 6.8). Rolled billets or extrusion billets form the starting material for the first three processes. The first group includes the tube roll piercing process — the Mannesmann process — together with a cold Pilger mill. The extrusion process is used in the second and third methods. Cast tubes are the starting material for the fourth process. The comparison indicates that copper tube production is undergoing a change. The favorable hot workability of copper makes it possible to extrude a thin-wall tube with dimensions very close to those of the finished product. This eliminates the first expensive cold working step. The press is the decisive factor in the production sequence from the point of view of both quality and profitability. This also applies to the production of aluminum tubes.

Bibliographic References

1. Billigmann, J., and Feldmann, H.: Stauchen und Pressen, Karl Hanser Verlag, Munich (1973), 2nd ed.
2. EWAA (The European Wrought Aluminium Association). Untersuchungen über die Wirtschaftlichkeit von Aluminium-Halbzeug. 1a. Produktivitätsvergleich No. 6b (1968). 1b. Produktivitätsvergleich No. 13 (1971). 1c. Produktivitätsvergleich No. 12 (1969).
3. Laue, K.: Wirtschaftlichkeit und Leistungssteigerung beim Strangpressen, Z. f. Metallkunde 60 (1969) p. 891/897.
4. Anonymous: Making Par as an Aluminium Extruder (interview with R. T. Ferguson), Iron Age 203 (1969) p. 54/57.
5. Ferguson, R. T.: Evaluating Extrusion Plant Operations, Paper No. 2, Int. Extr. Technol. Seminar, New Orleans (1969), Light Metal Age 7 (1969) p. 6/18.
6. Tuschy, E.: Fertigungsverfahren für nahtlose Rohre; Paper presented at the Extrusion Conference, Osnabrück (1968).

7. Future Developments

Machine technology in extrusion — as in all branches of industry — has reached a high degree of development and is capable of translating the present-day knowledge of process technology and requirements into industrial practice. However, every industry recognizes that material and personnel costs are increasing each year and it is not always possible to match these higher costs by raising the selling price. Extrusion plants also have to meet the stringent demands of their customers for improved quality, reduction in wall thickness, and more complicated sections (which are labor-saving for the customer). These demands provide a continuous driving force for the advancement of extrusion technology. From the present-day stand of scientific knowledge and production technology it can be predicted with a high degree of certainty that extrusion technology will advance mainly along the following lines.

7.1. Equipment

7.1.1. Press Capacity

The already recognized trend of increasing the rate of production by using bigger extrusion presses will continue for mass production plants. Presses with capacities as high as 600 MN are even now under consideration. On the other hand the small universal presses will still retain their importance for small batch extrusion.

7.1.2. Auxiliary Equipment

Frequently, the auxiliary equipment and not the extrusion press determines the output of the plant and sometimes also the quality of the extruded products. Improvements are, therefore, being continually made in this field. One urgent requirement, for example, in section extrusion is the automation of the stretcher jaws and also the final cutting to length. Extrusion at faster exit speeds will necessitate the development of a more efficient cooling system. Automatic pullers on the runout table have been used in the past only in certain cases, but they offer so many advantages that they will become essential items in any efficient extrusion plant, at least for those involved in mass production.

7.2. Production Technology

Production technology will have to concentrate to an increasing extent on three main areas:

(*a*) Increasing the extrusion speed.
(*b*) Improving the quality and uniformity of the product.
(*c*) Extrusion of new materials — for example, glass.

The metallurgical knowledge and production technology available today offer numerous possibilities that have not been put into practice at all or only to a limited degree.

7.2.1. Extrusion Speed

Extrusion at a constant temperature (isothermal extrusion), which has been discussed for a long time but used only to a limited extent, may increase in importance because of economical factors. Modern presses already offer displacement-dependent speed control and an important task in the near future for speed control will be the determination of sufficient suitably reliable extrusion parameters.

An equally important requirement in this context is the empirical and systematic determination of the optimum extrusion temperature as a function of the press parameters. This will help in achieving the true maximum extrusion speeds. Extensive knowledge of the causes of hot shortness in the various alloys must also be obtained, together with possible metallurgical and extrusion technological means of controlling the development of hot shortness.

Significantly higher extrusion speeds than those used now can be attained in cold or warm extrusion, especially with the difficult-to-extrude alloys. This requires the development or further development of new technology and its introduction into practice. Cold or warm extrusion processes, which include lubricated direct, hydrostatic and also indirect extrusion, might, therefore, increase in importance in the future.

The lack of suitable lubricants for many temperature ranges hinders the further application of lubricated extrusion to some alloy groups. However, economical pressures will certainly result in solutions to these problems.

7.2.2. Quality

The large variation in longitudinal and transverse material properties in products extruded by conventional direct extrusion often results in serious difficulties in quality control and higher costs because of the amount of wastage. This will further the use of extrusion processes in the future that are not associated with these property variations. These include indirect extrusion and lubricated direct extrusion (warm or cold).

7.3. Tooling

7.3.1. Service Life

The low die life is the weak point in the extrusion of alloys at temperatures above 800 °C. This affects both the economics of the process and the quality (dimensional tolerances). It remains to be seen whether special hard alloys—for example, sintered materials or ceramics—will provide a solution in the future.

7.3.2. Die Design

Although the erosion and machining operations used in die production have been widely developed and partly automated, considerable problems are still encountered in die and extrusion tooling design for complicated sections or when the extrusion is not subjected to further working — for example, drawing. The problem is that the section extruded from a new die that corresponds exactly to the original drawing frequently has unpredicted dimensional discrepancies. The die then has to be corrected, usually several times, and this costs both time and money. The future task in die design is to leave purely practical guesswork behind and to develop a systematic method of calculation, drawing on a large volume of stored data, that will make it possible to determine in advance the correct die apertures and bearing lengths with sufficient accuracy that no expensive die correction will be needed during production.

7.3.3. Mechanical Properties

If the tendency to reduce extrusion temperatures persists — that is, warm or cold extrusion — the tooling, including the die set, the stem and the container, will have to withstand higher stresses. The selection of the optimum steel, the tool design and the associated stress analysis will, thus, increase in importance.

Appendix 1: Symbols Used in This Book

α = Angle of taper

Δ_T = Temperature rise

ϵ_t = Elastic compressive or tensile strains in the individual container components

ϵ_n = Relative contraction allowance

η_F = Deformation efficiency factor

λ = Thermal conductivity of the extruded material

μ_M = Coefficient of mandrel friction

μ_i = Coefficient of internal friction

μ_F = Coefficient of friction between billet surface and container wall

ρ = Density

$\sigma_{1,2,3}$ = Normal principal stresses

σ_m = Mean stress

σ_M = Tensile stress in mandrel

σ_b = Bending stress

σ_R = Reference stress

σ_o = Design stress

σ_t = Tangential stresses in the container resulting from the operating pressure p_{ri} and the shrinkage stress p_{sn}

σ_r = Radial stresses in the container resulting from the operating pressure p_{ri} and the shrinkage stress p_{sn}

σ_a = Axial stresses in the container resulting from the operating pressure p_{ri} and the shrinkage stress p_{sn}

σ_{tT} = Effective tangential operating stress resulting from the superimposition of the stresses from the extrusion load and the shrinkage stresses

σ_{rT} = Effective radial operating stress resulting from the superimposition of the stresses from the extrusion load and the shrinkage stresses

τ = Shear stress

τ_s = Measured shear stress

φ_{Fr} = Strain to fracture

φ = Logarithmic strain

$\dot{\varphi}$ = Strain rate

$\dot{\varphi}_o$ = Instantaneous strain rate

φ_p = Strain during piercing

ψ = Strain rate dependent function of internal friction (Geleji)

ψ^* = Necking

A_o = Cross sectional area of the container

A_B = Cross sectional area of the billet

A_1 = Cross sectional area of the extruded product

A_M = Cross sectional area of the mandrel

A = Instantaneous cross section of the specimen

A in % = Elongation to fracture

A_L	=	Cross sectional area of the inner liner
A_T	=	Area of the tongue
A^*	=	Constant
B^*	=	Constant
C	=	Circumference (also U)
C^*	=	Constant
D_o	=	Container diameter
D_B	=	Billet diameter
D_C	=	Circumscribing circle diameter
D_M	=	Mandrel diameter
D_T	=	Outside diameter of the tool set
D_L	=	Diameter of the inner liner
D_{DB}	=	Diameter of the dummy block
D_1	=	Diameter of the die
D_2	=	Diameter of the backing ring
D_{1000}	=	Diameter of the inner liner, related to a specific extrusion pressure of ≈ 1000 N/mm^2 (≈ 100 kp/mm^2)
D_{SS}	=	Diameter of the solid stem
D_{HSI}	=	Inside diameter of the hollow stem
D_{HSO}	=	Outside diameter of the hollow stem
E	=	Modulus of elasticity
F	=	Load (compression load, tensile load, torsion load)
F_{id}	=	Ideal extrusion load
F_{FD}	=	Load resulting from friction along the die land
F_p	=	Piercing load
F_{PS}	=	Shearing load for piercing
F_e	=	Total load for the section
F_F	=	Frictional load
F_o	=	Total load for a round bar of identical area
F_T	=	Total (extrusion) load
F_{FM}	=	Load resulting from mandrel friction
K^*	=	Constant
L	=	Instantaneous billet length
L_o	=	Initial billet length
L_B	=	Depth of the backing ring
L_M	=	Mandrel length
L_D	=	Depth of the die

L_1	=	Length of the extruded product
L_T	=	Total depth of the tool set
L_C	=	Length of container
L_{DB}	=	Thickness of dummy block
L_D + L_B	=	Total depth of die and backing ring
M	=	Bending moment
N	=	Number of revolutions
P	=	Power, capacity (press)
Q	=	Area load
R	=	Extrusion ratio
R_m	=	Tensile strength
$R_{p0.2}$	=	0.2% proof stress
T	=	Exit temperature
T_s	=	Solidus temperature
T_o	=	Reference temperature
T_B	=	Billet temperature
T_C	=	Container temperature
U	=	Circumference (also C)
U_o	=	Circumference of the circle of identical area
U_E	=	Outside circumference of the extruded product
U_I	=	Inside circumference of the extruded product
U_n	=	Diameter ratio
V	=	Deforming volume
W_T	=	Total deformation work
W_{id}	=	Ideal deformation work
W_S	=	Shearing work
W_F	=	Work to overcome friction
Z^*	=	Relative extrudability index
Z	=	Section modulus

a	=	Thermal diffusivity
a^*	=	Constant
a_f	=	Difficulty factor
b_t	=	Width of tongue
b^*	=	Constant
b_{min}	=	Minimum opening width
b	=	Heat penetration factor
c	=	Deepest channel in the section

c_p	= Specific heat at constant pressure	k_{fo}	= Flow stress at temperature T_o
d	= Diameter of the extruded product or equivalent diameter	k_{wo}	= Deformation resistance for a specified cross section
d^*	= Constant	l_T	= Length of tongue
dl	= Change in length	m^*	= Constant
d_{1i}	= Inside diameter of the inner liner	n	= Number of strands
d_{1a}	= Outside diameter of the inner liner	p_{as}	= Axial stress
		$\overline{p}$	= Mean extrusion pressure
d_{2i}	= Inside diameter of the liner holder	p	= Extrusion pressure
d_{2a}	= Outside diameter of the liner holder	p_{sn}	= Shrinkage pressure between liners
d_{3i}	= Inside diameter of the outer mantle	p_{ri}	= Radial internal specific pressure on the individual container components
d_{3a}	= Outside diameter of the outer mantle	p_{ra}	= Radial external specific pressure on the individual container components
e	= Distance from the center of gravity	s	= Length of the die land
f_s	= Shape factor	s_{min}	= Minimum wall thickness (of the extruded product)
f^*	= Constant	t	= Time
f_f	= Die land friction factor	t_t	= Length of taper
f_E	= Section factor	v_a	= Exit speed
h	= Height of the extruded product, depth of the die	v_R	= Ram speed
		v_{RA}	= Maximum ram speed according to the extrudability of the alloy
k_f	= Flow stress		
k_{fm}	= Mean flow stress	v_{RP}	= Maximum ram speed according to the press capacity
k_w	= Deformation resistance		
k_{wm}	= Mean deformation resistance	x	= Length of deformation zone

Appendix 2

DIN Numbers, Designations, AISI Equivalents, and Compositions of Steels

DIN No.	Designation	AISI	C	Si	Mn	Cr	Mo	W	V	Co	Ni	Nb	Others
1.0065	St 37	–	0.17	0.15	0.35	–	–	–	–	–	–	–	–
1.0070	St 70	–	0.45	0.15	0.35	–	–	–	–	–	–	–	–
1.0075	St 42	C, C1	0.20	0.15	0.35	–	–	–	–	–	–	–	–
1.0401	C15	–	0.15	0.25	0.45	–	–	–	–	–	–	–	–
1.0503	C45	C1042	0.45	0.25	0.65	–	–	–	–	–	–	–	–
1.0570	St 52	–	0.20	0.50	0.45	–	–	–	–	–	–	–	–
1.0601	C60	C1060	0.60	0.25	0.75	–	–	–	–	–	–	–	–
1.1192	Cq45	–	0.45	0.25	0.65	–	–	–	–	–	–	–	–
1.1645	C105W2	W1	1.05	0.20	0.22	–	–	–	–	–	–	–	–
1.2243	61CrSiV5	–	0.61	0.9	0.8	1.2	–	–	0.1	–	–	–	–
1.2311	40CrMnMo7	–	0.40	0.3	1.5	2.0	0.2	–	–	–	–	–	–
1.2323	48CrMoV67	–	0.48	0.3	0.8	1.5	0.8	–	0.3	–	–	–	–
1.2343	X38CrMoV51	H11	0.38	1.0	0.4	5.3	1.1	–	0.4	–	–	–	–
1.2344	X40CrMoV51	H13	0.40	1.0	0.4	5.3	1.4	–	1.0	–	–	–	–
1.2365	X32CrMoV33	H10	0.32	0.3	0.3	3.0	2.8	–	0.5	–	–	–	–
1.2367	X40CrMoV53	–	0.40	0.4	0.5	5.0	3.0	–	0.9	–	–	–	–
1.2542	45WCrV7	S1	0.45	1.0	0.3	1.1	–	2.0	0.2	–	–	–	–
1.2547	45WCrV77	–	0.45	1.0	0.3	1.7	–	2.0	0.2	–	–	–	–
1.2564	X30WCrV41	–	0.30	1.0	0.4	1.0	–	3.8	0.2	–	–	–	–
1.2567	X30WCrV53	–	0.30	0.2	0.3	2.4	–	4.3	0.6	–	–	–	–
1.2581	X30WCrV93	H20/21	0.30	0.2	0.3	2.7	–	8.5	0.4	–	–	–	–
1.2584	X60WCrVMo94	–	0.60	0.3	0.3	4.0	0.5	9.0	0.7	–	–	–	–
1.2603	45CrVMoW58	–	0.45	0.6	0.4	1.5	0.5	0.5	0.8	–	–	–	–
1.2606	X37CrMoW51	H12, A8	0.37	1.0	0.5	5.3	1.5	1.3	0.3	–	–	–	–
1.2622	X60WCrMoV94	–	0.60	0.3	0.3	4.0	0.9	9.0	0.7	–	–	–	–
1.2625	X33WCrVMo1212	H23	0.33	0.2	0.3	12.0	0.5	12.0	1.1	–	–	–	–
1.2662	X30WCrCoV93	–	0.30	0.2	0.3	2.3	–	8.5	0.3	2.0	–	–	–
1.2678	X45CoCrWV555	H19	0.45	0.4	0.4	4.5	0.5	4.5	2.0	4.5	–	–	–
1.2710	45NiCr6	–	0.45	0.3	0.7	1.4	–	–	–	–	1.7	–	–
1.2713	55NiCrMoV6	L6,6F2	0.55	0.3	0.6	0.7	0.3	–	0.1	–	1.7	–	–
1.2714	56NiCrMoV7	6F3, L6	0.56	0.3	0.7	1.0	0.5	–	0.1	–	1.7	–	–
1.2731	X50NiCrWV1313	–	0.50	1.3	0.7	13.0	–	2.5	0.5	–	13.0	–	–
1.2758	X50WNiCrVCo1212	–	0.50	1.4	0.6	4.0	0.7	12.5	1.1	1.6	11.5	–	–
1.2767	X45NiCrMo4	–	0.45	0.2	0.4	1.3	0.3 or 0.5	–	–	–	4.0	–	–
1.2826	60MnSi4	S4	0.60	0.9	1.0	–	–	–	–	–	–	–	–

DIN Numbers, Designations, AISI Equivalents, and Compositions of Steels

DIN No.	Designation	AISI	C	Si	Mn	Cr	Mo	W	V	Co	Ni	Nb	Others
1.2887	X31CrWCoMoV129	–	0.31	–	–	11.5	0.8	9.0	0.5	1.3	–	–	–
1.2888	X20CoCrWMo109	–	0.20	0.3	0.5	10.0	2.0	5.5	–	10.0	–	–	–
1.4021	X20Cr13	420	0.20	0.5	0.5	13.0	–	–	–	–	–	–	–
1.4024	X15Cr13	403	0.15	0.5	0.5	13.0	–	–	–	–	–	–	–
1.4301	5CrNi189	304	0.05	0.5	1.0	18.5	–	–	–	–	9.0	–	–
1.4340	X40CrNi274	–	0.40	1.0	0.8	27.0	–	–	–	–	4.5	–	–
≈1.4515	X15CrTi25	–	0.15	0.5	0.5	25.0	–	–	–	–	–	–	Ti1.1
1.4541	X10CrNiTi189	321	0.10	0.5	1.0	18.0	–	–	–	–	10.0	–	Ti0.3
1.4550	10CrNiNb189	347	0.10	0.5	1.0	18.0	–	–	–	–	10.0	0.4	–
1.4571	10CrNiMoTi1810	316Ti	0.10	0.5	1.0	17.5	2.2	–	–	–	12.0	–	Ti0.3
1.4876	X10NiCrAlTi3220	–	0.10	0.5	0.8	21.0	–	–	–	–	32.0	–	Ti0.4/Al0.4
1.4980	X5NiCrTi2615	660	0.05	0.5	0.8	15.0	1.3	–	0.3	–	25.0	–	B0.05/Ti0.3
2.4989	X40CoCrNiMoWNb432020	–	0.40	0.5	0.8	20.0	4.0	4.0	–	–	20.0	4.0	Fe≦/5.0
1.5415	15Mo3	–	0.15	0.2	0.6	0.2	0.3	–	–	–	–	–	–
1.7015	15Cr3	5117	0.15	0.2	0.5	0.5	–	–	–	–	–	–	–
1.7335	13CrMo44	–	0.13	0.2	0.7	1.0	0.6	–	–	–	–	–	–
1.7380	10CrMo910	–	0.10	0.3	0.7	2.2	1.1	–	–	–	–	–	–
1.7737	45CrMoV67	–	0.45	0.3	0.7	1.4	0.7	–	0.3	–	–	–	–

Appendix 3

Approximate Chemical Compositions of Materials Mentioned in This Book

Material	AA	Fe	Si	Cu	Mn	Mg	Cr	Zn	Other
Aluminum and Aluminum Alloys									
Al99.5	1050	<0.4	<0.25	..	..	..	..	..	..
Al99.6	1060	<0.35	<0.25	..	..	..	..	..	..
Al99Cu	1100	<1.0	<1.0	0.1	..	..	..	..	..
AlMgSi0.5	6060	0.1	0.45	..	..	0.50	..	..	..
AlMgSi0.8	..	..	1.0	..	..	0.8	..	..	..
AlMgSi1	6082	..	1.0	..	0.7	0.9	..	..	..
AlMgSiCuMn.....	6261	..	0.55	0.25	0.25	0.85	..	..	..
E-AlMgSi0.5	6201	..	0.7	..	..	0.75	..	..	0.06 B
AlSi5...............	4043	..	5.3	..	..	..	..	..	..
AlSi5Mg...........	4543	..	6.0	..	..	0.25	..	..	..
AlMgSiPb........	(6262)	..	1.0	..	0.7	0.9	..	..	1.75 Pb + Bi
AlMn...............	3103	..	..	..	1.1	..	..	..	..
AlMg1	..	..	..	..	..	0.9	..	..	..
AlMg2.5Cr........	5052	..	..	..	..	2.5	0.25	..	..
AlMg3	5754	..	..	..	..	3.1	..	..	..
AlMg4.5	5082	..	..	..	..	4.5	..	..	..
AlMg5Mn	5056A	..	..	..	0.35	5.0	..	..	..
AlMg3.5Mn......	5154A	..	..	..	0.30	3.5	..	..	..
AlMg2.7MnCr ...	5454	..	..	..	0.75	2.7	0.12	..	..
AlMg4.5Mn.......	5083	..	..	..	0.70	4.5	0.12	..	..
AlMg1Mn1........	3004	..	..	..	1.2	1.1	..	..	..
AlCuMg1.........	2017A	..	0.5	4.0	0.7	0.7	..	..	0.25 Zr + Ti
AlCuMg2..........	2024	..	..	4.3	0.6	1.6	..	..	0.20 Zr + Ti
AlCuMgPb........	2030	..	..	4.0	..	0.9	..	..	1.2 Pb
AlCuBiPb.........	2011	..	..	5.5	..	..	..	..	0.4 Pb + 0.4 Bi
AlCuSiMn	2014	..	0.85	4.5	0.8	0.5	..	..	0.20 Zr + Ti
AlZn4.5Mg1	7020	..	..	..	0.3	1.2	0.20	4.5	0.15 Zr
AlZnMgCu0.5 ...	..	..	..	0.75	0.25	3.2	0.20	4.7	..
AlZnMgCu1.5....	7075	..	..	1.6	..	2.5	0.25	5.6	0.25 Zr + Ti
AlZnMgCu2.5....	7050	..	..	2.3	..	2.3	..	6.2	0.12 Zr

Magnesium and Magnesium Alloys

Material	Al	Mn	Zn	Zr	Mg
Mg	. .	. .	. .	. .	99.90
MgMn	. .	1.5	. .	. .	rem
MgMn2	. .	2.0	. .	. .	rem
MgAl1Zn	0.5	0.3	0.2	. .	rem
MgAl3Zn	3.5	0.35	0.4	. .	rem
MgAl5Zn	4.5	0.6	1.2	. .	rem
MgAl6Zn	6.0	0.35	0.3	. .	rem
MgAl8Zn	8.5	0.30	0.4	. .	rem
MgZn2Zr	. .	. .	2.0	0.6	rem
MgZn3Zr	. .	. .	3.0	0.7	rem

Titanium and Titanium Alloys

Material	Al	Cr	Mn	Mo	Sn	V	Zr	Ti
Ti	. .	. .	. .	. .	. .	. .	. .	99.9
TiAl6V4	6.0	. .	. .	. .	. .	4.0	. .	rem
TiAl7Mo4	7.0	. .	. .	4.0	. .	. .	. .	rem
TiAl6V6Sn2	6.0	. .	. .	. .	2.0	6.0	. .	rem
TiAl6Zr4Sn2Mo2	6.0	. .	. .	2.0	2.0	. .	4.0	rem
TiAl5Sn2.5	5.0	. .	. .	. .	2.5	. .	. .	rem
TiAl8Mo1V1	8.0	. .	. .	1.0	. .	1.0	. .	rem
TiAl4Mn4	4.0	. .	4.0	. .	. .	. .	. .	rem
TiV13Cr11Al3	3.0	11.0	. .	. .	. .	13.0	. .	rem

Copper and Copper Alloys

Material	Al	Fe	Mn	Ni	Pb	Si	Sn	Zn	Other	Cu
E-Cu	. .	. .	. .	. .	. .	. .	. .	. .	. .	99.90
SE-Cu	. .	. .	. .	. .	. .	. .	. .	. .	. .	99.90
SF-Cu	. .	. .	. .	. .	. .	. .	. .	. .	. .	99.90
CuZn1.5	. .	. .	. .	. .	. .	. .	. .	1.5	. .	rem
CuZn10	. .	. .	. .	. .	. .	. .	. .	9.5	. .	rem
CuZn20	. .	. .	. .	. .	. .	. .	. .	19.5	. .	rem
CuZn28	. .	. .	. .	. .	. .	. .	. .	27.5	. .	rem
CuZn30	. .	. .	. .	. .	. .	. .	. .	29.5	. .	rem
CuZn33	. .	. .	. .	. .	. .	. .	. .	32.5	. .	rem
CuZn35	. .	. .	. .	. .	. .	. .	. .	34.5	. .	rem
CuZn37	. .	. .	. .	. .	. .	. .	. .	36.5	. .	rem
CuZn40	. .	. .	. .	. .	. .	. .	. .	39.5	. .	rem
CuZn20Al	2.0	. .	. .	. .	. .	. .	. .	19.5	. .	rem
CuZn28Sn	. .	. .	. .	. .	. .	. .	1.0	27.5	. .	rem
CuZn31Si	. .	. .	. .	0.3	0.4	1.0	. .	27.0	. .	rem
CuZn35Ni	0.9	0.3	2	2.5	0.4	. .	0.3	34.1	. .	rem
CuZn38Pb1.5	. .	. .	. .	. .	1.5	. .	. .	37.5	. .	rem
CuZn39Pb3	. .	. .	. .	. .	3.0	. .	. .	38.5	. .	rem
CuZn40Pb2	. .	. .	. .	. .	2.0	. .	. .	40.0	. .	rem

(continued)

Material	Al	Fe	Mn	Ni	Pb	Si	Sn	Zn	Other	Cu
Copper and Copper Alloys (*continued*)										
CuZn40Mn	..	0.7	1.7	0.5	..	..	..	39.0	..	rem
CuZn40Al2	1.8	0.5	1.7	1.0	0.4	0.4	0.3	36.5	..	rem
CuSn2	..	..	..	..	..	..	2.0	..	..	rem
CuSn5	..	..	..	..	..	..	4.5	..	..	rem
CuSn6	..	..	..	..	..	..	6.5	..	..	rem
CuSn8	..	..	..	..	..	..	8.0	..	..	rem
CuSn10	..	..	..	..	..	..	10.0	..	..	rem
CuNi1.5Si	..	..	..	1.3	..	0.55	..	..	..	rem
CuNi2Si	..	..	..	2.0	..	0.65	..	..	..	rem
CuNi3Si	..	..	..	3.5	..	0.9	..	..	..	rem
CuNi5Fe	..	1.2	0.6	5.0	..	..	..	..	..	rem
CuNi10Fe	..	1.4	0.8	10.0	..	..	..	..	..	rem
CuNi20	..	..	..	21.0	..	..	..	..	..	rem
CuNi20Fe	..	0.8	1.0	21.0	..	..	..	..	..	rem
CuNi25	..	..	..	25.0	..	..	..	..	..	rem
CuNi30Mn	..	..	3.0	30.0	..	..	..	..	..	rem
CuNi30Fe	..	0.7	1.0	31.0	..	..	..	..	..	rem
CuNi44	..	..	1.0	44.0	..	..	..	..	..	rem
CuNi10Zn42Pb	..	..	..	10.0	1.2	..	..	42.0	..	rem
CuNi12Zn24	..	..	..	12.0	..	..	..	23.0	..	rem
CuNi12Zn30Pb	..	..	..	12.0	0.9	..	..	30.0	..	rem
CuNi18Zn20	..	..	..	18.0	..	..	..	20.0	..	rem
CuNi18Zn19Pb	..	..	..	18.0	0.9	..	..	20.0	..	rem
CuNi25Zn15	..	..	..	25.0	..	..	..	15.0	..	rem
CuAl5	5.0	..	..	..	..	..	..	..	..	rem
CuAl8Fe	7.5	2.0	..	..	..	..	..	..	..	rem
CuAl8Si	7.5	1.0	1.0	..	..	2.5	..	..	..	rem
CuAl10Fe	10.0	3.0	2.5	..	..	..	..	..	..	rem
CuAl10Ni	9.5	3.9	1.0	5.0	..	..	..	..	..	rem
CuSi3Mn	..	..	1.0	..	..	3.0	..	..	..	rem
CuCr	..	..	..	..	..	..	..	..	0.75 Cr	rem
CuBe2	..	..	..	0.4	..	..	..	..	2.0 Be	rem
CuAg	..	..	..	..	..	..	..	..	0.15 Ag	rem
CuZr	..	..	..	..	..	..	..	..	0.50 Zr	rem

Material	C	Cr	Mo	W	Nb	Fe	Ni	Co
Cobalt Alloys								
A L X	2.0	33.0	..	16.5	..	..	..	rem
Aknit Co50	2.2	27.0	..	14.0	..	..	..	rem
Celsit P	2.5	31.0	..	13.5	..	..	..	rem
Revolta	0.29	28.0	5.9	..	..	..	..	rem
Platit	1.4	28.0	..	5.0	..	..	..	rem
Stellite 1	2.5	33.0	..	13.0	..	..	..	rem
Stellite 251	0.3	28.0	..	..	2.0	18.0	..	rem
CoCr20Ni20W	0.40	20.0	4.00	4.0	..	<5.0	20.0	45.0

Material	C	Co	Cr	Al	Mn	Mo	Si	Ti	Other	Ni
Nickel and Nickel Alloys										
NiCr20Co18Ti	0.05	18.0	19.5	1.4	0.5	..	0.7	2.4	<5.00Fe	rem
NiCo15Cr15MoAlTi	0.16	15.0	15.0	5.0	0.5	4.0	0.5	4.0	(a)	rem
NiCr20TiAl	0.05	1.0	20.0	1.4	0.5	..	0.5	2.3	(b)	rem
NiCr20Ti	0.13	..	19.5	..	0.5	..	0.5	0.40	(b)	rem
NiMn2	0.1	..	..	..	2.0	..	0.2	..	(c)	rem
NiBe2	0.1	2.0 Be	..	..	1.0	..	0.1	..	(d)	rem
NiAl4Ti	0.15	..	..	4.5	0.4	..	1.0	..	(e)	rem
NiFe45	0.05	..	..	..	1.0	..	0.3	..	45.0 Fe	rem
NiCu30Fe	0.1	33.0 Cu	..	..	..	..	3.20	..	(f)	rem
NiCu30Al	0.23	29.5 Cu	..	2.80	..	..	..	0.50	(g)	rem

Material	C	Hf	Sn	Ti	W	Mo	Nb	Ta	Zr	Other
Molybdenum, Niobium, Tantalum and Zirconium Alloys										
TZM(h)	0.03	..	..	0.45	..	rem	..	..	0.08	..
Cermotherm	0.01	..	..	..	..	rem	..	..	..	(j)
NbW15Mo5Zr1	0.05	..	..	..	15.0	5.0	rem	..	1.0	..
TaHf10W5	..	10.0	..	..	5.0	..	..	rem	..	..
TaW10	..	..	..	..	10.0	..	..	rem	..	..
ZrSn1.5	..	..	1.5	..	..	..	..	..	rem	0.20 Ni
ZrNb1	..	..	..	..	..	..	1.0	..	rem	..

Material	C	Si	Mn	Cr	Mo	W	V	Co	Ni	Other	Fe
Iron Alloys and Steels											
FeNi40Cr13MoTi	0.05	0.12	0.24	12.5	6	..	..	..	44	(k)	rem
FeNi38Cr16	0.05	2.3	1.2	18	..	..	..	..	37	(m)	rem
FeNi32Cr20Ti	0.04	0.35	0.75	20.5	..	..	..	..	32	(m)	rem
FeNi32Cr20	0.05	0.5	0.75	21	..	..	..	..	32.5	(p)	rem

(a) 0.012 B, < 1.0 Fe, < 0.5 Zr. (b) < 5.00 Fe, < 0.50 Cu. (c) 0.2 Cu, 0.3 Fe, 0.15 Mg. (d) 0.2 Cu, 0.5 Fe, 0.1 Mg. (e) 0.2 Cu, 0.5 Fe, 0.15 Mg. (f) 1.50 Fe. (g) 1.00 Fe. (h) MoTi0.5Zr0.08. (j) 15.0 to 20.0 ZrO_2. (k) 0.015 B. (m) 0.5 max Cu. (n) 1.10 Ti, 0.15 Cu. (p) 0.38 Ti, 0.38 Al.

Index

NOTE. The symbol (F) or (T) following an entry in this index indicates that information on the subject is presented in a Figure or a Table.